The UK Mathematics Trust

Yearbook

2008 – 2009

This book contains an account of UKMT activities from 1st September 2008 to 31st August 2009. It contains all question papers, solutions and results as well as a variety of other information.

Published by the United Kingdom Mathematics Trust.
School of Mathematics, The University of Leeds, Leeds LS2 9JT
Telephone: 0113 343 2339
Website: http://www.ukmt.org.uk

Cover design: – The backdrop is a Penrose tiling whose complexity reflects the activities of the UKMT.

The photographs are

Front Cover:
St Paul's School, London: TMC winners

Back Cover:
Pupils celebrating at the Elms School;
Certificate winners at Westminster Choir School

ISBN 978-1-906001-10-0

Printed and bound in Great Britain by
H. Charlesworth & Co. Ltd, Wakefield

Contents

Foreword i

Background and history of the UKMT 1

Foundation of the Trust; Aims and Activities of the Trust; Structure and Membership of the Trust

An outline of the events 3

Junior competitions; Intermediate competitions; Senior competitions; Growth; Team Maths Challenge

Report from the Director 6

Sponsors' pages 7

The Junior Mathematical Challenge and Olympiad

JMC paper 11

JMC solutions and comments 15

JMO paper and solutions 23

JMO marking and results 31

The Intermediate Mathematical Challenge and its follow-up events

IMC paper 39

IMC solutions and comments 43

IMOK: Kangaroo papers and solutions 50

IMOK: Olympiad papers and solutions 65

IMOK: Comments on the Olympiad papers 91

IMOK: Medal winners 100

National Mathematics Summer School 108

The Senior Mathematical Challenge and British Mathematical Olympiads

SMC paper and solutions 116

SMC comments and high scorers 126

BMO Round 1 – paper and high scorers 132

BMO Round 2 – paper and high scorers 137

BMO Round 1 – solutions 141

BMO Round 2 – solutions 147

Olympiad Training 153

The International Mathematical Olympiad 156

49th International Mathematical Olympiad, Madrid 157

UKMT Mentoring Schemes 171

Team Maths Challenge 174

Senior Team Maths Challenge 210

Other aspects of the UKMT and other similar bodies overseas 229

Lists of volunteers involved in the UKMT's activities 233

UKMT Maths Challenges Dates 2008/09 239

UKMT Publications 240

Order Form 242

Announcement

It is with sadness that we have to report the recent death of Jim Wiegold. He was one of the first members of the UKMT Council and made contributions in the area on the IMO activities.

Foreword

This is the last yearbook introduction I shall write in my capacity as Chairman of the UK Mathematics Trust, and it is exciting to look back at the progress we have made in the last six years. Building on the remarkable legacy of my predecessor, our activities have continued to grow in scale and scope, and, thanks to excellent efforts both from volunteers and staff members we are in a strong position to continue to thrive in the future, even in the hard circumstances of the current economic climate.

The bedrock of our work remains the Junior, Intermediate and Senior Challenges, now taken by over 600,000 pupils across the UK every year. We know that the reason these are so clearly appreciated by schools and colleges is the content of the questions: the way they encourage thinking mathematically, the way some questions amuse and the depth in what appears at first glance to be a straightforward question. These questions do not come out of nowhere but are the result of the effort of many volunteers who devise and select such superb and well-balanced question papers. And thanks also to those who devise questions for our newer team challenge competitions, run them, mark Olympiad papers and staff our summer schools and other camps. Without them the core activities of the Trust simply would not take place.

In 2008-09 Senior Challenge entries continued to increase significantly from 80,660 entries in 2006 to 87,400 in 2007 and 92,550 in 2008. Coinciding as they do with a resurgence in numbers taking mathematics at A Level, this is a hopeful sign for the future of mathematics. Junior entries were at their highest ever level at 291,130, and Intermediate entries at 258,890 held roughly steady in the face of a reduction in the cohort figures.

Our team challenge competitions also continue to engage pupils: combining mathematics with communication and team-work skills. Entries in our competition for younger pupils increased from 1411 to 1500 schools this year and our new co-operation with the Further Maths Network for a senior competition went nationwide with 853 entries in its first year.

At the very top level in our competitions, we should be proud that the UK International Mathematical Olympiad team all achieved medals with one gold, three silvers and two bronzes. A number of very talented mathematicians have come through our student ranks in recent years and we wish them all the very best for the future. I must pay tribute to all those who make it so successful, through all the intensive activities that go on around the preparation for and participation in the IMO and other international competitions and activities.

It is invidious to pick out individuals for special thanks but I hope that a demitting Chairman may be forgiven for doing so. I would like to thank our office staff who have been such a wonderful team under the outstanding leadership of Mary Wimbury. And among our volunteers I would like to make special mention of two with whom I have worked closely throughout my tenure, Bill Richardson and Alan Slomson. Both put in enormous effort in specific ways, for example Bill in his work for the Challenges and on this Yearbook, and Alan in his role as Secretary of the Trust, but even more importantly I have been more appreciative than they might imagine of their continual support and wise counsel. To them, and to all our volunteers, I give my heartfelt thanks, and to the Trust and to my successor Frances Kirwan, I give all my good wishes for the future.

Bernard Silverman

St Peter's College, Oxford: August 2009

Introduction

Foundation of the Trust

National mathematics competitions have existed in the UK for several decades. Up until 1987 the total annual participation was something like 8,000. Then there was an enormous growth, from 24,000 in 1988 to around a quarter of a million in 1995 – without doubt due to the drive, energy and leadership of Dr Tony Gardiner. By the end of this period there were some nine or ten competitions for United Kingdom schools and their students organised by three different bodies: the British Mathematical Olympiad Committee, the National Committee for Mathematical Contests and the UK Mathematics Foundation. During 1995 discussions took place between interested parties which led to agreement to seek a way of setting up a single body to continue and develop these competitions and related activities. This led to the formation of the United Kingdom Mathematics Trust, which was incorporated as a company limited by guarantee in October 1996 and registered with the Charity Commission.

In just over ten years of its existence, the UKMT has continued to nurture and expand the number of competitions. As a result, over six hundred thousand students throughout the UK now participate in the challenges alone, and their teachers (as well as others) not only provide much valued help and encouragement, but also take advantage of the support offered to them by the Trust.

The Royal Institution of Great Britain is the Trust's Patron, and it and the Mathematical Association are Participating Bodies. The Association of Teachers of Mathematics, the Edinburgh Mathematical Society, the Institute of Mathematics and Its Applications, the London Mathematical Society and the Royal Society are all Supporting Bodies.

Aims and Activities of the Trust

According to its constitution, the Trust has a very wide brief, namely "to advance the education of children and young people in mathematics". To attain this, it is empowered to engage in activities ranging from teaching to publishing and lobbying. But its focal point is the organisation of mathematical competitions, from popular mass "challenges" to the selection and training of the British team for the annual International Mathematical Olympiad (IMO).

There are three main challenges, the UK Junior, Intermediate and Senior Mathematical Challenges. The number of challenge entries in 2008-2009 totalled 642,260, an increase of 1.5% over the previous year. The challenges were organised by the Challenges Subtrust (CS). The Challenges are open to all pupils of the appropriate age. Certificates are awarded for the best performances and the most successful participants are encouraged to enter follow-up competitions.

At the junior and intermediate levels, a total of around 8000 pupils enter the follow-up competitions. These consist of the Junior Mathematical Olympiad and a suite of papers forming the Intermediate Mathematical Olympiad and Kangaroo under the auspices of the Challenges Subtrust.

The British Mathematical Olympiad Committee Subtrust (BMOS) organises two rounds of the British Mathematical Olympiad. Usually about 800 students who have distinguished themselves in the Senior Mathematical Challenge are invited to enter Round 1, leading to about 100 in Round 2. From the latter, around twenty are invited to a training weekend at Trinity College, Cambridge. Additionally, an elite squad, identified largely by performances in the UKMT competitions, is trained at camps and correspondence courses throughout the year. The UK team is then selected for the annual International Mathematical Olympiad (IMO) which usually takes place in July. The IMO was held in the USA in 2001, the UK in 2002, Japan in 2003, Athens in 2004, Mexico in 2005, Slovenia in 2006, Vietnam in 2007, Madrid in 2008 and Bremen in 2009. The BMOS also runs a mentoring scheme for high achievers at senior, intermediate and junior levels.

Structure and Membership of the Trust

The governing body of the Trust is its Council. The events have been organised by three Subtrusts who report directly to the Council. The work of the Trust in setting question papers, marking scripts, monitoring competitions, mentoring students and helping in many other ways depends critically on a host of volunteers. A complete list of members of the Trust, its Subtrusts and other volunteers appears at the end of this publication.

Mary Wimbury continues in her role as Director. Rachel Greenhalgh has been on maternity leave and has once again reminded us of the amount of work she does by not being here to do it! (Baby Ben, who has already visited the offices, and will no doubt be taking the challenges before we know it!) Thanks are due to Beverley Detoeuf for her willingness to grasp every diverse new task quickly. Jo Williams joined us at the beginning of the 2008-09 academic year and eased the burden immeasurably. The existing office staff of Heather Macklin, Nicky Bray and Janet Clark also deserve thanks as do the packing office staff of David Coxon, John Dales, Claire Hall, Gwyneth Hartley, Jessica Raby-Cox, Stewart Ramsay and Mary Roberts. Teachers often ask by what happens when they send the challenge papers off to us. If, as the joke goes, mathematicians are machines for turning coffee into theorems, the packing office staff, helped by a few optical mark readers and some computers, are 'machines' for turning answer sheets into results to send back to you.

An outline of the events

A brief description of the challenges, their follow-up competitions and other activities is given here with much fuller information later in the book.

Junior competitions

The UK Junior Mathematical Challenge, typically held on the last Thursday in April, is a one hour, 25 question, multiple choice paper for pupils up to and including:

Y8 in England and Wales;

S2 in Scotland, and

Y9 in Northern Ireland.

Pupils enter their personal details and answers on a special answer sheet for machine reading. The questions are set so that the first 15 should be accessible to all participants whereas the remaining 10 are more testing.

Five marks are awarded for each correct answer to the first 15 questions and six marks are awarded for each correct answer to the rest. Each incorrect answer to questions 16–20 loses 1 mark and each incorrect answer to questions 21–25 loses 2 marks. Penalty marking is used to discourage guessing.

Certificates are awarded on a proportional basis:– Gold about 6%, Silver about 14% and Bronze about 20% of all entrants. Each centre also receives one 'Best in School Certificate'.

The Junior Mathematical Olympiad is the follow-up competition to the JMC. It is normally held six weeks after the JMC and between 1000 and 1200 high scorers in the JMC are invited to take part. It is a two-hour paper which has two sections. Section A contains ten questions and pupils are required to give the answer only. Section B contains six questions for which full written answers are required. It is made clear to candidates that they are not expected to complete all of Section B and that little credit will be given to fragmentary answers. Gold, silver and bronze medals are awarded to very good candidates. In 2009 a total of 224 medals was awarded. All candidates who sat the paper received a certificate; the top 25% got Certificates of Distinction and the others Certificates of Participation. In addition, the top 50 students were given book prizes.

Intermediate competitions

The UK Intermediate Mathematical Challenge is organised in a very similar way to the Junior Challenge. One difference is that the age range goes up to Y11 in England and Wales, to S4 in Scotland and Y12 in Northern Ireland. The other difference is the timing; the IMC is held on the first Thursday in February. All other arrangements are as in the JMC.

There are five follow-up competitions under the overall title 'Intermediate Mathematical Olympiad and Kangaroo' (IMOK). Between 400 and 550 in each of Years 9, 10 and 11 (English style) sit an Olympiad paper (Cayley, Hamilton and Maclaurin respectively). In 2009, each of these was a two-hour paper and contained six questions all requiring full written solutions. A total of around 5000 pupils from the three year groups took part in a Kangaroo paper. In the European Kangaroo papers, which last an hour, there are 25 multiple-choice questions. The last ten questions are more testing than the first fifteen and correct answers gain six marks as opposed to five. (Penalty marking is not applied.) The same Kangaroo paper (designated 'Pink') was taken by pupils in Years 10 and 11 and a different one, 'Grey', by pupils in Year 9. In 2009, all five papers were sat on the same day – Thursday 19th March. All pupils received one of three types of certificate: Participation, Merit or Distinction (the last being available only to those who sat an Olympiad paper) and a specially designed UKMT key fob. In addition, the top 50 students in each year group were given a book. Performance in the Olympiad papers and the IMC was a major factor in determining pupils to be invited to one of a pair of five-day summer schools early in July.

Senior competitions

In 2008, the UK Senior Mathematical Challenge was held on Thursday 6th November. Like the other Challenges, it is a 25 question, multiple choice paper marked in the same way as the Junior and Intermediate Challenges. However, it lasts 1½ hours. Certificates (including Best in School) are awarded as with the other Challenges. The follow-up competitions are organised by the British Mathematical Olympiad Subtrust.

The first is BMO1, which was held on Thursday 4th December 2008. About 800 are usually invited to take part. The paper lasted 3½ hours and contained six questions to which full written solutions are required.

About 100 high scorers are then invited to sit BMO2, which was held on Thursday 29th January 2009. It also lasted 3½ hours but contained four, very demanding, questions.

The results of BMO2 are used to select a group of students to attend a

Training Session at Trinity College, Cambridge at Easter. As well as being taught more mathematics and trying numerous challenging problems, this group sits a 4½ hour 'mock' Olympiad paper. On the basis of this and all other relevant information, a group of about eight is selected to take part in correspondence courses and assignments which eventually produce the UK Olympiad Team of six to go forward to the International Mathematical Olympiad in July.

The growth of the Challenges

In the 2005 UKMT Yearbook, we showed the growth of the Challenges since UKMT was established and this has now been updated. The graphs below show two easily identifiable quantities, the number of schools and the number of entries. In each case, the lines, from top to bottom, represent the Junior, Intermediate and Senior Challenges. As those involved in the UKMT firmly believe that the Challenges are a very worthwhile endeavour, we hope that the upward trends continue.

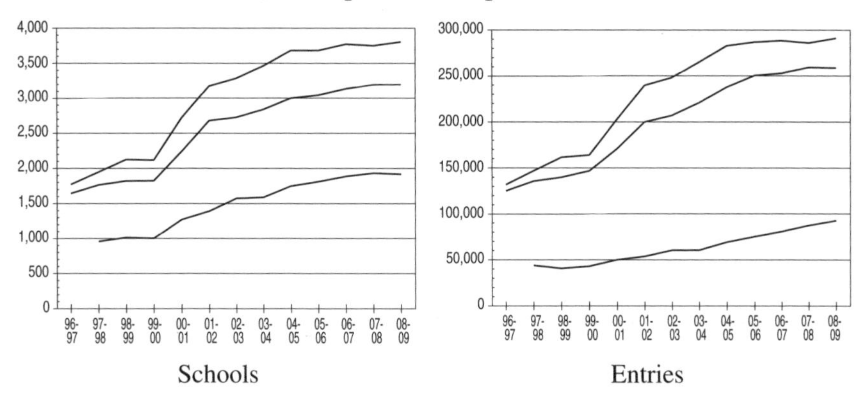

Schools

Entries

Team Maths Challenge

This event is the successor of the Enterprising Mathematics UK which was run in conjunction with the IMO in 2002. A team consists of four pupils who are in Year 9 (English style) or below with at most two members being in Year 9. Almost 1400 schools took part in Regional Finals and seventy teams competed in the National Final held in London on Monday 22nd June. In addition almost 900 schools took part in the Senior Team Maths Challenge. The final which involved 58 teams was held in the Camden Centre in February.

Report from the Director

The year 2008-09 was another busy one for the Trust. We re-launched our website just before Christmas providing a cleaner, clearer and more modern overview of the Trust's activities. Early in May our main offices moved within Leeds University to newly modernised and much more appropriate accommodation. We are very grateful to the Mathematics Department for this. We also trialled electronic BACS payment for discretionary entries for the British Mathematical Olympiad and teachers' meetings and in 2009-10 are rolling this out for the challenges: another way we hope to make it easier for schools to participate in our activities.

As detailed in the Chairman's foreword, entries to our main competitions remained strong. Although it was extremely disappointing that the exceptionally bad weather disrupted the Intermediate Challenge, it was heartening to see how keen so many schools were to sit the IMC despite the problems. Our newest venture, the Senior Team Challenge (run jointly with the Further Maths Network), got off to a good start with over 800 schools and colleges nationally taking part. We hope to grow it to reach the 1500 teams taking part in our team challenge event for younger pupils.

As is often said, but cannot be said often enough, UKMT would not be what it is without the people involved: the teachers in schools that organise for pupils to take part in our activities; the volunteers who set the questions and run the competitions and the office staff ensuring smooth administration of the challenges. They are all due my thanks.

Our Volunteers' Day, held in October 2008, was a welcome innovation. This provided volunteers' with the opportunity to find out about the activities of the Trust they were not directly involved in and facilitated getting involved in new areas. We intend to repeat the event in January 2010.

Mary Wimbury

The Actuarial Profession

The Actuarial Profession
making financial sense of the future

Profile

The Institute of Actuaries in England and Wales and the Faculty of Actuaries in Scotland are the two professional bodies for UK actuaries, working together across the UK as 'The Actuarial Profession'.

What is an actuary?

Actuaries apply their statistical and mathematical expertise and knowledge to the financial world. They look at what has happened in the past and use it to make predictions about the future, developing strategies that are appropriate given the risks involved and the probability levels required.

Actuaries work in many areas that directly benefit the public through their work in life and non-life insurance, advising pension funds, savings, capital projects, investments, healthcare and risk management. Such work offers management opportunities, with actuaries having a commercial as well as a technical role.

Training and development

To qualify as an actuary you'll need to complete the profession's exams. Most actuarial trainees take the exams whilst working for actuarial employers. Exemptions from some of the exams may be awarded to students who have studied to an appropriate standard in a relevant degree, or have studied actuarial science at postgraduate level. Qualification typically takes 3-6 years. Newly qualified actuaries can earn from £53,000 and over £100,000 as you gain more experience.

International outlook

The UK qualification is already highly valued throughout the world, with 28 per cent of members based overseas. Mutual recognition agreements with other overseas actuarial bodies facilitate the ability of actuaries to move and work in other parts of the world and create a truly global profession.

For more information on qualifications and careers visit our website at

www.actuaries.org.uk

Man Group is a leading global provider of
alternative investment products and solutions.
www.mangroupplc.com

Man Group plc

Winton Capital Management

Winton is a state-of-the-art hedge fund that specialises in using advanced mathematical and statistical techniques to invest in markets on behalf of our clients. Winton was founded in 1997 and our fund has returned an average of 18% a year since inception. That means if you had given us £1,000 in 1997, you would now have over £5,000.

We employ more than 70 researchers holding postgraduate and doctorate degrees covering a wide range of fields, including mathematical statistics, astrophysics, electronic engineering and economics. Our offices are at the Oxford Science Park, Cambridge and in Kensington and Hammersmith (London).

Winton's success as a company is founded upon the mathematical skills of our employees but we also know the value of maths based skills in other areas of life.

Doctors need to be able to understand and present meaningful probabilities to patients to allow them to make informed decisions about their treatment. If a test for a disease is 99% accurate and your result comes back positive, it doesn't mean it's a 99% certainty you've got it!

Governments need to make use of sophisticated statistical analysis to ensure that they can effectively monitor the results of their policies.

Everyone needs to be able to understand the workings and risks of credit cards and mortgages to ensure their own welfare and the health of the wider economy.

The next generation of children in Britain will require more than ever before the proper mathematical skills as they negotiate a modern world racing forward on a wave of engineering, computer science and public statistics. We are therefore proud to support the UK Mathematics Trust whose work is significant in the promotion of mathematics in schools.

If you would like to know more about Winton Capital please contact Emma Watkins at e.watkins@wintoncapital.com.

The Junior Mathematical Challenge and Olympiad

The Junior Mathematical Challenge was held on Thursday 30th April 2009 and over 247,000 pupils took part. Approximately 1200 pupils were invited to take part in the Junior Mathematical Olympiad which was held on Tuesday 16th June. In the following pages, we shall show the question paper and solutions leaflet for both the JMC and JMO.

We start with the JMC paper, the front of which is shown below in a slightly reduced format.

UK JUNIOR MATHEMATICAL CHALLENGE

THURSDAY 30th APRIL 2009

Organised by the **United Kingdom Mathematics Trust from the School of Mathematics, University of Leeds**

The Actuarial Profession
making financial sense of the future

RULES AND GUIDELINES (to be read before starting)

1. Do not open the paper until the Invigilator tells you to do so.
2. Time allowed: **1 hour**.
   No answers, or personal details, may be entered after the allowed hour is over.
3. The use of rough paper is allowed; **calculators** and measuring instruments are **forbidden**.
4. Candidates in England and Wales must be in School Year 8 or below.
   Candidates in Scotland must be in S2 or below.
   Candidates in Northern Ireland must be in School Year 9 or below.
5. **Use B or HB pencil only**. Mark *at most one* of the options A, B, C, D, E on the Answer Sheet for each question. Do not mark more than one option.
6. *Do not expect to finish the whole paper in 1 hour.* Concentrate first on Questions 1-15. When you have checked your answers to these, have a go at some of the later questions.
7. Five marks are awarded for each correct answer to Questions 1-15.
   Six marks are awarded for each correct answer to Questions 16-25.
   Each incorrect answer to Questions 16-20 loses 1 mark.
   Each incorrect answer to Questions 21-25 loses 2 marks.
8. Your Answer Sheet will be read only by a *dumb machine*. **Do not write or doodle on the sheet except to mark your chosen options**. The machine 'sees' all black pencil markings even if they are in the wrong places. If you mark the sheet in the wrong place, or leave bits of rubber stuck to the page, the machine will 'see' a mark and interpret this mark in its own way.
9. The questions on this paper challenge you to **think**, not to guess. You get more marks, and more satisfaction, by doing one question carefully than by guessing lots of answers.
   The UK JMC is about solving interesting problems, not about lucky guessing.

The UKMT is a registered charity

http://www.ukmt.org.uk

1. What is the value of $9002 - 2009$?

A 9336 B 6993 C 6339 D 3996 E 3669

2. How many of the six faces of a die (shown below) have fewer than three lines of symmetry?

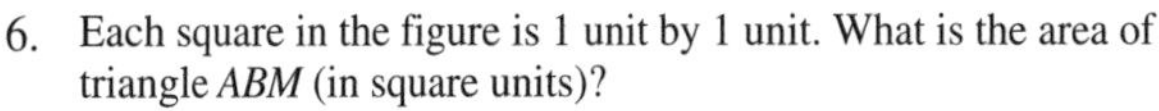

A 2 B 3 C 4 D 5 E 6

3. Which of the following is correct?

A $0 \times 9 + 9 \times 0 = 9$ B $1 \times 8 + 8 \times 1 = 18$ C $2 \times 7 + 7 \times 2 = 27$
D $3 \times 6 + 6 \times 3 = 36$ E $4 \times 5 + 5 \times 4 = 45$

4. Which of the following points is *not* at a distance of 1 unit from the origin?

A (0, 1) B (1, 0) C (0, −1) D (−1, 0) E (1, 1)

5. Which of the following numbers is divisible by 7?

A 111 B 1111 C 11 111 D 111 111 E 1 111 111

6. Each square in the figure is 1 unit by 1 unit. What is the area of triangle *ABM* (in square units)?

A 4 B 4.5 C 5 D 5.5 E 6

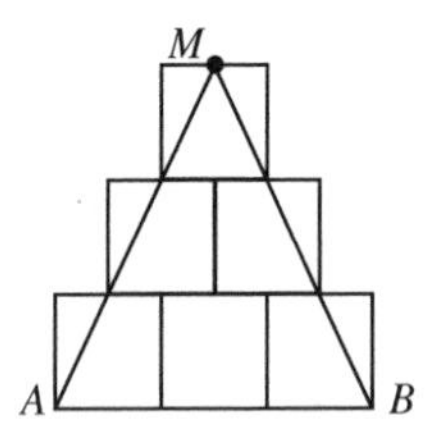

7. How many minutes are there from 11:11 until 23:23 on the same day?

A 12 B 720 C 732 D 1212 E 7212

8. The figure on the right shows an arrangement of ten square tiles. Which labelled tile could be removed, but still leave the length of the perimeter unchanged?

A B C D E

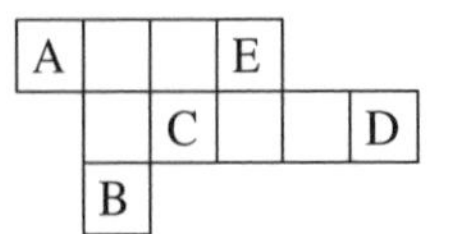

9. How many different digits appear when $\frac{20}{11}$ is written as a recurring decimal?

A 2 B 3 C 4 D 5 E 6

10. The diagram shows three squares of the same size. What is the value of x?

A 105 B 120 C 135 D 150 E 165

11. In a sequence of numbers, each term after the first three terms is the sum of the previous three terms. The first three terms are −3, 0, 2 . Which is the first term to exceed 100?

A 11th term B 12th term C 13th term D 14th term E 15th term

12. Gill is 21 this year. At the famous visit to the clinic in 1988, her weight was calculated to be 5kg, but she now weighs 50kg. What has been the percentage increase in Gill's weight from 1988 to 2009?

A 900% B 1000% C 5000% D 9000% E 10 000%

13. The sum of ten consecutive integers is 5. What is the largest of these integers?

A 2 B 3 C 4 D 5 E more information needed

14. Karen was given a mark of 72 for Mayhematics. Her average mark for Mayhematics and Mathemagics was 78. What was her mark for Mathemagics?

A 66 B 75 C 78 D 82 E 84

15. In Matt's pocket there are 8 watermelon jellybeans, 4 vanilla jellybeans and 4 butter popcorn jellybeans. What is the smallest number of jellybeans he must take out of his pocket to be certain that he takes at least one of each flavour?

A 3 B 4 C 8 D 9 E 13

---

16. The kettle in Keith's kitchen is 80% full. After 20% of the water in it has been poured out, there are 1152 ml of water left. What volume of water does Keith's kitchen kettle hold when it is full?

A 1400 ml B 1600 ml C 1700 ml D 1800 ml E 2000 ml

17. The tiling pattern shown uses two sizes of square, with sides of length 1 and 4. A very large number of these squares is used to tile an enormous floor in this pattern. Which of the following is closest to the ratio of the number of grey tiles on the floor to the number of white tiles?

A 1:1 B 4:3 C 3:2 D 2:1 E 4:1

18. Six friends are having dinner together in their local restaurant. The first eats there every day, the second eats there every other day, the third eats there every third day, the fourth eats there every fourth day, the fifth eats there every fifth day and the sixth eats there every sixth day. They agree to have a party the next time they all eat together there. In how many days' time is the party?

A 30 days B 60 days C 90 days D 120 days E 360 days

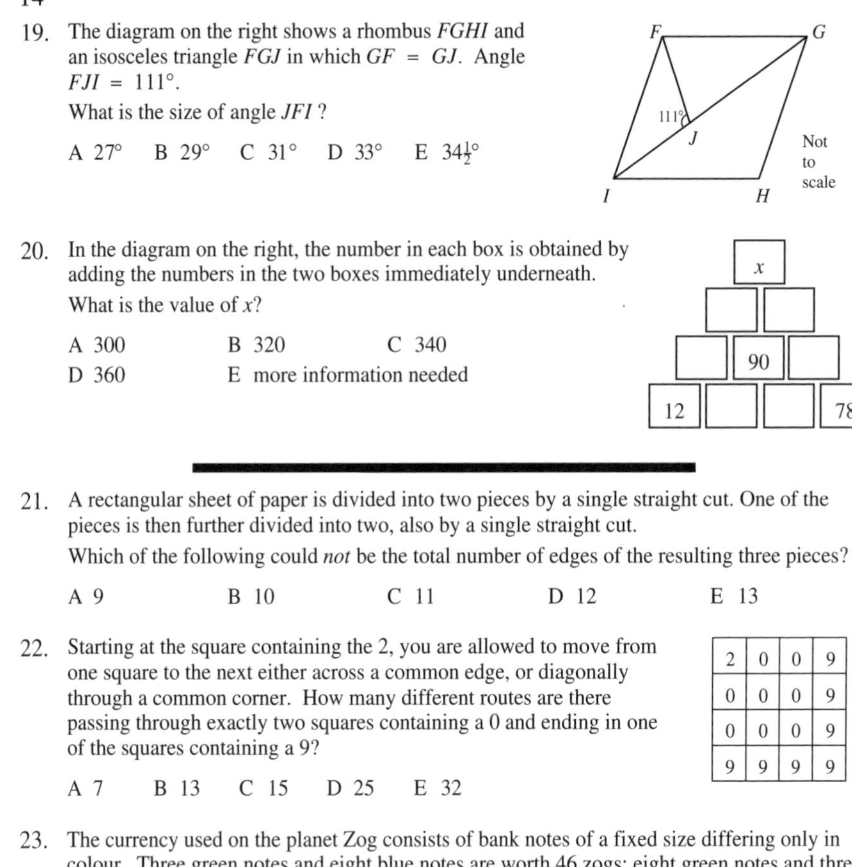

19. The diagram on the right shows a rhombus $FGHI$ and an isosceles triangle FGJ in which $GF = GJ$. Angle $FJI = 111°$.

    What is the size of angle JFI ?

    A $27°$ B $29°$ C $31°$ D $33°$ E $34\frac{1}{2}°$

20. In the diagram on the right, the number in each box is obtained by adding the numbers in the two boxes immediately underneath.

    What is the value of x?

    A 300 B 320 C 340
    D 360 E more information needed

21. A rectangular sheet of paper is divided into two pieces by a single straight cut. One of the pieces is then further divided into two, also by a single straight cut.

    Which of the following could *not* be the total number of edges of the resulting three pieces?

    A 9 B 10 C 11 D 12 E 13

22. Starting at the square containing the 2, you are allowed to move from one square to the next either across a common edge, or diagonally through a common corner. How many different routes are there passing through exactly two squares containing a 0 and ending in one of the squares containing a 9?

    A 7 B 13 C 15 D 25 E 32

2	0	0	9
0	0	0	9
0	0	0	9
9	9	9	9

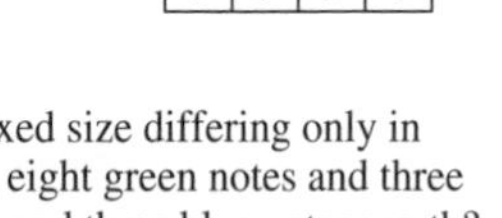

23. The currency used on the planet Zog consists of bank notes of a fixed size differing only in colour. Three green notes and eight blue notes are worth 46 zogs; eight green notes and three blue notes are worth 31 zogs. How many zogs are two green notes and three blue notes worth?

    A 13 zogs B 16 zogs C 19 zogs D 25 zogs E 27 zogs

24. The parallelogram $WXYZ$ shown in the diagram on the right has been divided into nine smaller parallelograms. The perimeters, in centimetres, of four of the smaller parallelograms are shown. The perimeter of $WXYZ$ is 21 cm.

    What is the perimeter of the shaded parallelogram?

    A 5 cm B 6 cm C 7 cm D 8 cm E 9 cm

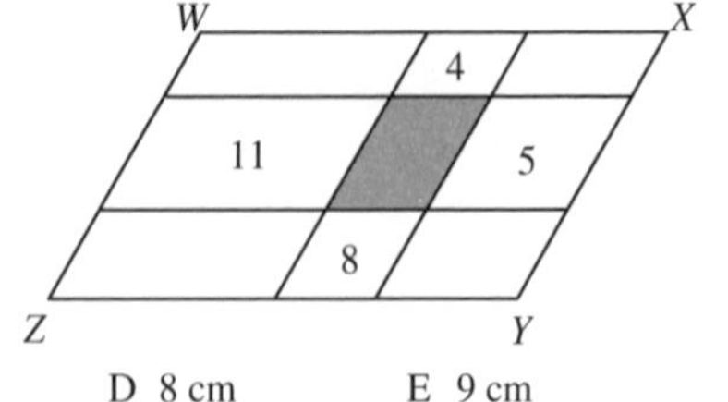

25. In Miss Quaffley's class, one third of the pupils bring a teddy bear to school. Last term, each boy took 12 books out of the library, each girl took 17 books and each teddy bear took 9 books. In total, 305 books were taken out. How many girls are there in Miss Quaffley's class?

    A 4 B 7 C 10 D 13 E 16

The JMC solutions

The usual solutions leaflet was issued.

UK JUNIOR MATHEMATICAL CHALLENGE

THURSDAY 30th APRIL 2009

Organised by the **United Kingdom Mathematics Trust from the School of Mathematics, University of Leeds**

http://www.ukmt.org.uk

The Actuarial Profession
making financial sense of the future

SOLUTIONS LEAFLET

This solutions leaflet for the JMC is sent in the hope that it might provide all concerned with some alternative solutions to the ones they have obtained. It is not intended to be definitive. The organisers would be very pleased to receive alternatives created by candidates.

The UKMT is a registered charity

1. **B** $9002 - 2002 = 7000$ so $9002 - 2009 = 7000 - 7 = 6993$.

2. **B** Each of faces 1, 4 and 5 has four axes of symmetry, whilst each of faces 2, 3 and 6 has two axes of symmetry only.

3. **D** The values of the left-hand sides of the expressions are 0, 16, 28, 36 and 40 respectively.

4. **E** Each of points A, B, C and D is 1 unit from the origin, but the point (1, 1) is at a distance $\sqrt{2}$ units from the origin.

5. **D** The problem may be solved by dividing each of the alternatives in turn by 7, but the prime factorisation of 1001, i.e. $1001 = 7 \times 11 \times 13$, leads to the conclusion that 111 111, which is 111×1001, is a multiple of 7.

6. **B** Triangle ABM has base 3 units and height 3 units, so its area is $\frac{1}{2} \times 3 \times 3$ units^2, that is $4\frac{1}{2}$ units^2.

7. **C** The time difference is 12 hours and 12 minutes, that is 732 minutes.

8. **E** Removing tile A or tile B or tile D has the effect of reducing the perimeter by a distance equal to twice the side of one tile, whilst removing tile C increases the perimeter by that same distance. Removing tile E, however, leaves the length of the perimeter unchanged.

9. **A** $\frac{20}{11} = 1\frac{9}{11} = 1.818181\ldots$, so only two different digits appear.

10. **B** The triangle in the centre of the diagram is equilateral since each of its sides is equal in length to the side of one of the squares. The sum of the angles at a point is 360°, so $x = 360 - (90 + 90 + 60) = 120$.

11. **C** The first thirteen terms of the sequence are −3, 0, 2, −1, 1, 2, 2, 5, 9, 16, 30, 55, 101, ….

12. **A** The increase in Gill's weight is 45 kg, which is 9 times her weight in 1988. So the percentage increase in weight is 900%.
(*The problem refers to* Q14 *in the very first Schools Mathematical Challenge – the forerunner of the current Junior and Intermediate Mathematical Challenges – in* 1988. *This was* '*Weighing the baby at the clinic was a problem. The baby would not keep still and caused the scales to wobble. So I held the baby and stood on the scales while the nurse read off* 78 kg. *Then the nurse held the baby while I read off* 69 kg. *Finally I held the nurse while the baby read off* 137 kg. *What is the combined weight of all three* (*in* kg)?
A 142 B 147 C 206 D 215 E 284.')

13. **D** Let the ten consecutive integers be $x - 4, x - 3, x - 2, x - 1, x, x + 1, x + 2, x + 3, x + 4$ and $x + 5$ respectively. The sum of these is $10x + 5$ so $10x + 5 = 5$, that is $x = 0$. Hence the largest of the integers is 5.

The profile of marks obtained is shown below.

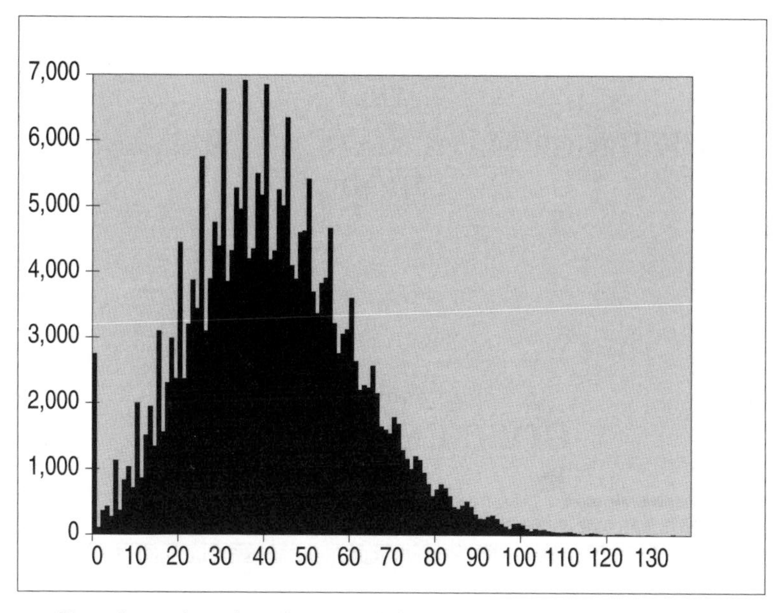

Bar chart showing the actual frequencies in the 2009 JMC

On the basis of the standard proportions used by the UKMT, the cut-off marks were set at

GOLD – 72 or over SILVER – 57 to 71 BRONZE – 45 to 56

A sample of one of the certificates is shown on the next page.

The Junior Mathematical Olympiad is the follow-up competition to the Challenge. It was decided that candidates who obtained a JMC score of 100 or over were eligible to take part in the JMO. This resulted in 1165 candidates being invited.

THE UNITED KINGDOM JUNIOR MATHEMATICAL CHALLENGE

The UK JMC encourages mathematical reasoning, precision of thought, and fluency in using basic mathematical techniques to solve non-standard problems. It is targeted at the top third of pupils in English and Welsh School Years 7-8 (S1 and S2 in Scotland and Years 8-9 in Northern Ireland).

The problems on the UK JMC are designed to make students think, and sometimes smile. Most are accessible to younger students, yet still challenge those with more experience; they are also meant to be memorable and enjoyable.

Mathematics controls more aspects of the modern world than most people realise – from CDs, cash machines, telecommunications and airline booking systems to production processes in engineering, efficient distribution and stock-holding, investment strategies and 'whispering' jet engines. The scientific and industrial revolutions flowed from the realisation that mathematics was both the language of nature, and also a way of analysing – and hence controlling – our environment. In the last fifty years old and new applications of mathematical ideas have transformed the way we live.

All these developments depend on mathematical thinking – a mode of thought whose essential style is far more permanent than the wave of technological change which has made so many recent changes possible. The problems on the UK JMC reflect this style – a style which pervades all mathematics – by challenging students to think clearly about simple, yet unfamiliar problems.

The UK JMC has grown from a national challenge first run in 1988. In 2008 over 241,000 entries were received and over 3,500 schools took part. Certificates were awarded to the highest scoring 40% of candidates (6% Gold, 13% Silver, 21% Bronze).

There is an Intermediate version for those in Years 9 to 11, and a Senior version for those in Years 12 and 13. All three events are organised by the United Kingdom Mathematics Trust and are administered from the School of Mathematics at the University of Leeds.

Further information on the UKMT and its activities can be found at www.ukmt.org.uk

The Junior Mathematical Olympiad

UK Junior Mathematical Olympiad 2009

Organised by The United Kingdom Mathematics Trust

Tuesday 16th June 2009

RULES AND GUIDELINES : READ THESE INSTRUCTIONS CAREFULLY BEFORE STARTING

1. Time allowed: 2 hours.
2. **The use of calculators, measuring instruments and squared paper is forbidden.**
3. All candidates must be in *School Year 8 or below* (England and Wales), *S2 or below* (Scotland), *School Year 9 or below* (Northern Ireland).
4. For questions in Section A *only the answer is required.* Enter each answer neatly in the relevant box on the Front Sheet. Do not hand in rough work. Write in blue or black pen or pencil.

   For questions in Section B you must give *full written solutions*, including clear mathematical explanations as to why your method is correct.

   Solutions must be written neatly on A4 paper, starting each question on a fresh sheet.

   Sheets must be STAPLED together in the top left corner with the Front Sheet on top.

   Do not hand in rough work.
5. Questions A1-A10 are relatively short questions. Try to complete Section A within the first 45 minutes so as to allow well over an hour for Section B.
6. Questions B1-B6 are longer questions requiring *full written solutions.*
   This means that each answer must be accompanied by clear explanations and proofs.
   Work in rough first, then set out your final solution with clear explanations of each step.
7. These problems are meant to be challenging! Do not hurry. Try the earlier questions in each section first (they tend to be easier). Try to finish whole questions even if you can't do many. A good candidate will have done most of Section A and given solutions to at least two questions in Section B.
8. Answers must be FULLY SIMPLIFIED, and EXACT using symbols like π, fractions, or square roots if appropriate, but NOT decimal approximations.

DO NOT OPEN THE PAPER UNTIL INSTRUCTED BY THE INVIGILATOR TO DO SO!

Section A

A1 What is the value of $200^2 + 9^2$?

A2 The diagram shows a regular hexagon inside an equilateral triangle. The area of the larger triangle is 60 cm^2. What is the area of the hexagon?

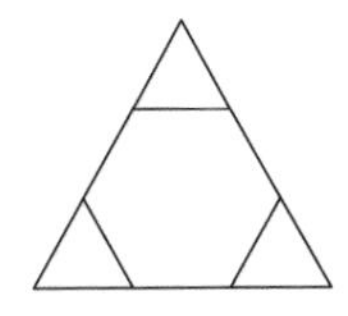

A3 The positive whole numbers a, b and c are all different and $a^2 + b^2 + c^2 = 121$. What is the value of $a + b + c$?

A4 The sum of three numbers is 2009. The sum of the first two numbers is 1004 and the sum of the last two is 1005. What is the product of all three numbers?

A5 Andrea's petrol tank holds up to 44 litres of fuel. She goes to the garage when her tank is a quarter full and puts more petrol in the tank until it is two-thirds full. How many litres of petrol does she put in the tank?

A6 The shorter sides of a right-angled isosceles triangle are each 10 cm long. The triangle is folded in half along its line of symmetry to form a smaller triangle. How much longer is the perimeter of the larger triangle than that of the smaller?

A7 Dean runs on a treadmill for thirty minutes. To keep his mind active as well as his legs, he works out what fraction of the total time has passed at each half minute and minute from the start. How many of the results of his calculations can be expressed in the form $\frac{1}{n}$, where n is an integer greater than 1?

A8 The diagram shows a curve made from seven semicircular arcs, the radius of each of which is 1 cm, 2 cm, 4 cm or 8 cm. What is the length of the curve?

A9 A book has 89 pages, but the page numbers are printed incorrectly. Every third page number has been omitted, so that the pages are numbered 1, 2, 4, 5, 7, 8, … and so on. What is the number on the last printed page?

A10 Gill piles up fourteen bricks into the shape shown in the diagram. Each brick is a cube of side 10 cm and, from the second layer upwards, sits exactly on top of the brick below.
Including the base, what is the surface area of Gill's construction?

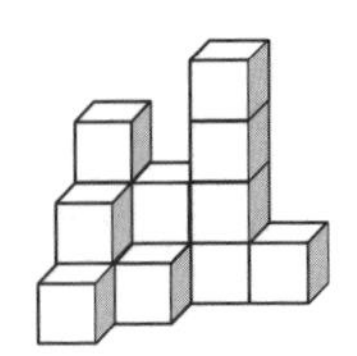

Section B

Your solutions to Section B will have a major effect on your JMO results. Concentrate on one or two questions first and then **write out full solutions** (not just brief 'answers').

B1 In 2007 Alphonse grew twice the number of grapes that Pierre did. In 2008 Pierre grew twice the number of grapes that Alphonse did. Over the two years Alphonse grew 49 000 grapes, which was 7600 less than Pierre. How many grapes did Alphonse grow in 2007?

B2 $ABCD$ is a square. The point E is outside the square so that CDE is an equilateral triangle. Find angle BED.

B3 Tom left a motorway service station and travelled towards Glasgow at a steady speed of 60 mph. Tim left the same service station 10 minutes after Tom and travelled in the same direction at a steady speed, overtaking Tom after a further 1 hour 40 minutes. At what speed did Tim travel?

B4 The diagram shows a polygon $ABCDEFG$, in which $FG = 6$ and $GA = AB = BC = CD = DE = EF$. Also $BDFG$ is a square. The area of the whole polygon is exactly twice the area of $BDFG$.
Find the length of the perimeter of the polygon.

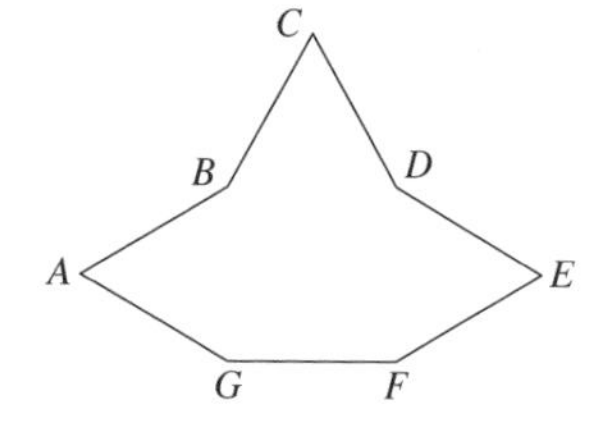

B5 An ant wishes to make a circuit of the board shown, visiting each square exactly once and returning to the starting square. At each step the ant moves to an adjacent square across an edge. Two circuits are considered to be the same if the first follows the same path as the second but either starts at a different square or follows the same path in reverse. How many such circuits are possible?

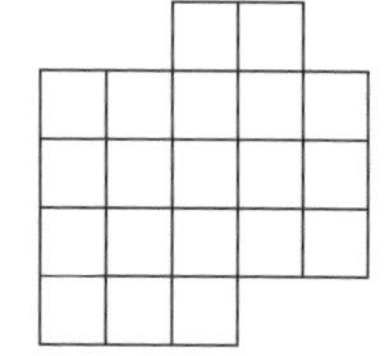

B6 I want to choose a list of n different numbers from the first 20 positive integers so that no two of my numbers differ by 5. What is the largest value of n for which this is possible? How many different lists are there with this many numbers?

UK Junior Mathematical Olympiad 2009 Solutions

A1 40081 $200^2 + 9^2 = 40000 + 81 = 40081$.

A2 40 cm² Since the hexagon is regular, it has interior angles of 120° and can be dissected into six congruent triangles. The small triangles have three angles of 60° and are therefore equilateral with side equal to that of the hexagon. The three triangles inside the large triangle but outside the hexagon are also equilateral with the same side length as the hexagon. So the area of the hexagon is $\frac{6}{9}\left(= \frac{2}{3}\right)$ of the area of the original triangle.

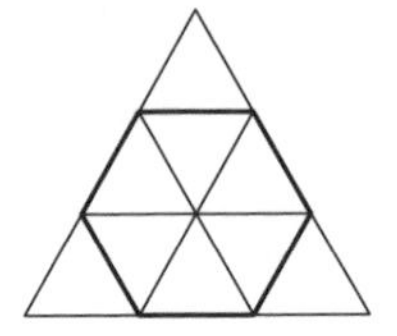

A3 17 It is clear that each of a, b and c must be less than or equal to 10. A brief inspection will show that the only combination of different square numbers which total 121 is $81 + 36 + 4$.

More formally, the problem can be analysed by considering the remainders after dividing the square numbers less than 121 (1, 4, 9, 16, 25, 36, 49, 64, 81 and 100) by three: the remainders are 1, 1, 0, 1, 1, 0, 1, 1, 0 and 1.

When 121 is divided by 3, the remainder is 1. Therefore $a^2 + b^2 + c^2$ must also leave a remainder of 1. Now we can deduce that two of the three squares must leave a remainder of 0 and so be multiples of 3. There are three square numbers below 121 which are multiples of three: 9, 36 and 81. Checking these, we see that 81 and 36 are the only pair to have a sum which differs from 121 by a perfect square, namely 4. So $a + b + c = 9 + 6 + 2 = 17$.

A4 0 The sum of the first two numbers and the last two numbers is $1004 + 1005 = 2009$. This counts the middle number twice. But the sum of all three numbers is 2009, so the middle number is 0. Hence the product of all three numbers is 0.

[*Alternatively*: Let the three numbers be a, b and c.

We have $a + b = 1004,$

$b + c = 1005$

and $a + b + c = 2009.$

Adding the first two equations gives

$$a + 2b + c = 2009$$

and subtracting the third equation from this gives

$$b = 0.$$

Thus the product $abc = 0$.]

A5 $18\frac{1}{3}$ The volume of petrol that Andrea put in, as a fraction of the volume of the tank, is the difference between $\frac{2}{3}$ and $\frac{1}{4}$, which is $\frac{5}{12}$. So she put in $\frac{5}{12}$ of 44 litres and $\frac{5}{12} \times 44 = \frac{5 \times 44}{12} = \frac{5 \times 11}{3} = \frac{55}{3} = 18\frac{1}{3}$.

A6 10 cm Since the original triangle is isosceles and right-angled, folding it produces a smaller triangle, also isosceles and right-angled. By Pythagoras' Theorem, the hypotenuse of the original triangle is $\sqrt{200} = 10\sqrt{2}$ cm. Hence the difference between the perimeters of the two triangles is $(10 + 10 + 10\sqrt{2}) - (5\sqrt{2} + 5\sqrt{2} + 10) = 10$ cm.

Alternatively: Let the length of the shorter sides of the new triangle be x cm, shown below. Then the perimeter of the original triangle is $(20 + 2x)$ cm and the perimeter of the new triangle is $(10 + 2x)$ cm. Hence the difference between the perimeters of the two triangles is 10 cm.

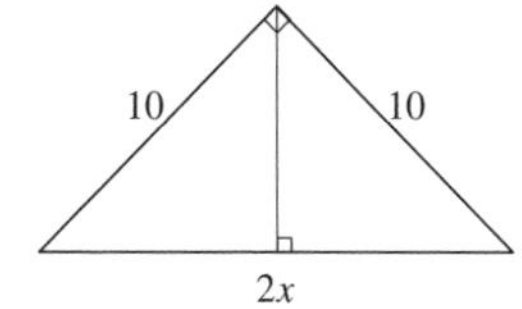

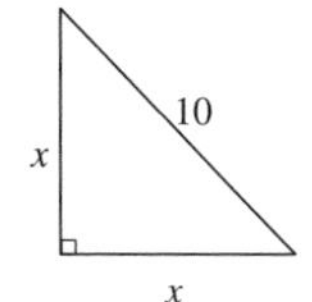

A7 11 As a fraction of 30 minutes, 30 seconds is $\frac{1}{60}$. So we are considering fractions with a denominator of 60. To obtain a fraction of the required form, the numerator must be a factor of 60 (and less than 60). The numerator can therefore be 1, 2, 3, 4, 5, 6, 10, 12, 15, 20 or 30.

A8 22π cm The length of a semicircular arc of radius r is πr and so the total perimeter is $(2 \times (1 + 2 + 4) + 8)\pi = 22\pi$ cm.

A9 133 After every two numbers, one is omitted. Because $89 = 2 \times 44 + 1$, there must be 44 page numbers missing and so the number on the last page is $89 + 44 = 133$.

A10 5000 cm^2 Views from the front and back, the top and bottom, and the two sides are as shown below:

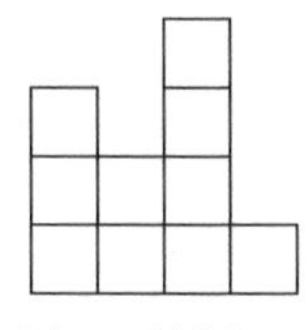

2 lots of 10 faces

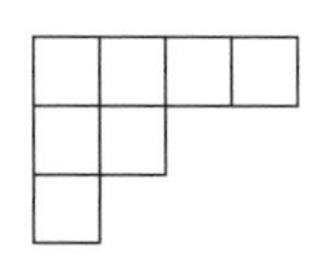

2 lots of 7 faces

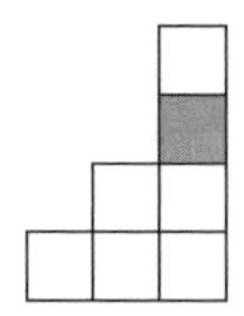

2 lots of 8 faces (one hidden from each side)

Each square face has a surface area of 100 cm^2. Hence the total surface area of Gill's shape is $(20 + 14 + 16) \times 100$ cm^2 $= 5000$ cm^2.

B1 In 2007 Alphonse grew twice the number of grapes that Pierre did. In 2008 Pierre grew twice the number of grapes that Alphonse did. Over the two years Alphonse grew 49 000 grapes, which was 7600 less than Pierre. How many grapes did Alphonse grow in 2007?

Solution

Suppose Pierre grew p grapes in 2007. Then, in 2007, Alphonse grew $2p$ grapes.
Thus, in 2008, Alphonse grew $49\,000 - 2p$ and so Pierre grew $98\,000 - 4p$.
Over the two years, the number of grapes Pierre grew was

$$p + (98\,000 - 4p) = 49\,000 + 7600$$

so $$41\,400 = 3p$$

and $$p = 13\,800.$$

Hence, in 2007, Alphonse grew $2 \times 13\,800 = 27\,600$ grapes.

B2 *ABCD* is a square. The point *E* is outside the square so that *CDE* is an equilateral triangle. Find angle *BED*.

Solution

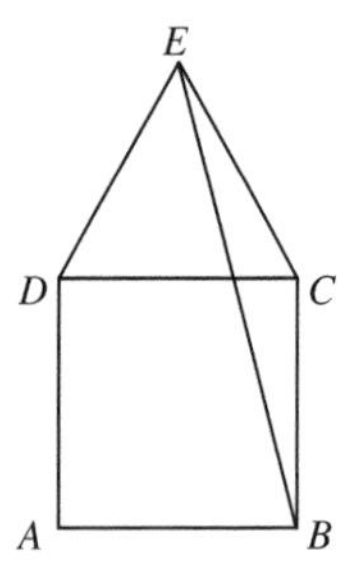

Since *ABCD* is a square, $\angle BCD = 90°$; and since *CDE* is an equilateral triangle, $\angle DCE = 60°$.
Thus $\angle BCE = \angle BCD + \angle DCE = 90° + 60° = 150°$.

Because *CDE* is an equilateral triangle, $EC = DC$ and also, because *ABCD* is a square, $DC = CB$. Hence $EC = CB$ and *ECB* is an isosceles triangle.

So $\angle CEB = \angle CBE = \frac{1}{2}(180 - 150)° = 15°$, and hence $\angle BED = \angle CED - \angle CEB = 60° - 15° = 45°$.

B3 Tom left a motorway service station and travelled towards Glasgow at a steady speed of 60 mph. Tim left the same service station 10 minutes after Tom and travelled in the same direction at a steady speed, overtaking Tom after a further 1 hour 40 minutes. At what speed did Tim travel?

Solution

Tom travels for 10 minutes longer than Tim, a time of 1 hour and 50 minutes.
Travelling at a speed of 60 mph (or 1 mile per minute), Tom travels a distance of 110 miles.
Tim travelled the same distance in 1 hour and 40 minutes ($1\frac{2}{3}$ hours),
so his speed, in mph, was $110 \div 1\frac{2}{3} = 110 \times \frac{3}{5} = 22 \times 3 = 66$ mph.

B4 The diagram shows a polygon *ABCDEFG*, in which $FG = 6$ and $GA = AB = BC = CD = DE = EF$. Also *BDFG* is a square. The area of the whole polygon is exactly twice the area of *BDFG*. Find the length of the perimeter of the polygon.

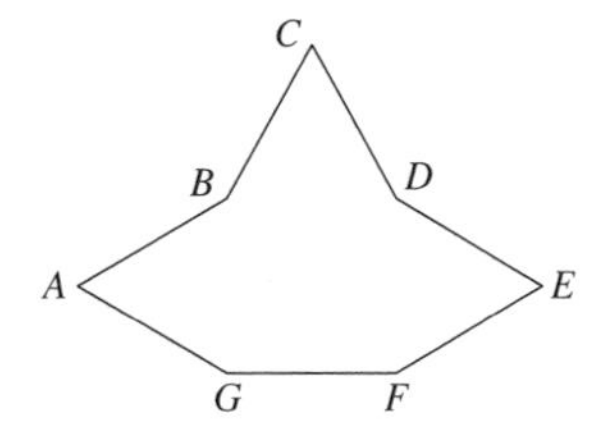

Solution

The area of square *BDFG* is $6 \times 6 = 36$ square units.
So the total area of the three triangles *ABG*, *BCD* and *DEF* is also 36 square units.
These three triangles are congruent and so each has an area of 12 square units.

The area of each triangle is $\frac{1}{2} \times$ base $\times$ height and the base is 6 units and hence we have $\frac{1}{2} \times 6 \times$ height $= 12$, so the height is 4 units.

Let X be the midpoint of BD Then CX is perpendicular to the base BD (since BCD is an isosceles triangle).

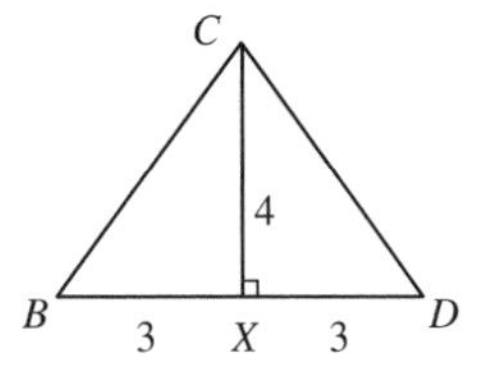

By Pythagoras' Theorem, $BC = \sqrt{3^2 + 4^2} = 5$ units.

Therefore the perimeter of *ABCDEFG* is $6 \times 5 + 6 = 36$ units.

B5 An ant wishes to make a circuit of the board shown, visiting each square exactly once and returning to the starting square. At each step the ant moves to an adjacent square across an edge. Two circuits are considered to be the same if the first follows the same path as the second but either starts at a different square or follows the same path in reverse. How many such circuits are possible?

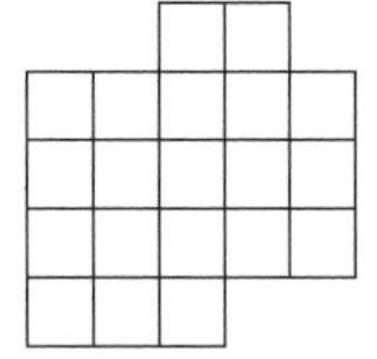

Solution

From Figure 1, we see that there is only one possible route through each of the corner squares, shown shaded, so the ant's path through these squares is as indicated.
There is then only one possible route through square X, giving Figure 2.

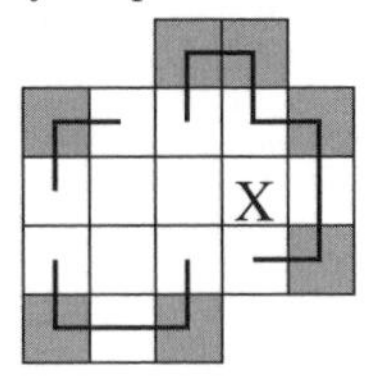

Figure 1

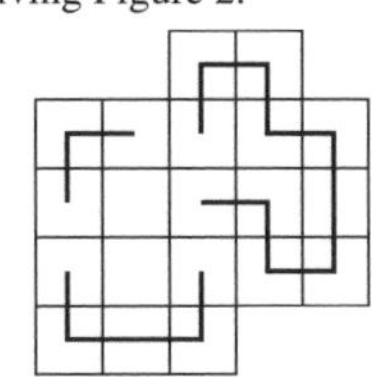

Figure 2

Now consider the shaded square in Figure 3.

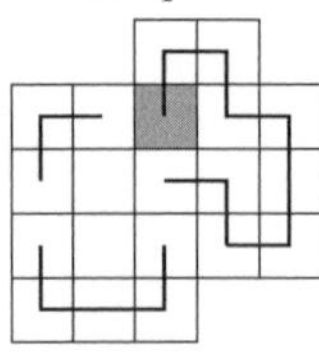

Figure 3

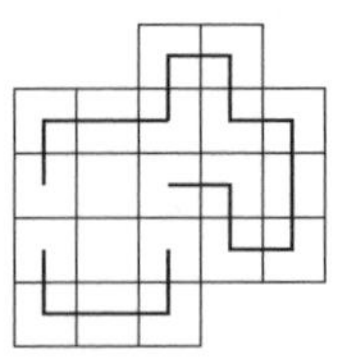

Figure 4

If the path joined this square to the square below, then a closed loop would be formed and the ant could not complete a circuit of the board. Hence the path joins the shaded square to the square on its left (Figure 4).

There are now only two squares which the ant's path has not visited. If a path through all the squares did not join these two, then two loops would be formed instead of a single circuit. We deduce that the path joins these two squares and then there are only two ways of completing the path, as shown in Figure 5.

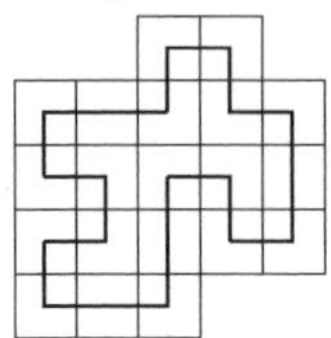

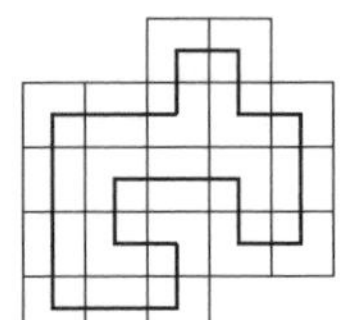

Figure 5

B6 I want to choose a list of n different numbers from the first 20 positive integers so that no two of my numbers differ by 5. What is the largest value of n for which this is possible? How many different lists are there with this many numbers?

Solution

Any such list contains at most two numbers from the set $\{1, 6, 11, 16\}$, at most two numbers from the set $\{2, 7, 12, 17\}$, and likewise from each of the sets $\{3, 8, 13, 18\}$, $\{4, 9, 14, 19\}$ and $\{5, 10, 15, 20\}$. Hence there are at most $5 \times 2 = 10$ numbers altogether. The list of ten numbers, 1, 2, 3, 4, 5, 11, 12, 13, 14, 15 shows that a selection is indeed possible.

From each of these sets of four numbers of the form $\{a, a + 5, a + 10, a + 15\}$, there are three pairs which do not differ by 5, namely $(a, a + 10\}$, $\{a, a + 15\}$ and $\{a + 5, a + 15\}$. Since we are choosing a pair from each of five such sets, there will be $3^5 = 243$ different lists.

The marking and results

The pupils' scripts began arriving very rapidly and the marking took place in Leeds the weekend following the paper, 20th and 21st June. The discussions as to how marks should be given and for what were ably led by Alex Voice who also directed the marking team of Dean Bunnell, David Crawford, Mary-Teresa Fyfe, Gwyn Gardiner, Tony Gardiner, Valeriu Gutu, Carl James, Andrew Jobbings, Peter Neumann, Sylvia Neumann, Stephen Power, Jenny Ramsden, Bill Richardson, Paul Russell, John Slater and Alan Slomson.

As has been stated, the object of the JMO is for pupils to be *challenged*, possibly in ways they have not been before. Some participants may find all of Section B rather beyond them, but it is hoped that they achieve a degree of satisfaction from Section A. Satisfaction is an important aspect of this level of paper; nevertheless, those who do succeed in tackling Section B deserve credit for that and such credit is mainly dependent on getting solutions to questions in Section B which are 'perfect' or very nearly so. The awarding process is somewhat complicated, some might say bizarre. Firstly there are certificates which come in two versions, Participation and Distinction. All who took part are awarded a certificate with about a quarter obtaining a Certificate of Distinction. There were book prizes for the top fifty. The book prize for 2009 was *How Many Socks Make a Pair* by Rob Eastaway. Finally, there were medals of the traditional Gold, Silver, Bronze varieties of design introduced in 2004.

The paper itself was found to be of a similar standard to the 2008 paper. The numbers of medals awarded were: 35 Gold, 66 Silver and 124 Bronze.

The list below includes all the medal winners in the 2009 JMO. Within each category, the names are in alphabetical order.

Special mention should be made of Joshua Degromoboy, George Fortune, Gabriel Gendler and Freddie Illingworth who repeated their 2008 gold medal success. But particular congratulations are due to Noah Fechtorpradine and Liam Hughes for gaining gold in 2007, 2008 and 2009!

The results and all the extras (books, book plates, certificates and medals) were sent away with reasonable chance of reaching schools before pupils departed for their summer holidays.

GOLD MEDALS

Matthew Almond	Sheldon School
Boris Anderson	Royal Grammar School, Guildford
Osaid Ather	St Christopher's School, Hove
Charlie Chen	Homefield, Sutton, Surry
Lixian Chiew	United World College of South East Asia
Wanfung Chui	West Island School, Hong Kong
Stijn Degraaf	Colet Court School, London
Joshua Degromoboy	Bournemouth School
Raymond Ding	Manchester Grammar School
Noah Fechtorpradine	British School of Boston, USA
George Fortune	Altrincham Grammar School for Boys
Gabriel Gendler	Queen Elizabeth's School, Barnet, Herts
Liam Hughes	Welland Park Community College
Freddie Illingworth	Dragon School, Oxford
Junghwan Jang	Sir James Henderson School, Milan
Yun seok Kang	Garden International School, Kuala Lumper
Jungmin Kang	British International School, Vietnam
Edward Kirkby	Amery Hill School, Hants
Seunghun Koh	Dubai British School
Haihao Liu	Island School, Hong Kong
Harry Metrebian	Beacon School, Amersham
Alistair Miller	Hampton School, Middlesex
Rachel Newhouse	Skipton Girls' High School
Shinhyng Park	Fulford School
Robert Phillips	Cheadle Hulme School
Katya Richards	School of St Helen and St Katharine, Abingdon
Morgan Rogers	Belvidere School, Shrewsbury
Kohei Shimahara	Hall School, Wimbledon

Jonghoon Shin	South Island School, Hong Kong
Kieran Sockalingam	Royal Latin School, Buckingham
Caitlin Stark	George Watson's College, Edinburgh
Sanjay Willder	Colet Court School, London
Oliver Woollard	Brookfield School, Southampton
Susan Xue	Marymount Int. Sch., Kingston upon Thames
Gloria Yin	St Paul's Girls' School, London

SILVER MEDALS

James Astles	Salesian College, Farnborough
Samuel Bodansky	The Grammar School at Leeds
Sam Booth	Cardinal Wiseman HS, Middlesex
Theo Caplan	Colet Court School, London
Clement Chan	King Edward's School, Birmingham
Jordan Chong	Colet Court School, London
Horace Chu	German Swiss International School
Dominic Clark	Abbeyfield School, Chippenham
James Clarke	Milbourne Lodge School, Esher
Michael Cui	Magdalen College School, Oxford
Hoagy Cunningham	Charter School, London
Aatreyee Das	Heckmondwike Grammar School
Arron Dhesi	King Edward's School, Birmingham
Robert Eady	Brentwood School
Madhi Elango	Queen Elizabeth's School, Barnet, Herts
Helen Fishwick	St Paul's Girls' School, London
Barnaby Fogg	Queen Elizabeth High School, Gainsborough
Allison Fok	South Island School, Hing Kong
Elizabet Fox	Abbey College, Ramsey, Cambridgeshire
Alistair Garfoot	Old Buckenham Hall School,
Ben Garland	Colet Court School, London
Peter Gerlagh	Altrincham Grammar School for Boys
David Gibson	High School of Glasgow

Ian Gibson	High School of Glasgow
Matthew Gill	All Saints CEVC Middle School, Sudbury
Ben Grant	Tapton School, Sheffield
Jaeho Han	British International School, Vietnam
Alex Harris	Perse School, Cambridge
Thomas Hill	The Hall School, Hampstead
Andrew Huang	Taipei European School
Gareth Jones	Clifton College Prep School, Bristol
Stephen Jones	Magdalen College School, Oxford
Taehun Kim	Frankfurt International School
Sathya Kongara	Kendrick School, Reading
Kai Laddiman	Heathfield Community College
Jaebeen Lee	Bristol Grammar School
Seungjee Lee	St Paul's Girls' School, London
Yebin Lee	St Paul's Girls' School, London
Renhui Lu	Overseas Family School, Singapore
Ben Macrae	Hampton School, Middlesex
Hugo Marrow	Westminster Under School
Domhnall Mcguigan	Edinburgh Academy
Akari Mikita	United World College of South East Asia
Anurag Modi	Queen Elizabeth's Grammar School, Horncastle
George Moore	Oathall Community College
Matthew Parker	Newland House School, Twickenham
Ramsay Pyper	Windlesham House School, West Sussex
Ethan Ren	Cardiff High School
Oliver Sale	Summer Fields School, Oxford
Andy Shaw	Garden International School, Kuala Lumpur
Matthew Shin	Tiffin School, Kingston-upon-Thames
Richard Simon	Abberley Hall School, Worcester
Eshan Singhal	Haberdashers' Aske's School for Boys, Elstree
Nancy Singleton	Loreto College, St Albans
David Sydenham	Colchester Royal Grammar School

Jed Thompson	Westminster Under School
Kavin Vijayakumar	Bancrofts School, Woodford Green
Jonathan Wall	King Edward VI Grammar School, Chelmsford
Callum Watson	Balfron High School
Alistair Webb	Island School, Hong Kong
Ravi Willder	Colet Court School, London
Natasha Wilson	Newlands School
Terence Wu	King Edward VI Camp Hill BS, Birmingham
Joanna Yass	North London Collegiate School
Sebastian Zimmer	Latymer Upper School
Aaron Zolnailucas	Watford Grammar School for Boys

BRONZE MEDALS

Michelle Ahn	South Island School
Charlott Austin	Colchester County High School for Girls
Samuel Banks	Lawrence Sheriff School, Rugby
Danny Bav	Queen Mary's Grammar School, Walsall
Sahil Bavisha	Haberdashers' Aske's School for Boys, Elstree
Lucy Biddle	Wells Cathedral School, Somerset
William Biggs	Beaumont School, St Albans
Joe Blythe	Queen Elizabeth Grammar School, Wakefield
Jenny Burrywes	Churcher's College, Petersfield
James Butcher	Weydon School, Farnham
Karan Chadda	Mountbatten School, Romsey
Michael Chang	St Martins, Ampleforth
Guy Cheng	German Swiss International School
Will Choi	Elstree School
Ga hou Chuen	German Swiss International School
Daniel Clark	Woodhouse Grove School, Bradford
Jessica Climer	King Edward VI Camp Hill Girls' School
Melissa Clubley	Little Heath School, Reading
Eleanor Cook	Oundle and King's Cliffe Middle School
Matthew Coster	Beechwood Park, St Albans
Samuel Coy	Forest School, London

Jack Drury	King Edward VI Aston School, Birmingham
Sean Earley	Wilson's School, Wallington
Eric Edmond	Manchester Grammar School
Jack Evans	Winterfold House School, Kidderminster
Tim Fox	Fitzharrys School, Abingdon
Jiali Gao	Wolverhampton Girls' High School
Adi George	Colet Court School, London
Shaya Ghadimi	King's College School, Wimbledon Common
Edward Grogan	Dragon School, Oxford
Ale x Gunasekera	Abingdon School
Siddhart Gupta	Judd School, Tonbridge
Monica Gupta	Tiffin Girls' School, Kingston-upon-Thames
Georgina Hansen	St Paul's Girls' School, London
Benjamin Hanser	St Gregory the Great School
Jack Hardcastle	St John's College, Hampshire
Hikaru Hotta	Bangkok Patana School
Michael Hulskamp	St Martins, Ampleforth
Willie Hung	Taipei European School
Akash Jayasekara	Westminster Under School
Chance Jeong	Vienna International School
Piers Kasas	Colet Court School, London
Robert Keen	The Priory Academy, Lincoln
Simon Kelly	Lancaster Royal Grammar School
Helen Kim	Lady Eleanor Holles School, Middlesex
Ben Kitson	Sevenoaks School, Kent
Philip Knott	Wilson's School, Wallington, Surrey
Jae Ko	Tapton School, Sheffield
Ben Lavelle	Warwick School, Warwick
Roy Lee	Bishops Stortford College Junior School
Jacob Lee	Overseas Family School, Singapore
Rowan Lee	Nottingham High School
Elizabet Lee	Loughborough High School
Edward Li	Latymer Upper School
Sophia Li	De Stafford School, Caterham

11. The diagram below shows a pattern which repeats every 12 dots.

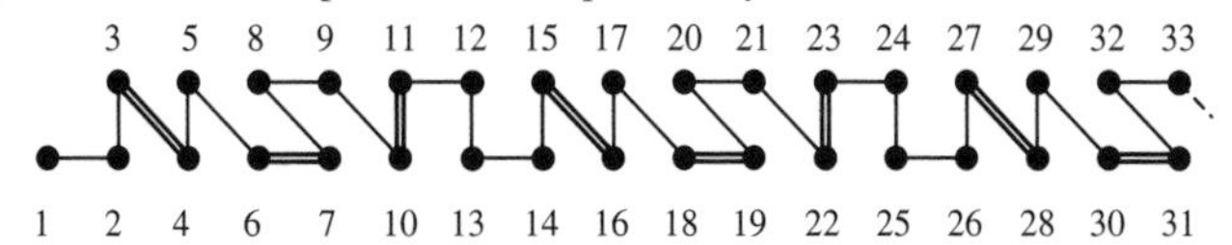

Which of the following does the piece between 2007 and 2011 look like?

A 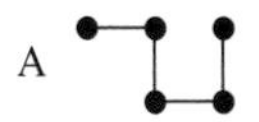 B 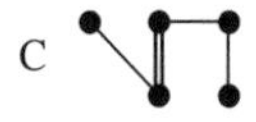 C D E

12. The diagram shows a square inside a regular hexagon. What is the size of the marked angle at X?

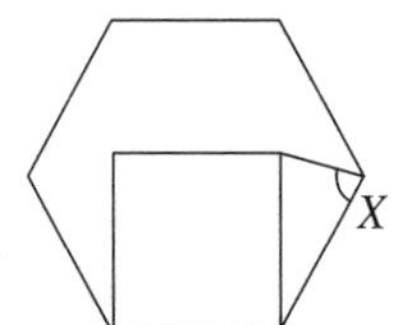

A 45° B 50° C 60° D 75° E 80°

13. The diagram on the right shows a rectangle with sides of length 5 cm and 4 cm. All the arcs are quarter-circles of radius 2 cm. What is the total shaded area in cm^2?

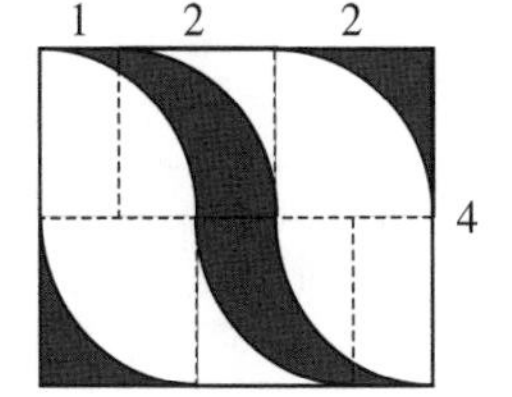

A $12 - 2\pi$ B 8 C $8 + 2\pi$ 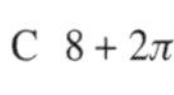
D 10 E $20 - 4\pi$

14. Catherine's computer correctly calculates $\frac{66^{66}}{2}$. What is the units digit of its answer?

A 1 B 2 C 3 D 6 E 8

15. What is the value of $\frac{1}{x+2}$, given that $\frac{1}{x} = 3.5$?

A $\frac{7}{9}$ B $\frac{7}{16}$ C $\frac{9}{7}$ D $\frac{7}{4}$ E $\frac{16}{7}$

16. How many different positive integers n are there for which n and $n^3 + 3$ are both prime numbers?

A 0 B 1 C 2 D 3 E infinitely many

17. PQR is a triangle and S is a point on QR.
$QP = QR = 9$ cm and $PR = PS = 6$ cm.
What is the length of SR?

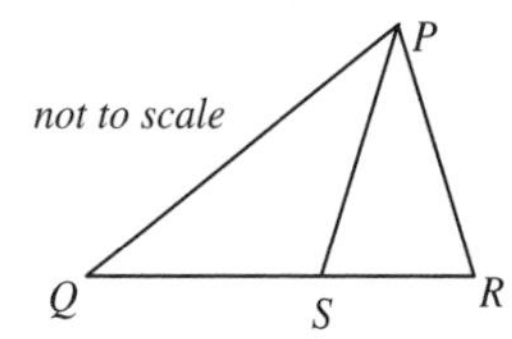

A 1cm B 2cm C 3cm D 4cm E 5cm

18. If p, q are distinct primes less than 7, what is the largest possible value of the highest common factor of $2p^2q$ and $3pq^2$?

A 60 B 45 C 36 D 20 E 15

19. Driving to Birmingham airport, Mary cruised at 55 miles per hour for the first two hours and then flew along at 70 miles per hour for the remainder of the journey. Her average speed for the entire journey was 60 miles per hour. How long did Mary's journey to Birmingham Airport take?

A 6 hours B $4\frac{1}{2}$ hours C 4 hours D $3\frac{1}{2}$ hours E 3 hours

20. A square, of side two units, is folded in half to form a triangle. A second fold is made, parallel to the first, so that the apex of this triangle folds onto a point on its base, thereby forming an isosceles trapezium. What is the perimeter of this trapezium?

A $4 + \sqrt{2}$ B $4 + 2\sqrt{2}$ C $3 + 2\sqrt{2}$ D $2 + 3\sqrt{2}$ E 5

21. There are lots of ways of choosing three dots from this 4 by 4 array. How many triples of points are there where all three lie on a straight line (not necessarily equally spaced)?

A 8 B 16 C 20 D 40 E 44

22. A square is divided into eight congruent triangles, as shown. Two of these triangles are selected at random and shaded black.

What is the probability that the resulting figure has at least one axis of symmetry?

A $\frac{1}{4}$ B $\frac{4}{7}$ C $\frac{1}{2}$ D $\frac{5}{7}$ E 1

23. The diagram shows part of a tiling pattern which is made from two types of individual tiles: 8 by 6 rectangular white tiles and square black tiles. If the pattern is extended to cover an infinite plane, what fraction is coloured black?

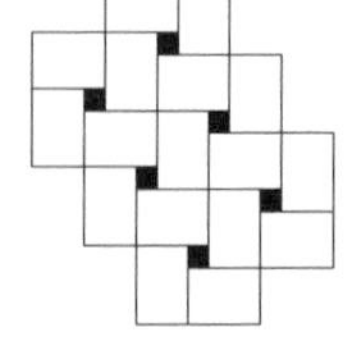

A $\frac{1}{12}$ B $\frac{1}{13}$ C $\frac{1}{25}$ D $\frac{1}{37}$ E $\frac{1}{40}$

24. What is the largest number of the following statements that can be true at the same time?

$$0 < x^2 < 1, \quad x^2 > 1, \quad -1 < x < 0, \quad 0 < x < 1, \quad 0 < x - x^2 < 1$$

A 1 B 2 C 3 D 4 E 5

25. One coin among N identical-looking coins is a fake and is slightly heavier than the others, which all have the same weight. To compare two groups of coins you are allowed to use a set of scales with two pans which balance exactly when the weight in each pan is the same. What is the largest value of N for which the fake coin can be identified using a maximum of two such comparisons?

A 4 B 6 C 7 D 8 E 9

The IMC solutions

As with the Junior Challenge, a solutions leaflet was sent out.

UK INTERMEDIATE MATHEMATICAL CHALLENGE

THURSDAY 5th FEBRUARY 2009

Organised by the **United Kingdom Mathematics Trust**
from the School of Mathematics, University of Leeds

http://www.ukmt.org.uk

The Actuarial Profession
making financial sense of the future

SOLUTIONS LEAFLET

This solutions leaflet for the IMC is sent in the hope that it might provide all concerned with some alternative solutions to the ones they have obtained. It is not intended to be definitive. The organisers would be very pleased to receive alternatives created by candidates.

The UKMT is a registered charity

1. B $1 + 2^3 + 4 \times 5 = 1 + 8 + 20 = 29$.

2. D The first five non-prime positive integers are 1, 4, 6, 8, 9.

3. C The values of these expressions are 5, 8, 9, 8, 5 respectively.

4. A The two acute angles in the quadrilateral in the centre of the diagram are both $(180 - 2x)°$ and the two obtuse angles are both $y°$, so $360 - 4x + 2y = 360$. So $y = 2x$.

5. D Let the number be x. Then $x^2 = 2x^3$, that is $x^2(1 - 2x) = 0$. So $x = 0$ or $x = \frac{1}{2}$. However, x is positive, so the only solution is $x = \frac{1}{2}$.

6. A $\frac{4}{5} = \frac{12}{15}$ and $-\frac{2}{3} = -\frac{10}{15}$, so the number half way between these is $\frac{1}{2}\left(\frac{-10}{15} + \frac{12}{15}\right)$, that is $\frac{1}{15}$.

7. C As can be seen from the diagram, the square whose vertices are the centres of the original four circles has side of length 2 units and this distance is equal to the diameter of the circle through X, Y, Z and T.

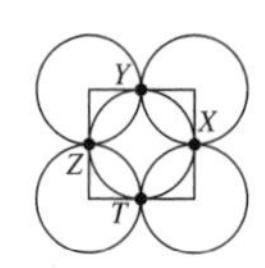

8. A The small square on top will be in the upper half of the divided figure. Now consider the figure formed by moving this square to become an extra square on the left of the second row, as shown. It may now be seen from the symmetry of the figure that the line PX splits the new figure in half – with that small square in the upper half. So the line PX does the same for the original figure.

9. B The ratio of goats to sheep is 100:155 = 20:31.

10. D There are 51 houses numbered from 100 to 150 inclusive. Of these, 17 are multiples of 3, 11 are multiples of 5 and 4 are multiples of both 3 and 5. So the number of houses Fiona can choose from is $51 - (17 + 11 - 4) = 27$.

11. E Note that 2004 is a multiple of 3 (since its digit sum is a multiple of 3) and also a multiple of 4 (since its last two digits form a multiple of 4). So 2004 is a multiple of 12 and hence the part of the pattern between 2007 and 2011 is the same as the part of the pattern between 3 and 7.

12. D Let Y and Z be the points shown. The interior angle of a regular hexagon is 120°, so $\angle XZY = 120° - 90° = 30°$. The side of the square has the same length as the side of the regular hexagon, so $YZ = XZ$. Hence triangle XYZ is isosceles and $\angle ZXY = \angle ZYX = \frac{1}{2}(180° - 30°) = 75°$.

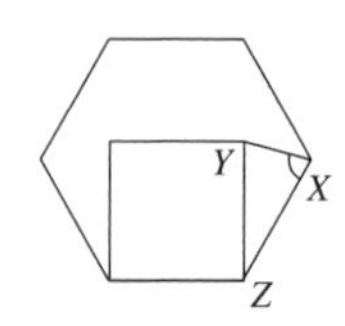

13. A If the shaded regions in the top-right and bottom-left corners of the diagram are moved as shown, the area of the shaded region in both the top half and bottom half of the diagram is now that of a 3×2 rectangle which has a quarter of a circle of radius 2 removed from it.
So the total shaded area is
$2\left(3 \times 2 - \frac{1}{4} \times \pi \times 2^2\right) \text{cm}^2 = (12 - 2\pi)\,\text{cm}^2$.

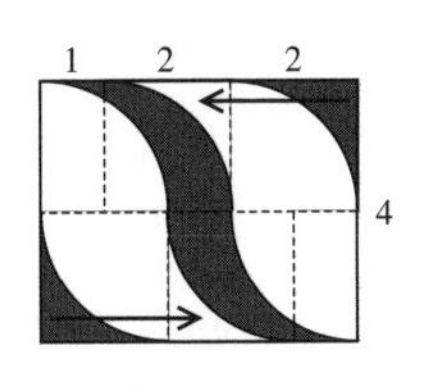

14. E If n is a positive integer then the units digit of 66^n is 6. So when a power of 66 is divided by 2, the units digit of the quotient is either 3 or 8. Now 66^{66} is clearly a multiple of 4, so $\frac{1}{2}(66^{66})$ is even and therefore has units digit 8 rather than 3.

15. B As $\dfrac{1}{x} = 3.5 = \dfrac{7}{2}$, $x = \dfrac{2}{7}$. So $x + 2 = \dfrac{16}{7}$. Hence $\dfrac{1}{x+2} = \dfrac{7}{16}$.

16. B If n is an odd prime, then $n^3 + 3$ is an even number greater than 3 and therefore not prime. The only even prime is 2 (which some would say makes it very odd!) and when $n = 2$, $n^3 + 3 = 11$ which is also prime. So there is exactly one value of n for which n and $n^3 + 3$ are both prime.

17. D Triangles PRS and QPR are similar because: $\angle PSR = \angle QRP$ (since $PR = PS$) and $\angle PRS = \angle QPR$ (since $QP = QR$). Hence $\dfrac{SR}{RP} = \dfrac{RP}{PQ}$, that is $\dfrac{SR}{6} = \dfrac{6}{9}$, that is $SR = 4$.

18. B For all positive integer values of p and q, $2p^2q$ and $3pq^2$ have a common factor of pq. They will also have an additional common factor of 2 if $q = 2$ and an additional common factor of 3 if $p = 3$. As the values of p and q are to be chosen from 2, 3 and 5, the largest possible value of the highest common factor will occur when $p = 3$ and $q = 5$. For these values of p and q, $2p^2q$ and $3pq^2$ have values 90 and 225 respectively, giving a highest common factor of 45.

19. E Let the time for which Mary drove at 70 mph be t hours. Then the total distance covered was $(55 \times 2 + 70 \times t)$ miles. Also, as her average speed over $(2 + t)$ hours was 60 mph, the total distance travelled was $60(2 + t)$ miles.

Therefore $110 + 70t = 120 + 60t$, that is $10t = 10$, that is $t = 1$.

So, in total, Mary's journey took 3 hours.

20. D As can be seen from the figures below, the perimeter of the trapezium is $2 + 3\sqrt{2}$.

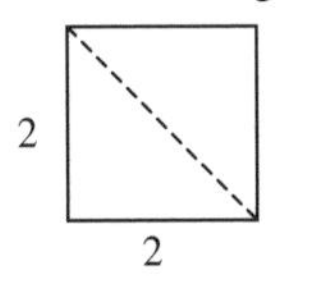

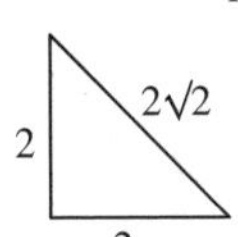

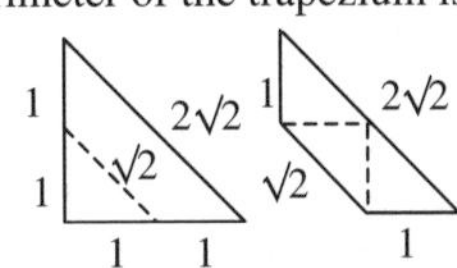

21. E Consider the top row of four dots. One can obtain a triple of dots by eliminating any one of the four – so there are four such triples. The same is true for each of the four rows, each of the four columns and the two main diagonals, giving 40 triples. In addition there are four diagonal lines consisting of exactly three dots, so there are 44 triples in total.

22. D If the first triangle selected to be shaded is a corner triangle, then the final figure will have at least one axis of symmetry provided that the second triangle selected is one of five triangles. For example, if A is chosen first then there will be at least one axis of symmetry in the final figure if the second triangle selected is B, D, E, G or H. The same applies if an inner triangle is selected first: for example, if B is chosen first then there will be at least one axis of symmetry in the final figure if the second triangle selected is A, C, F, G or H.

So, irrespective of which triangle is selected first, the probability that the final figure has at least one axis of symmetry is $\frac{5}{7}$.

23. C Firstly, note that the black squares have side 2 units. The pattern may be considered to be a tessellation of the shape shown on the right. So the ratio of squares to rectangles is 1:2 and hence the fraction coloured black is $\frac{4}{4 + 2 \times 48} = \frac{4}{100} = \frac{1}{25}$.

24. C Reading from the left, we number the statements I, II, III, IV and V. Statement I is true if and only if $-1 < x < 1$; statement II is true if $x > 1$ or if $x < -1$. By considering the graph of $y = x - x^2$, which intersects the x-axis at (0, 0) and (1, 0) and has a maximum at $(\frac{1}{2}, \frac{1}{4})$, it may be seen that statement V is true if and only if $0 < x < 1$.

We see from the table below that a maximum of three statements may be true at any one time.

	$x < -1$	$x = -1$	$-1 < x < 0$	$x = 0$	$0 < x < 1$	$x = 1$	$x > 1$
True statement(s)	II	none	I, III	none	I, IV, V	none	II

25. E As it is known that the fake coin is heavier than all of the others, it is possible in one comparison to identify which, if any, is the fake in a group of three coins: simply compare any two of the three coins – if they do not balance then the heavier coin is the fake, whereas if they do balance then the third coin is the fake. This means that it is possible to find the fake coin when $N = 9$ using two comparisons: the coins are divided into three groups of three and, using the same reasoning as for three individual coins, the first comparison identifies which group of three coins contains the fake. The second comparison then identifies which of these three coins is the fake. However, it is not possible to identify the fake coin in a group of four coins in one comparison only, so it is not always possible to identify the fake coin using two comparisons when $N = 10$. If less than four are put on each side for the first comparison and they balance, then there are more than three left and the fake coin amongst these cannot be identified in one further comparison. Alternatively, if more than three are put on each side for the first comparison and they do not balance, then the fake coin in the heavier group cannot be identified in one further comparison.

The answers

The table below shows the proportion of pupils' choices. The correct answer is shown in bold. [The percentages are rounded to the nearest whole number.]

Qn	A	B	C	D	E	Blank
1	2	**49**	4	44	1	1
2	3	9	17	**51**	15	5
3	1	4	**87**	4	3	1
4	**40**	8	7	9	30	6
5	5	5	11	**61**	15	3
6	**54**	7	12	5	16	4
7	8	10	**59**	8	9	5
8	**56**	21	12	4	3	3
9	25	**36**	17	6	13	2
10	16	13	20	**33**	14	3
11	7	13	15	23	**36**	6
12	14	11	20	**35**	15	5
13	**19**	12	17	6	35	10
14	4	9	44	22	**14**	7
15	16	**29**	12	17	14	11
16	9	**17**	7	5	16	46
17	1	4	35	**16**	2	42
18	5	**14**	7	3	10	61
19	2	5	4	11	**30**	46
20	5	7	5	**7**	4	70
21	3	10	11	13	**13**	50
22	12	6	9	**7**	8	57
23	7	4	**7**	5	4	72
24	7	9	**11**	5	2	65
25	9	5	4	6	**4**	72

IMC 2009: Some comments on the pupils' choice of answers as sent to schools in the letter with the results

The mean score of 36 was significantly lower than in 2008, despite the Problem Group‹s attempt to set an easier paper. None of the early questions turned out to be disasters, but with the exception of Question 3, none was found to be really easy.

It is pleasing to report some progress on the BODMAS front. In 2007 only 5% of the students gave the right answer to a question for which knowledge of the BODMAS convention was needed. Last year 30% of the pupils gave the correct answer to a similar question. This year 49% gave the correct answer to Question 1. While this is pleasing, it remains a matter for concern that 44% of the pupils chose the answer which follows from interpreting $1 + 23 + 4 \times 5$, wrongly, as $(1 + 23 + 4) \times 5$. The importance of BODMAS was explained in the comments on the 2008 IMC. These are reprinted in UKMT Yearbook for 2007-8 on page 48.

Although 88% of the students gave the correct answer to Question 3, the response to Question 9, also involving percentages, was rather disappointing, although more chose the correct answer than any other.

We hope that teachers will be able to find the time for some follow up work on some of these questions. The Geometry questions 4, 12 and 17, and the Algebra question 15 are particularly worthy of attention.

As always, we welcome comments on the questions, and, particularly, their level of difficulty.

The profile of marks obtained is shown below.

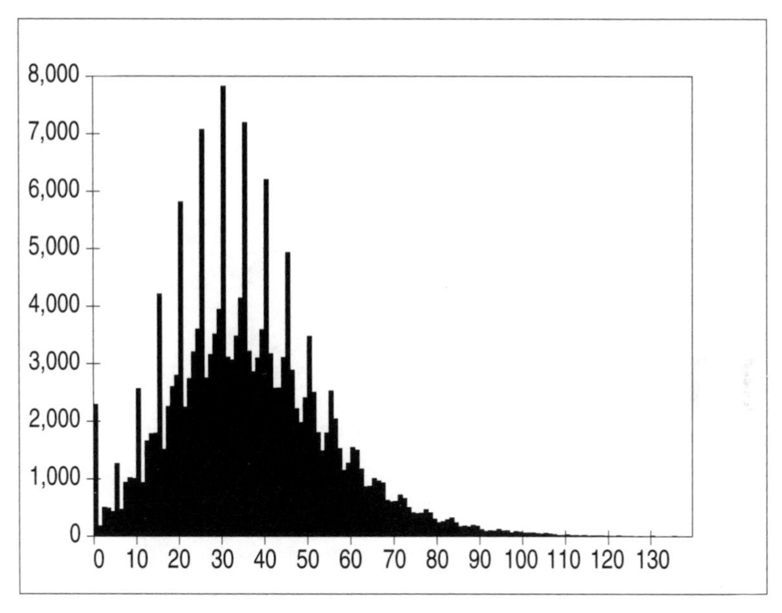

Bar chart showing the actual frequencies in the 2009 IMC

On the basis of the standard proportions used by the UKMT, the cut-off marks were set at

GOLD – 66 or over SILVER – 51 to 65 BRONZE – 39 to 50

The certificates were virtually identical in design to those used for the JMC.

The cut-off scores for the follow-up competitions were

Year (E&W)		Minimum mark	Event		Minimum mark	Event
11		99	Maclaurin		77	Kangaroo Pink
10		90	Hamilton		77	Kangaroo Pink
9		83	Cayley		66	Kangaroo Grey

The Intermediate Mathematical Olympiad and Kangaroo

(a) *Kangaroo*

The 2009 European Kangaroo (a multiple choice paper with 25 questions) took place on Thursday 19th March. It was also held in many other countries across Europe and beyond with over three million candidates. As in previous years, the UKMT constructed two Kangaroo papers.

EUROPEAN 'KANGAROO' MATHEMATICAL CHALLENGE
'GREY'
Thursday 19th March 2009

Organised by the United Kingdom Mathematics Trust and the Association Kangourou Sans Frontières

This competition is being taken by 5 million students in over 40 countries worldwide.

RULES AND GUIDELINES (to be read before starting):

1. Do not open the paper until the Invigilator tells you to do so.
2. Time allowed: **1 hour**.
   No answers, or personal details, may be entered after the allowed hour is over.
3. The use of rough paper is allowed; **calculators** and measuring instruments are **forbidden**.
4. Candidates in England and Wales must be in School Year 9 or below.
   Candidates in Scotland must be in S2 or below.
   Candidates in Northern Ireland must be in School Year 10 or below.
5. **Use B or HB pencil only**. For each question mark *at most one* of the options A, B, C, D, E on the Answer Sheet. Do not mark more than one option.
6. Five marks will be awarded for each correct answer to Questions 1 - 15.
   Six marks will be awarded for each correct answer to Questions 16 - 25.
7. *Do not expect to finish the whole paper in 1 hour*. Concentrate first on Questions 1-15. When you have checked your answers to these, have a go at some of the later questions.
8. The questions on this paper challenge you **to think**, not to guess. Though you will not lose marks for getting answers wrong, you will undoubtedly get more marks, and more satisfaction, by doing a few questions carefully than by guessing lots of answers.

Enquiries about the European Kangaroo should be sent to: Maths Challenges Office, School of Mathematics, University of Leeds, Leeds, LS2 9JT.
(Tel. 0113 343 2339)
http://www.ukmt.org.uk

2009 European Grey Kangaroo

1. Which of the following calculations results in an even number?

   A $2 \times 0 + 0 + 9$ B $2 + 0 + 0 + 9$ C $200 - 9$ D $200 + 9$ E 200×9

2. The star on the right is formed from 12 identical equilateral triangles. The length of the perimeter of the star is 36 cm. What is the length of the perimeter of the shaded hexagon?

   A 12 cm B 18 cm C 24 cm D 30 cm E 36 cm

3. The product of four different positive integers is 100. What is the sum of these four integers?

   A 10 B 12 C 14 D 15 E 18

4. In the diagram on the right, QSR is a straight line, $\angle QPS = 12°$ and $PQ = PS = RS$. What is the size of $\angle QPR$?

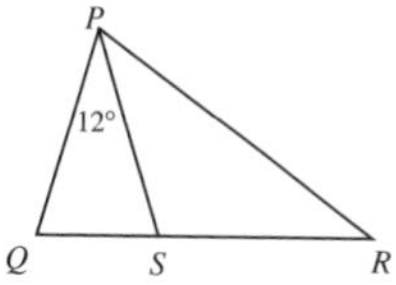

   A 36° B 42° C 54° D 60° E 84°

   P 12° Q S R

5. Which of the following knots consist of more than one loop of rope?

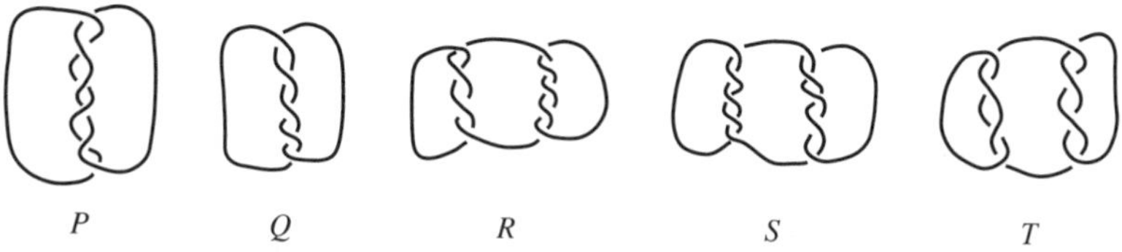

   P Q R S T

   A P, R and T B R, S and T C P, R, S and T
   D all of P, Q, R, S and T E none of A, B, C or D

6. How many positive integers n exist for which n^2 has the same number of digits as n^3 ?

   A 0 B 3 C 4 D 9 E infinitely many

7. The diagram on the right shows nine points in a square array. What is the smallest number of points that need to be removed in order that no three of the remaining points are in a straight line?

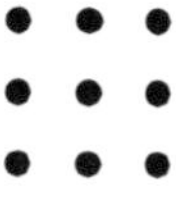

   A 1 B 2 C 3 D 4 E 7

8. Nick measured all six of the angles in two triangles – one acute-angled and one obtuse-angled. He remembered that four of the angles were 120°, 80°, 55° and 10°. What is the size of the smallest angle of the acute-angled triangle?

   A 5° B 10° C 45° D 55° E more information needed

9. The diagram shows four circles each of which touches the largest square and two adjacent circles. A second square has its vertices at the midpoints of the sides of the largest square and the central square has its vertices at the centres of the circles. What is the ratio of the total shaded area to the area of the outer square?

   A $\pi : 12$ B $1 : 4$ C $(\pi + 2) : 16$ D $1 : 3$ E $\pi : 4$

10. A magical island is inhabited entirely by knights (who always tell the truth) and knaves (who always tell lies). One day 25 of the islanders were standing in a queue. The first person in the queue said that everybody behind was a knave. Each of the others in the queue said that the person immediately in front of them in the queue was a knave. How many knights were there in the queue?

A 0 B 12 C 13 D 24 E more information needed

11. The diagram shows a solid with six triangular faces. At each vertex there is a number and two of the numbers are 1 and 5, as shown. For each face the sum of the numbers at the three vertices of each face is calculated, and all the sums are the same. What is the sum of all five numbers at the vertices?

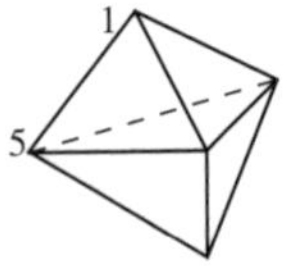

A 9 B 12 C 17 D 18 E 24

12. In the equation $\frac{E\times I\times G\times H\times T}{F\times O\times U\times R} = T\times W\times O$, the same letter stands for the same digit and different letters stand for different digits.
How many different possible values are there for the product $T\times H\times R\times E\times E$?

A 1 B 2 C 3 D 4 E 5

13. In each of the squares in the grid, one of the letters P, Q, R and S must be entered in such a way that adjacent squares (whether connected by an edge or just a corner) do not contain the same letter. Some of the letters have already been entered as shown.
What are the possibilities for the letter in the shaded square?

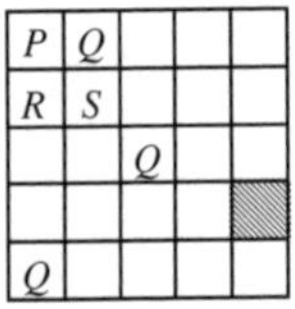

P	*Q*			
R	*S*			
		Q		
Q				

A only *Q* B only *R* C only *S* D either *R* or *S*, but no others
E it is impossible to complete the grid

14. The diagram shows a regular 9-sided polygon (a *nonagon* or an *enneagon*) with two of the sides extended to meet at the point *X*.
What is the size of the acute angle at *X*?

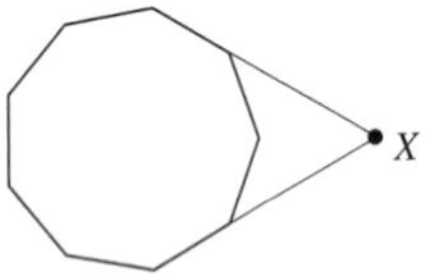

A 40° B 45° C 50° D 55° E 60°

15. The diagram shows the first three patterns in a sequence in which each pattern has a square hole in the middle. How many small shaded squares are needed to build the **tenth** pattern in the sequence?

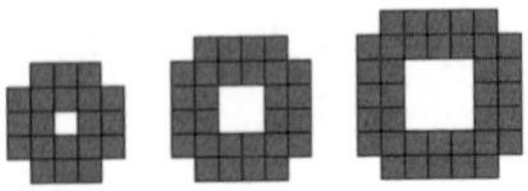

A 76 B 80 C 84 D 92 E 100

16. How many ten-digit numbers are there which contain only the digits 1, 2 or 3, and in which any pair of adjacent digits differs by 1?

A 16 B 32 C 64 D 80 E 100

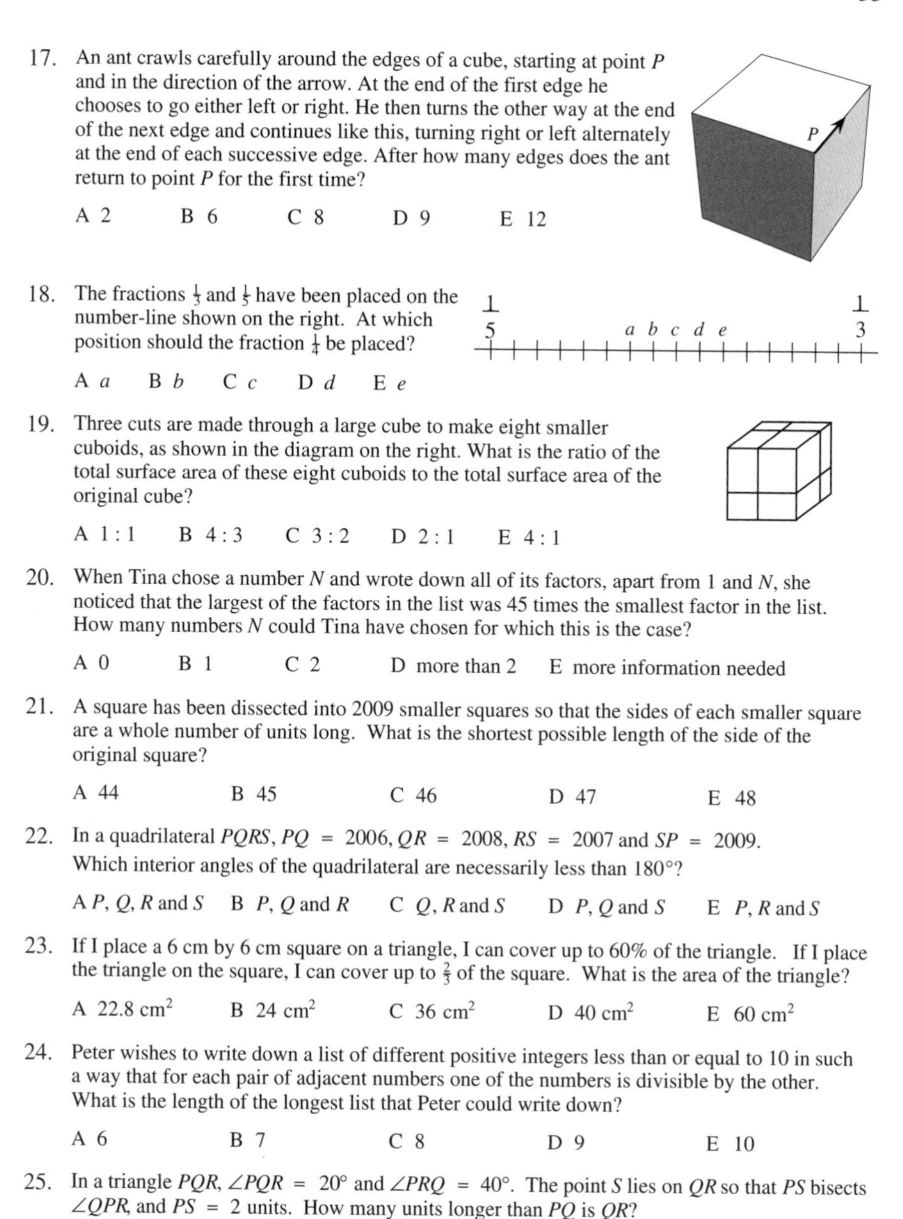

17. An ant crawls carefully around the edges of a cube, starting at point P and in the direction of the arrow. At the end of the first edge he chooses to go either left or right. He then turns the other way at the end of the next edge and continues like this, turning right or left alternately at the end of each successive edge. After how many edges does the ant return to point P for the first time?

    A 2 B 6 C 8 D 9 E 12

18. The fractions $\frac{1}{3}$ and $\frac{1}{5}$ have been placed on the number-line shown on the right. At which position should the fraction $\frac{1}{4}$ be placed?

    A a B b C c D d E e

19. Three cuts are made through a large cube to make eight smaller cuboids, as shown in the diagram on the right. What is the ratio of the total surface area of these eight cuboids to the total surface area of the original cube?

    A 1 : 1 B 4 : 3 C 3 : 2 D 2 : 1 E 4 : 1

20. When Tina chose a number N and wrote down all of its factors, apart from 1 and N, she noticed that the largest of the factors in the list was 45 times the smallest factor in the list. How many numbers N could Tina have chosen for which this is the case?

    A 0 B 1 C 2 D more than 2 E more information needed

21. A square has been dissected into 2009 smaller squares so that the sides of each smaller square are a whole number of units long. What is the shortest possible length of the side of the original square?

    A 44 B 45 C 46 D 47 E 48

22. In a quadrilateral $PQRS$, $PQ = 2006$, $QR = 2008$, $RS = 2007$ and $SP = 2009$. Which interior angles of the quadrilateral are necessarily less than 180°?

    A P, Q, R and S B P, Q and R C Q, R and S D P, Q and S E P, R and S

23. If I place a 6 cm by 6 cm square on a triangle, I can cover up to 60% of the triangle. If I place the triangle on the square, I can cover up to $\frac{2}{3}$ of the square. What is the area of the triangle?

    A 22.8 cm^2 B 24 cm^2 C 36 cm^2 D 40 cm^2 E 60 cm^2

24. Peter wishes to write down a list of different positive integers less than or equal to 10 in such a way that for each pair of adjacent numbers one of the numbers is divisible by the other. What is the length of the longest list that Peter could write down?

    A 6 B 7 C 8 D 9 E 10

25. In a triangle PQR, $\angle PQR = 20°$ and $\angle PRQ = 40°$. The point S lies on QR so that PS bisects $\angle QPR$, and $PS = 2$ units. How many units longer than PQ is QR?

    A 1 B 1.5 C 2 D 4 E more information needed

Solutions to the 2009 European Grey Kangaroo

1. **E** The values of the expressions are: A 9; B 11; C 191; D 209 and E 1800.

2. **B** The perimeter of the star is formed from 12 sides of the equilateral triangles and that of the hexagon from 6 sides. So the perimeter of the hexagon is $\frac{1}{2} \times 36 = 18$ cm.

3. **E** Since $100 = 2 \times 2 \times 5 \times 5$, the only possible product of four *different* positive integers which equals 100 is $1 \times 2 \times 5 \times 10$. The sum of these integers is $1 + 2 + 5 + 10 = 18$.

4. **C** Observing that triangle PQS is isosceles, we have $\angle PSQ = \frac{1}{2}(180° - 12°) = 84°$ and hence $\angle PSR = 180° - 84° = 96°$.
Since triangle PRS is also isosceles, we have $\angle SPR = \frac{1}{2}(180° - 96°) = 42°$.
Hence $\angle QPR = 12° + 42° = 54°$.

5. **A** The diagrams below show that only P, R and T are made from more than one loop.

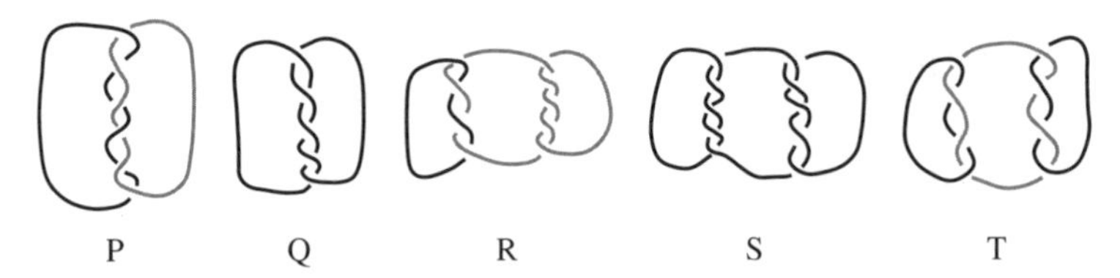

6. **B** Firstly note that if $n \geqslant 10$, then $n^3 \geqslant 10n^2$ so n^3 will have at least one more digit than n^2. For all $n < 10$, we have $n^2 < 100$, so n^2 has either 1 or 2 digits, but n^3 has 3 digits for $n > 4$ since $5^3 = 125$, so we need only consider $n = 1, 2, 3$ or 4. For $n = 1$ and 2, n^2 and n^3 both have one digit; for $n = 4$, $n^2 = 16$ and $n^3 = 64$ both have two digits. However for $n = 3$, $n^2 = 9$ has one digit while $n^3 = 27$ has two digits.

7. **C** At least one point must be removed from each of the three horizontal lines; so at least three points need to be removed. However, removing the three points lying on either diagonal does what is required.

8. **C** We shall refer to the acute-angled triangle as triangle A and the obtuse-angled triangle as triangle B. The 120° angle must belong to B; so the sum of its other two angles is 60°. Therefore the 80° angle must belong to A. If the 10° angle also belonged to A, that would make A a right-angled triangle, which it is not. So the 10° angle belongs to B. The final angle in B must be $180° - 120° - 10° = 50°$. So the 55° angle is in A and the final angle of A is $180° - 80° - 55° = 45°$.

9. **B** First, note that the middle-sized square passes through the centres of the four circles. Each side of the middle-sized square together with the edges of the outer square creates a right-angled isosceles triangle with angles of 45°. Thus the angles these sides make with the inner square are also 45°. Each side of the middle-sized square bisects the area of a circle. The inner half of that circle is made up of two shaded segments with angles of 45° which together are equal in area to the unshaded right-angled segment. Thus the total shaded area is exactly equal to the area of the inner square and hence equal to one-quarter of the area of the outer square.

10. B The first person cannot be telling the truth since if all the others are knaves, this contradicts that they are telling the truth when they say the person in front is a knave!

The second person says the first is a knave so is telling the truth; he is a knight. The third says this knight is a knave so is lying; he is a knave. Continuing in this way we see that there is an alternating sequence of 13 knaves and 12 knights.

11. C Let the numbers at two of the other vertices be u and v, as shown in the diagram on the right. The three faces sharing the vertex labelled with the number 1 all have the same sum. Then $1 + v + u = 1 + 5 + u$ and so $v = 5$. Similarly, $1 + v + 5 = 1 + v + u$ so $u = 5$. Hence the sum for each face is $1 + 5 + 5$, i.e. 11, and we see that the number at the bottom vertex is 1. The total of all the vertices is $1 + 5 + 5 + 5 + 1 = 17$.

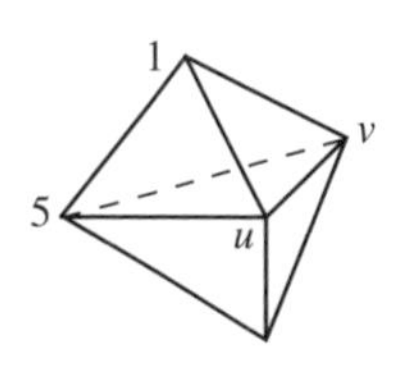

12. A If we rewrite the equation we get the product $E\times I\times G\times H\times T = T\times W\times O\times F\times O\times U\times R$. There are 10 different letters here, so each number from 0 to 9 must be represented by one of the letters. So one letter is 0. Any product where this letter appears is 0. Hence both sides must include this letter. The only letter on both sides is T. Hence $T = 0$ and the product $T\times H\times R\times E\times E = 0$.

13. D It is clear that there is a unique way to complete the top three rows, as shown on the right (start in the second square of the third row). Thereafter it is possible to complete the fourth row with R and S alternating and the fifth row $QPQPQ$.

P	*Q*	*P*	*Q*	*P*
R	*S*	*R*	*S*	*R*
Q	*P*	*Q*	*P*	*Q*
Q				

14. E The exterior angles of a regular nonagon are $360° \div 9 = 40°$, whence the interior angles are $180° - 40° = 140°$. In the arrowhead quadrilateral whose rightmost vertex is X, three of the angles are $40°$, $40°$ and $360° - 140° = 220°$ and these add up to $300°$. So the angle at X is $60°$.

[It is now possible to see that the entire nonagon can fit neatly inside an equilateral triangle and so the angle at X is $60°$.]

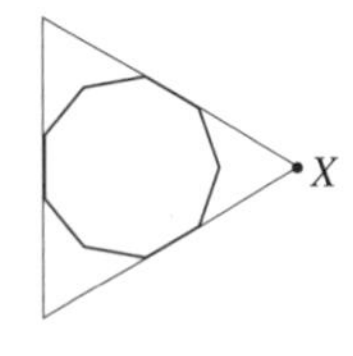

15. D One way to proceed is to regard the pattern as four arms, each two squares wide, with four corner pieces of three squares each. So for the nth pattern, we have $4 \times 2 \times n + 4 \times 3 = 8n + 12$. For $n = 10$, we need $8 \times 10 + 12$, i.e. 92 squares.

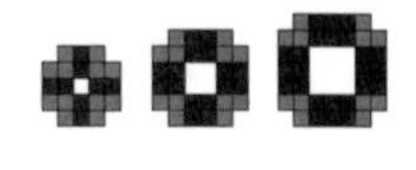

[Alternatively, it is possible to see the pattern as a complete square with the four corners and a central square removed. So for the nth pattern, we have a complete $(n + 4)(n + 4)$ square with the four corners and a central $n \times n$ square removed. Hence the number of squares is $(n + 4)^2 - n^2 - 4 = 8n + 12$.

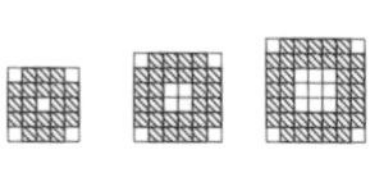

16. C The digits 1 and 3 will always be followed by the digit 2. The digit 2 can be followed by either 1 or 3. Hence the digit 2 appears exactly five times in a ten-digit number, in alternate positions.

If the first digit is 2, then in each even position we have two choices, 1 or 3. This gives $2 \times 2 \times 2 \times 2 \times 2 = 32$ possibilities. Otherwise, the second digit is 2 and in each odd position we have two choices. So again there are 32 possibilities, making a total of 64.

17. B At Q the ant can choose first to go left to T, then right to W. Otherwise, at Q he can go right to R and then left to W. Note that W is the corner diagonally opposite to P and is reached by either route after three edges (and no fewer). So after exactly three more edges, the ant must reach the corner opposite W, that is, P.

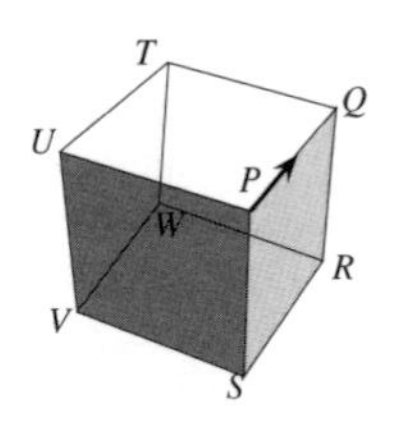

18. A The difference between $\frac{1}{3}$ and $\frac{1}{5}$ is $\frac{1}{3} - \frac{1}{5} = \frac{2}{15}$. This section of the number line is divided into 16 intervals, each of length $\frac{2}{15} \div 16 = \frac{1}{120}$. The difference between $\frac{1}{4}$ and $\frac{1}{5}$ is $\frac{1}{4} - \frac{1}{5} = \frac{1}{20} = \frac{6}{120}$, and hence $\frac{1}{4}$ is six smaller intervals from $\frac{1}{5}$, at point a.

19. D After the cuts, eight smaller cuboids are formed and so we can conclude that the cuts are parallel to the faces of the large cube. Each of the smaller cuboids has three matching pairs of faces, one on the outside of the large cube and one inside. So the total surface area of the smaller cuboids is twice the surface area of the cube.

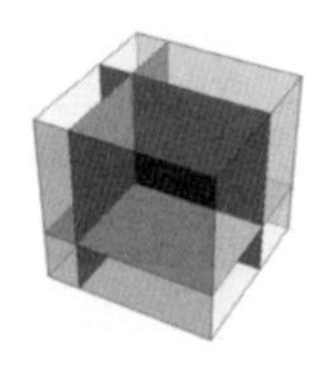

20. C Let the smallest prime factor of N be p, whence the second largest factor, and the highest factor Tina wrote down, is $\frac{N}{p}$. Now we have $\frac{N}{p} = 45p$ whence $N = 45p^2$. Since N is a multiple of 45, it has prime factors of 3 and 5 and, because p is the smallest prime factor of N, we can conclude that p can be only 2 or 3. Hence either $N = 45 \times 2^2 = 180$ or $N = 45 \times 3^2 = 405$.

21. B It is clear that a 44×44 square would be too small to accommodate 2009 squares, because $44 \times 44 = 1936$. Now $45 \times 45 = 2025$, which is 16 squares too many. However, if we use 18 squares as shown in the diagram to form two 3×3 squares we get a total of 2009.

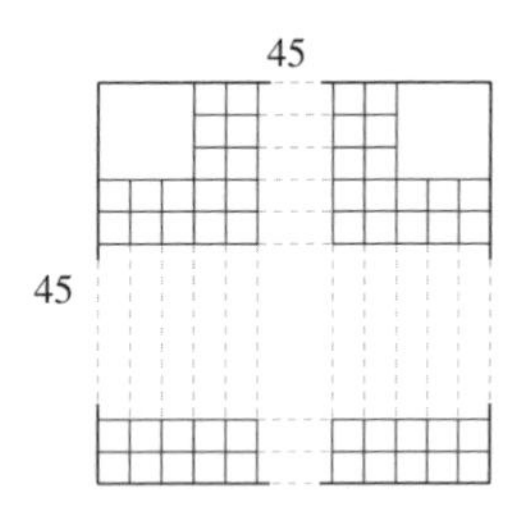

22. E Consider first a general case where in a quadrilateral $TUVW$ the interior angle at T is more than 180°. Let UT be extended to meet VW at X.

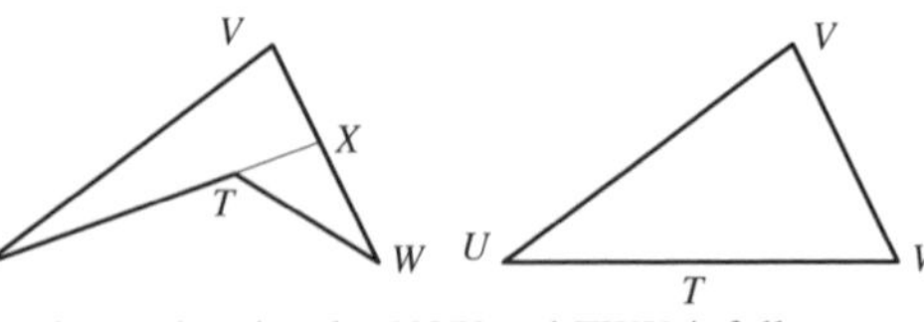

Then, by the triangle equality applied to the triangles UXV and TWX, it follows that

$$UX < UV + VX$$

and $$TW < TX + XW.$$

Adding these inequalities gives $$UX + TW < UV + VX + TX + XW,$$

that is

$UT + TX + TW < UV + VX + TX + VW.$

Hence $$UT + TW < UV + VX + XW,$$

that is $$UT + TW < UV + VW.$$

In the case where the angle at T is 180°, UVW is a triangle and by the triangle equality $UW < UV + VW$, that is, again, $UT + TW < UV + VW$.

Thus if the interior angle at a given vertex of a quadrilateral is θ where $\theta \geqslant 180°$ the sum of the lengths of the sides adjacent to this vertex is less than the sum of the lengths of the other two sides.

[The above argument appears as Proposition 21 in Book 1 in the ancient treatise on geometry, *The Elements*, by the Greek mathematician Euclid. There is an excellent online version (at http://tinyurl.com/6neb9e) which readers might like to consult.]

In this case, we have that $QP + PS = 2006 + 2009 = 2008 + 2007 = QR + RS$, from which it immediately follows by the above result that the interior angles at P and at R must each be less than 180°. Also $PS + SR = 2009 + 2007 > 2006 + 2008 = PQ + QR$. Again it follows from the above result that the interior angle at S must be less than 180°. However the angle at Q need not be less than 180°. For example, this occurs in the case where $PR = 4000$ and Q is an interior point of the triangle PRS.

23. D Suppose that the triangle and the square are placed so that the area of overlap is as large as possible. The area of the square is 36 cm^2. The area of overlap is $\frac{2}{3}$ of this, namely 24 cm^2. This is 60% of the area of the triangle. So the area of the triangle is $\frac{10}{6} \times 24 = 40$ cm^2.

24. D Suppose it is possible to make a list of all ten numbers.

The number 7 must be at one end and must be next to 1 since 7 has no other factors or multiples under 10. Without loss of generality we can assume 7 is the first number, followed by 1.

The number 5 only has two possible adjacent numbers, 1 and 10. The same is true for 9 which can only be next to 1 or 3. Hence either we must start with 7, 1, 5, 10 and end with 9; or we start with 7, 1, 9, 3 and end in 5. Either way this means that 1 cannot be next to any other numbers.

The diagram below shows the only possible connections that can be used. It is clearly impossible to link all ten numbers together without using 2 twice. If the sequence starts 7, 1, 5, 10 then the only possibility after 10 is 2 but the only possibility before 6 is 2 which means 2 has to appear twice; or if the sequence starts 7, 1, 9, 3, 6 then the only possibility after 6 is 2 and the only possibility before 10 is 2 so 2 is used twice.

However, the diagram suggests a possible list of nine numbers: 6, 3, 9, 1, 5, 10, 2, 4, 8.

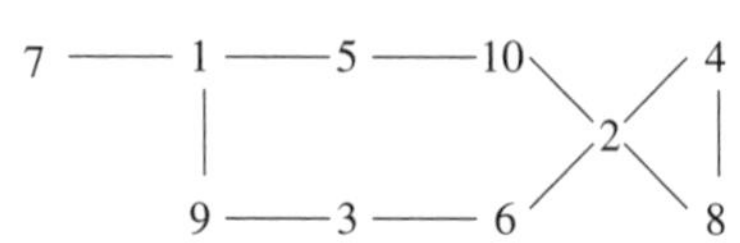

25. C Consider triangle PQR. Using the angle sum of a triangle, $\angle QPR = 180° - 40° - 20° = 120°$. Thus $\angle QPS = 60°$ and, by using the exterior angle property, $\angle PST = 80°$.

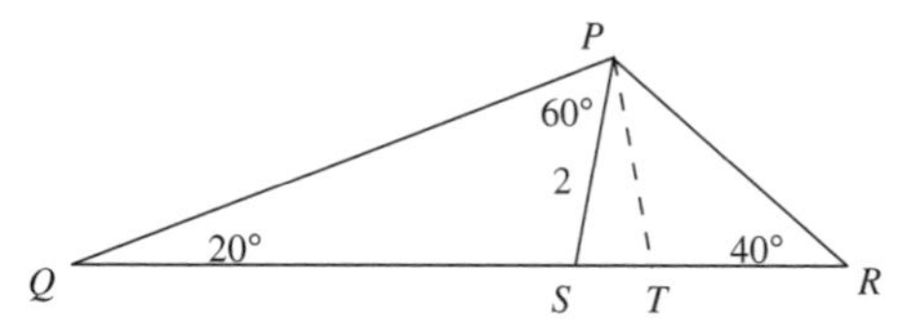

Let T be the point on QR such that $QT = QP$ which means that triangle PQT is isosceles. Hence $\angle QTP = \frac{1}{2}(180° - 20°) = 80°$. Thus triangle PST is also isosceles and therefore $PT = 2$.

Since $\angle QTP = 80°$, it follows from the exterior angle property applied to triangle PTR that $\angle TPR = 40°$. Thus this triangle is also isosceles and so $TR = TP$ and so QR is 2 units longer than PQ.

2009 European Pink Kangaroo

1. The Woomera Marathon had 2009 participants. The number of participants beaten by Kanga was three times the number that beat Kanga. In what position did Kanga finish the marathon?

   A 500th   B 501st   C 503rd   D 1503rd   E 1507th

2. What is the value of $\frac{1}{2}$ of $\frac{2}{3}$ of $\frac{3}{4}$ of $\frac{4}{5}$ of $\frac{5}{6}$ of $\frac{6}{7}$ of $\frac{7}{8}$ of $\frac{8}{9}$ of $\frac{9}{10}$ of 1000?

   A 100   B 200   C 250   D 300   E none of these

3. The diagram shows a solid with six triangular faces. At each vertex there is a number. Two of the numbers are 1 and 5 as shown. For each face the sum of the numbers at the three vertices of that face is calculated, and all the sums are found to be the same. What is the sum of all five numbers at the vertices?

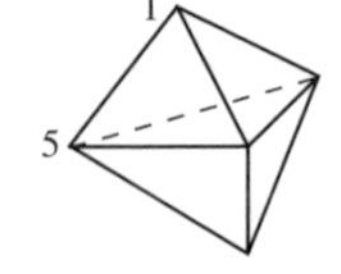

   A 9   B 12   C 17   D 18   E 24

4. How many positive integers n exist for which n^2 has the same number of digits as n^3 ?

   A 0   B 3   C 4   D 9   E infinitely many

5. The diagram shows a triangle and three circles whose centres are at the vertices of the triangle. The area of the triangle is 80 cm^2 and each of the circles has radius 2 cm. What is the area, in cm^2, of the shaded area?

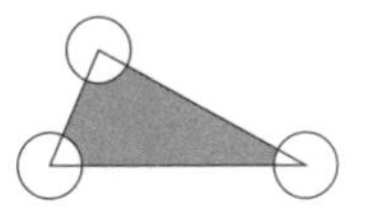

   A 76   B $80 - 2\pi$ C $40 - 4\pi$ D $80 - \pi$ E 78π

6. Leonard writes down a sequence of numbers. After the first two numbers, each number is the sum of the previous two numbers in the sequence. The fourth number is six and the sixth number is fifteen. What is the seventh number in the sequence?

   A 9   B 16   C 21   D 22   E 24

7. The three angle bisectors of triangle LMN meet at a point O as shown. Angle LNM is 68°. What is the size of angle LOM?

   A 120°   B 124°   C 128°   D 132°   E 136°

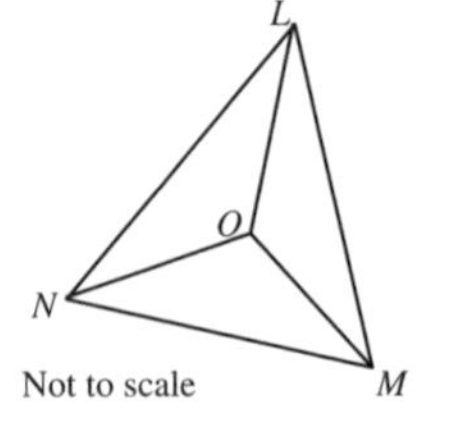

8. Mary sits four tests, each of which is out of 5 marks. Mary's average over the four tests is 4 marks. Which one of the following statements cannot be true?

   A Mary obtained a mark of 4 out of 5 in each test
   B Mary obtained a mark of 4 out of 5 twice
   C Mary obtained a mark of 1 out of 5 once
   D Mary obtained a mark of 3 out of 5 twice
   E Mary obtained a mark of 3 out of 5 three times

9. A magical island is inhabited entirely by knights (who always tell the truth) and knaves (who always tell lies). One day 25 of the islanders were standing in a queue. The first person in the queue said that everybody behind was a knave. Each of the others in the queue said that the person immediately in front of them in the queue was a knave. How many knights were there in the queue?

A 0 B 12 C 13 D 24 E more information needed

10. We define $a \oplus b = ab + a + b$. Given that $3 \oplus 5 = 2 \oplus x$, what is the value of x ?

A 3 B 4 C 5 D 6 E 7

11. The diagram shows two identical large circles and two identical smaller circles whose centres are at the corners of a square. The two large circles are touching, and they each touch the two smaller circles. The radius of the small circles is 1 cm. What is the radius of a large circle in centimetres?

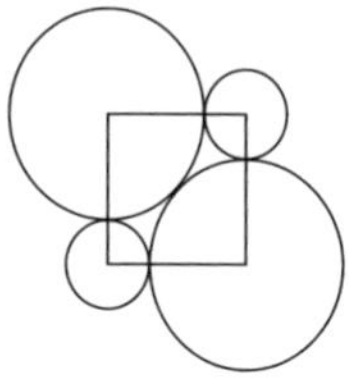

A $1 + \sqrt{2}$ B $\sqrt{5}$ C $\sqrt{2}$ D $\frac{5}{2}$ E $\frac{4}{5}\pi$

12. How many integers n exist such that the difference between $\sqrt{n}$ and 10 is less than 1?

A 19 B 20 C 39 D 40 E 41

13. Peter wishes to write down a list of different positive integers less than or equal to 10 in such a way that for each pair of adjacent numbers one of the numbers is divisible by the other. What is the length of the longest list that Peter could write down?

A 6 B 7 C 8 D 9 E 10

14. Three circular hoops are joined together so that they intersect at right-angles as shown. A ladybird lands on an intersection and crawls around the outside of the hoops by repeating this procedure: she travels along a quarter-circle, turns 90° to the right, travels along a quarter-circle and turns 90° to the left. Proceeding in this way, how many quarter-circles will she travel along before she first returns to her starting point?

A 6 B 9 C 12 D 15 E 18

15. Which of these decimals is less than $\frac{2009}{2008}$ but greater than $\frac{20009}{20008}$?

A 1.01 B 1.001 C 1.0001 D 1.00001 E 1.000001

16. If $a = 2^{25}$, $b = 8^8$ and $c = 3^{11}$, then which of these statements is true?

A $a < b < c$ B $b < a < c$ C $b < c < a$ D $c < a < b$ E $c < b < a$

17. How many ten-digit numbers are there which contain only the digits 1, 2 or 3, and in which any pair of adjacent digits differs by 1?

A 16 B 32 C 64 D 80 E 100

18. Roo has glued 2009 unit cubes together to form a cuboid. He opens a pack containing 2009 stickers and he has enough to place one sticker on each exposed face of each unit cube. How many stickers does he have left?

A fewer than 49 B 49 C 763 D 1246 E more than 1246

19. When Tina chose a number N and wrote down all of its factors, apart from 1 and N, she noticed that the largest of the factors in the list was 45 times the smallest factor in the list. How many numbers N could Tina have chosen for which this is the case?

A 0 B 1 C 2 D more than 2 E more information needed

20. A grocer places some oranges, peaches, apples and bananas in a row so that, somewhere in the row, each type of fruit can be found next to each other type of fruit. What is the smallest possible number of fruits in the row?

A 7 B 8 C 12 D 16 E 32

21. Barbara wants to place draughts on a 4×4 board in such a way that the number of draughts in each row and in each column are all different (she may place more than one draught in a square, and a square may be empty). What is the smallest number of draughts that she would need?

A 14 B 16 C 21 D 28 E 32

22. What is the smallest integer n such that the product

$$(2^2 - 1)(3^2 - 1)(4^2 - 1)\ldots(n^2 - 1)$$

is a perfect square?

A 6 B 8 C 16 D 27 E none of these

23. A kangaroo is sitting in the Australian outback. He plays a game in which he may only jump 1 metre at a time, either North, East, South or West. At how many different points could he end up after 10 jumps?

A 100 B 121 C 400 D 441 E none of these

24. Shakil wants to remove numbers from the set $\{1, 2, 3, \ldots, 16\}$ so that no two remaining numbers add to make a perfect square. What is the smallest number of numbers that he needs to remove?

A 6 B 7 C 8 D 9 E 10

25. A prime number is called 'strange' if either it is a one-digit prime, or if each of the numbers obtained by removing its first digit or its last digit are themselves strange primes. How many strange primes are there?

A 6 B 7 C 8 D 9 E 11

Solutions to the 2009 European Pink Kangaroo

1. **C** Kanga divides the other 2008 participants in the ratio 1:3, so has $2008 \div 4 = 502$ participants ahead of her. She comes in 503rd.

2. **A** When multiplying the fractions together, the denominator of each fraction, apart from the last, cancels with the numerator of the next fraction. We are left with the numerator 1 from the first fraction and the denominator 10 from the last, which gives $\frac{1}{10}$ of 1000, i.e. 100.

3. **C** Let the numbers at two of the other vertices be u and v, as shown in the diagram on the right. The three faces sharing the vertex labelled with the number 1 all have the same sum. Then $1 + v + u = 1 + 5 + u$ and so $v = 5$. Similarly, $1 + v + 5 = 1 + v + u$ so $u = 5$. Hence the sum for each face is $1 + 5 + 5$, i.e. 11, and we see that the number at the bottom vertex is 1. The total of all the vertices is $1 + 5 + 5 + 5 + 1 = 17$.

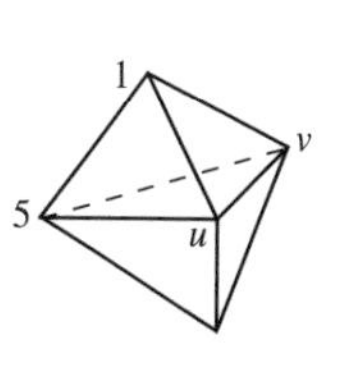

4. **B** Firstly note that if $n \geqslant 10$, then $n^3 \geqslant 10n^2$ so n^3 will have at least one more digit than n^2. For all $n < 10$, we have $n^2 < 100$, so n^2 has either 1 or 2 digits, but n^3 has 3 digits for $n > 4$ since $5^3 = 125$, so we need only consider $n = 1, 2, 3$ or 4. For $n = 1$ and 2, n^2 and n^3 both have one digit; for $n = 4$, $n^2 = 16$ and $n^3 = 64$ both have two digits. However for $n = 3$, $n^2 = 9$ has one digit while $n^3 = 27$ has two digits.

5. **B** The three angles of the triangle add to 180°, so the combined area of the three sectors of the circles that are inside the triangle add up to half a circle with area $\frac{1}{2} \times \pi \times 2^2 = \frac{4\pi}{2} = 2\pi$. So the grey area is $(80 - 2\pi)\,\text{cm}^2$.

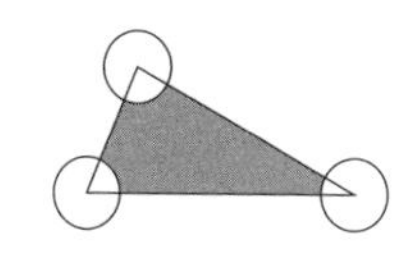

6. **E** If we let the fifth number be a, then the sixth number is $6 + a = 15$, so $a = 9$. The seventh number is the sum of the fifth and sixth numbers, $9 + 15 = 24$.

7. **B** Let $\angle OLM = \angle OLN = a°$, $\angle OML = \angle OMN = b°$ and $\angle LOM = c°$. Angles in a triangle add up to 180°, so from ΔLMN, $2a° + 2b° + 68° = 180°$ which gives $2(a° + b°) = 112°$ i.e. $a + b = 56$. Also, from ΔLOM, $a° + b° + c° = 180°$ and so $c = 180 - (a + b) = 180 - 56 = 124$.

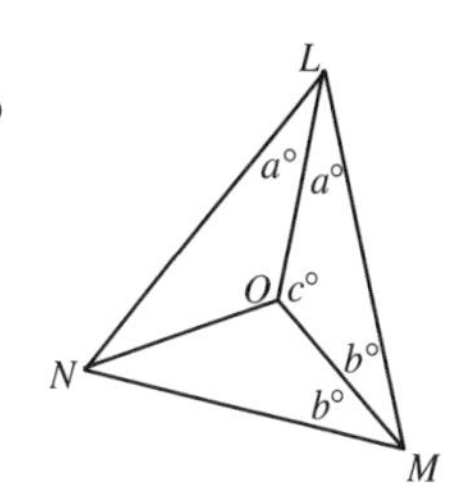

8. **E** Mary's average over four tests is 4 marks, so she has scored 16 marks in total. The first four options can give a total of 16 as follows:

A Mary achieved a mark of 4 out of 5 in each test: $4 + 4 + 4 + 4 = 16$

B Mary achieved a mark of 4 out of 5 twice: $4 + 4 + 3 + 5 = 16$

C Mary achieved a mark of 1 out of 5 once: $1 + 5 + 5 + 5 = 16$

D Mary achieved a mark of 3 out of 5 twice: $3 + 3 + 5 + 5 = 16$

Of the five cases given in the question, only the last one makes it impossible to score 16 marks since she has scored 9 marks from three tests, and would need 7 marks from the fourth test (which is only out of 5).

9. **B** The first person cannot be telling the truth since if all the others are knaves, this contradicts that they are telling the truth when they say the person in front is a knave!

The second person says the first is a knave so is telling the truth; he is a knight. The third says this knight is a knave so is lying; he is a knave. Continuing in this way we see that there is an alternating sequence of 13 knaves and 12 knights.

10. **E** $3 \oplus 5 = 3 \times 5 + 3 + 5 = 23$ and $2 \oplus x = 2x + 2 + x = 3x + 2$. These are equal, so $3x + 2 = 23$, i.e. $x = 7$.

11. **A** Let R be the radius of each of the larger circles. The sides of the square are equal to $R + 1$, the sum of the two radii. The diagonal of the square is $2R$. By Pythagoras, $(R + 1)^2 + (R + 1)^2 = (2R)^2$. Simplifying gives $2(R + 1)^2 = 4R^2$, i.e. $(R + 1)^2 = 2R^2$, so $R + 1 = \sqrt{2}R$ [$-\sqrt{2}R$ is not possible since $R + 1 > 0$]. Therefore $(\sqrt{2} - 1)R = 1$. Hence $R = \dfrac{1}{\sqrt{2} - 1} = \sqrt{2} + 1$.

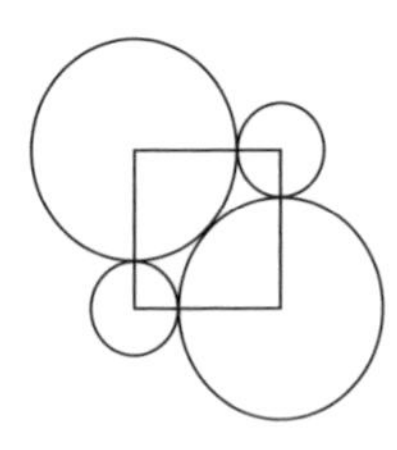

12. **C** We require that $9 < \sqrt{n} < 11$, or, equivalently, that $81 < n < 121$. Hence the possible integer values for n are the 39 values $n = 82, 83, \ldots, 119, 120$.

13. **D** Suppose it is possible to make a list of all ten numbers.

The number 7 must be at one end and must be next to 1 since 7 has no other factors or multiples under 10. Without loss of generality we can assume 7 is the first number, followed by 1.

The number 5 only has two possible adjacent numbers, 1 and 10. The same is true for 9 which can only be next to 1 or 3. Hence either we must start with 7, 1, 5, 10 and end with 9; or we start with 7, 1, 9, 3 and end in 5. Either way this means that 1 cannot be next to any other numbers.

The diagram below shows the only possible connections that can be used. It is clearly impossible to link all ten numbers together without using 2 twice. If the sequence starts 7, 1, 5, 10 then the only possibility after 10 is 2 but the only possibility before 6 is 2 which means 2 has to appear twice; or if the sequence starts 7, 1, 9, 3, 6 then the only possibility after 6 is 2 and the only possibility before 10 is 2 so 2 is used twice.

However, the diagram suggests a possible list of nine numbers: 6, 3, 9, 1, 5, 10, 2, 4, 8.

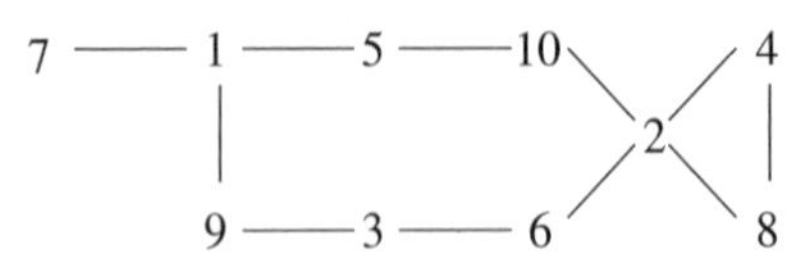

14. **A** We may suppose that the ant starts at the top. The diagram shows the six quarter-circles that she travels through before arriving back at the top.

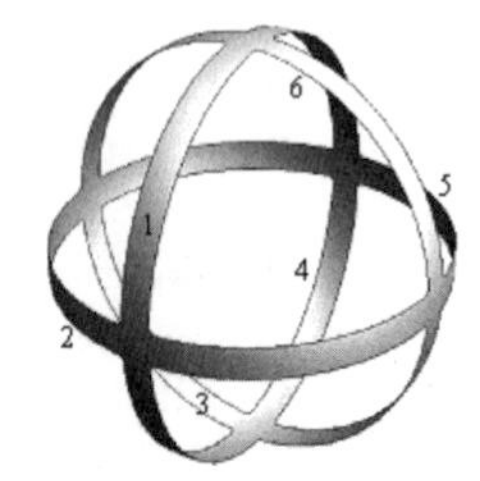

15. C The options are all of the form $1 + \frac{1}{n}$ so we need to find n such that $1 + \frac{1}{20008} < 1 + \frac{1}{n} < 1 + \frac{1}{2008}$. This means $2008 < n < 20008$. The choices for n are 100, 1000, 10000, 100000 and 1000000 but only 10000 satisfies the inequalities. We get $1 + \frac{1}{10000} = 1.0001$.

16. E By comparing b and c first, we have $b = 8^8 = (2^3)^8 = 2^{24} = (2^2)^{12} = 4^{12} > 3^{11} = c$ so $c < b$. But also $b = 2^{24} < 2^{25} = a$ so $b < a$. Together these give $c < b < a$.

17. C The digits 1 and 3 will always be followed by the digit 2. The digit 2 can be followed by either 1 or 3. Hence the digit 2 appears exactly five times in a ten-digit number, in alternate positions.

If the first digit is 2, then in each even position we have two choices, 1 or 3. This gives $2 \times 2 \times 2 \times 2 \times 2 = 32$ possibilities. Otherwise, the second digit is 2 and in each odd position we have two choices. So again there are 32 possibilities, making a total of 64.

18. C Any three positive integers that multiply to make 2009 would create viable cuboids. The prime factors of 2009 are $7 \times 7 \times 41$, so the options are $1 \times 1 \times 2009$, $1 \times 7 \times 287$, $1 \times 41 \times 49$ and $7 \times 7 \times 41$. The first three cuboids all have two faces which each require 2009 stickers (1×2009, 7×287 and 41×49 respectively) so Roo cannot cover them. The last cuboid has surface area $2 \times (7 \times 7 + 7 \times 41 + 41 \times 7) = 1246$, leaving $2009 - 1246 = 763$ stickers left over.

19. C Let the smallest prime factor of N be p, whence the second largest factor, and the highest factor Tina wrote down, is $\frac{N}{p}$. Now we have $\frac{N}{p} = 45p$ whence $N = 45p^2$. Since N is a multiple of 45, it has prime factors of 3 and 5 and, because p is the smallest prime factor of N, we can conclude that p can be only 2 or 3. Hence either $N = 45 \times 2^2 = 180$ or $N = 45 \times 3^2 = 405$.

20. B Each fruit can have at most two fruits next to it but each type of fruit must be next to three other types of fruit so there are at least two of every fruit. This means there are at least 8 fruits in total. In fact 8 are sufficient, as shown in the arrangement OABPOBAP (O or Orange, P for Peach, A for Apple, B for Banana).

21. A There are four rows and four columns, so we need eight different sums. The smallest eight sums (if possible) would be 0, 1, 2, 3, …, 7. Since each draught is counted towards the sum of a row and the sum of a column, we would need $\frac{1}{2}(0 + 1 + 2 + \ldots + 7) = 14$ draughts. The diagram shows it is possible to place 14 draughts on the board to create the eight smallest sums (the numbers in the cells represent how many draughts there are in each cell, and the column and row totals are shown).

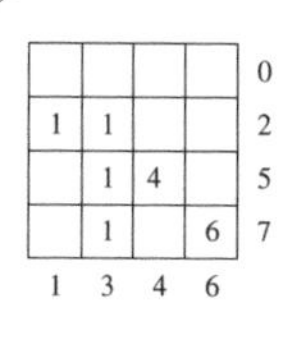

22. B We make use of two key facts. First, we have the factorization $n^2 - 1 = (n - 1)(n + 1)$. Second, when a square number is factorized, each prime factor appears an even number of times. Now $2^2 - 1 = 1 \times 3$. We next get a prime factor 3 with $4^2 - 1 = 3 \times 5$. We next get a factor 5 with $6^2 - 1 = 5 \times 7$. We next get a factor 7 with $8^2 - 1 = 7 \times 9$. As $9 = 3^2$, it does not require any further factors. Hence we need $n \geqslant 8$. Checking the product with $n = 8$, we get $(2^2 - 1)(3^2 - 1)(4^2 - 1)(5^2 - 1)(6^2 - 1)(7^2 - 1)(8^2 - 1) =$
$1 \times 3 \times 2 \times 4 \times 3 \times 5 \times 4 \times 6 \times 5 \times 7 \times 6 \times 8 \times 7 \times 9 =$
$2 \times 8 \times 3 \times 3 \times 4 \times 4 \times 5 \times 5 \times 6 \times 6 \times 7 \times 7 \times 9 =$
$4 \times 4 \times 3 \times 3 \times 4 \times 4 \times 5 \times 5 \times 6 \times 6 \times 7 \times 7 \times 3 \times 3 = (4 \times 3 \times 4 \times 5 \times 6 \times 7 \times 3)^2$.
So in fact $n = 8$ is sufficient, and is thus the minimum.

23. B Consider the kangaroo's starting position as the origin of coordinate axes, with East and North being the positive x and y directions, respectively, and one metre being one unit along the axes. We begin by considering the first quadrant. If the kangaroo's end point has coordinates (a, b), then a and b must be integers. Also, after 10 jumps, it must be that $a + b \leqslant 10$. Hence his end points are bounded by the right-angled triangle with vertices at $(10, 0)$, $(0, 10)$ and $(0, 0)$. He can finish at any point on the hypotenuse of this triangle since all these points satisfy $a + b = 10$ and so can be reached by a jumps East and b jumps North. But he can only end up at a point (a, b) on the other two edges or inside the triangle if $a + b$ is even. (He can certainly reach all such points in $a + b \leqslant 10$ jumps, and if $a + b$ is even, with $a + b < 10$, he can jump away and back again using up 2 jumps, and can repeat this until he has made 10 jumps, and so end up at (a, b).)

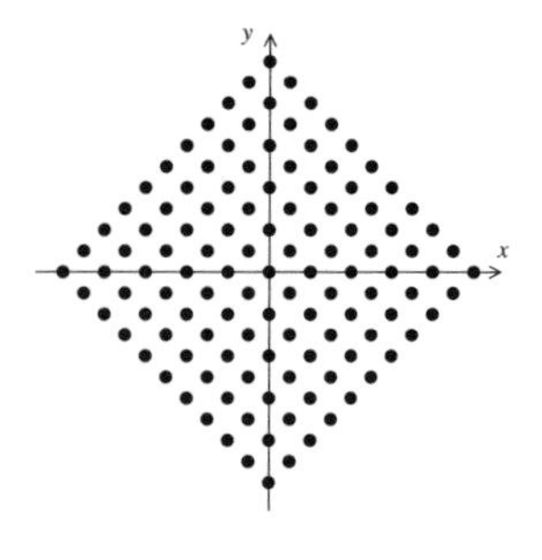

By symmetry we see that the possible end points form a square of side 11, and so there are 121 of them, as shown in the diagram.

24. C The following seven pairs add to 16 so at least one of each pair must be removed: (1, 15), (2, 14), (3, 13), (4, 12), (5, 11), (6, 10), (7, 9).

If removing these seven is sufficient, then we would be left with 8, 16 and seven others.

But	$16 + 9 = 25$	so we must remove 9 (and keep its partner 7).
	$7 + 2 = 9$	so we must remove 2 and keep 14.
	$14 + 11 = 25$	so we must remove 11 and keep 5.
	$5 + 4 = 9$	so we must remove 4 and keep 12.
	$12 + 13 = 25$	so we must remove 13 and keep 3.
	$3 + 1 = 4$	so we must remove 1 and keep 15.
	$15 + 10 = 25$	so we must remove 10 and keep 6.

But we have kept 3 and 6 which add to 9.

Hence it is not sufficient to remove only seven. If we remove the number 6, we obtain a set which satisfies the condition: {8, 16, 7, 14, 5, 12, 3, 15} or in ascending order {3, 5, 7, 8, 12, 14, 15, 16}. Hence eight is the smallest number of numbers that may be removed.

25. D The 1-digit primes are 2, 3, 5 and 7. Any two of these make a two-digit number which is strange if the result is a prime. A 2-digit prime cannot end in 2 or 5, and we can also exclude 27, 57 because they are divisible by 3; also 33 and 77 are divisible by 11. This leaves four 2-digit strange primes: 23, 53, 73, 37.

A 3-digit strange prime will be the concatenation of two 2-digit strange primes where the last digit of the first prime is the first digit of the second prime. The possibilities are: 23 and 37 to make 237; 53 and 37 to make 537; 73 and 37 to make 737; 37 and 73 to make 373. However, 237 and 537 are divisible by 3, and 737 is divisible by 11. This leaves only one 3-digit strange prime, 373. Therefore a 4-digit strange prime can only begin with 373 (making the second digit 7) and end with 373 (making the second digit 3) which is impossible. Since there are no 4-digit primes, we cannot make a strange prime with more than 4 digits. Hence there are nine strange primes: 2, 3, 5, 7, 23, 37, 53, 73, 373.

(b) *The IMOK Olympiad*

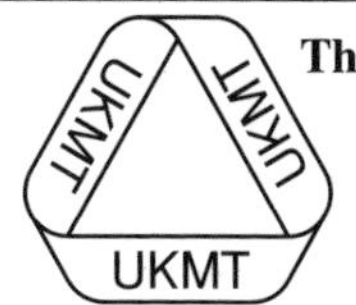

The United Kingdom Mathematics Trust

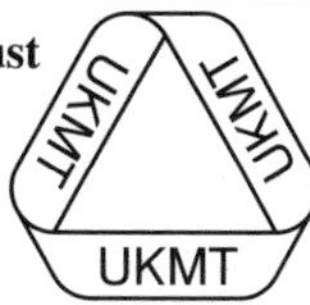

Intermediate Mathematical Olympiad and Kangaroo (IMOK)

Olympiad Cayley/Hamilton/Maclaurin Papers

Thursday 19th March 2009

READ THESE INSTRUCTIONS CAREFULLY BEFORE STARTING

1. Time allowed: 2 hours.
2. **The use of calculators, protractors and squared paper is forbidden.** Rulers and compasses may be used.
3. Solutions must be written neatly on A4 paper. Sheets must be STAPLED together in the top left corner with the Cover Sheet on top.
4. Start each question on a fresh A4 sheet.
   You may wish to work in rough first, then set out your final solution with clear explanations and proofs.
   Do not hand in rough work.
5. Answers must be FULLY SIMPLIFIED, and EXACT using symbols like π, fractions, or square roots if appropriate, but NOT decimal approximations.
6. Give full written solutions, including mathematical reasons as to why your method is correct.
   Just stating an answer, even a correct one, will earn you very few marks; also, incomplete or poorly presented solutions will not receive full marks.
7. **These problems are meant to be challenging!** The earlier questions tend to be easier; the last two questions are the most demanding.
   Do not hurry, but spend time working carefully on one question before attempting another. Try to finish whole questions even if you cannot do many: you will have done well if you hand in full solutions to two or more questions.

DO NOT OPEN THE PAPER UNTIL INSTRUCTED BY THE INVIGILATOR TO DO SO!

The United Kingdom Mathematics Trust is a Registered Charity.
Enquiries should be sent to: Maths Challenges Office,
School of Mathematics, University of Leeds, Leeds, LS2 9JT.
(Tel. 0113 343 2339)
http://www.ukmt.org.uk

2009 Olympiad Cayley Paper

All candidates must be in *School Year 9 or below* (England and Wales), *S2 or below* (Scotland), or *School Year 10 or below* (Northern Ireland).

1. An aquarium contains 280 tropical fish of various kinds. If 60 more clownfish were added to the aquarium, the proportion of clownfish would be doubled.
   How many clownfish are in the aquarium?

2. The boundary of the shaded figure consists of four semicircular arcs whose radii are all different. The centre of each arc lies on the line AB, which is 10 cm long.
   What is the length of the perimeter of the figure?

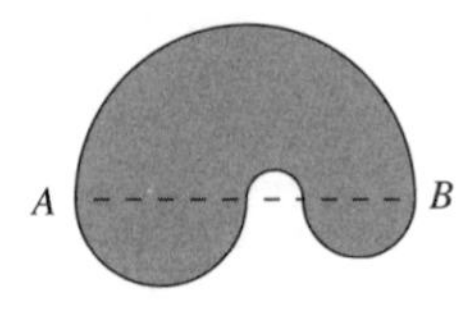

3. Two different rectangles are placed together, edge-to-edge, to form a large rectangle. The length of the perimeter of the large rectangle is $\frac{2}{3}$ of the total perimeter of the original two rectangles.

   Prove that the final rectangle is in fact a square.

4. In the rectangle $ABCD$, the side AB has length $\sqrt{2}$ and the side AD has length 1. Let the circle with centre B and passing through C meet AB at X.

   Find $\angle ADX$ (in degrees).

5. Two candles are the same height. The first takes 10 hours to burn completely whilst the second takes 8 hours to burn completely.
   Both candles are lit at midday. At what time is the height of the first candle twice the height of the second candle?

6. Teams A, B, C and D competed against each other once. The results table was as follows:

Team	Win	Draw	Loss	Goals for	Goals against
A	3	0	0	5	1
B	1	1	1	2	2
C	0	2	1	5	6
D	0	1	2	3	6

   (a) Find (with proof) which team won in each of the six matches.

   (b) Find (with proof) the scores in each of the six matches.

2009 Olympiad Hamilton Paper

All candidates must be in *School Year 10* (England and Wales), *S3* (Scotland), or *School Year 11* (Northern Ireland).

1. An aquarium contains 280 tropical fish of various kinds. If 60 more clownfish were added to the aquarium, the proportion of clownfish would be doubled.

   How many clownfish are in the aquarium?

2. Find the possible values of the digits p and q, given that the five-digit number '$p543q$' is a multiple of 36.

3. In the diagram, $ABCD$ is a rectangle with $AB = 16$ cm and $BC = 12$ cm. Points E and F lie on sides AB and CD so that $AECF$ is a rhombus.

   What is the length of EF?

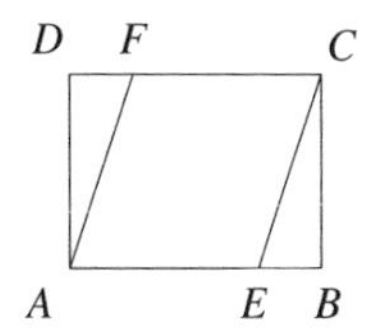

4. Four positive integers a, b, c and d are such that:

   the sum of a and b is half the sum of c and d;

   the sum of a and c is twice the sum of b and d;

   the sum of a and d is one and a half times the sum of b and c.

   What is the smallest possible value of $a + b + c + d$?

5. The diagram shows a triangle PTU inscribed in a square $PQRS$. Each of the marked angles at P is equal to 30°.

   Prove that the area of the triangle PTU is one third of the area of the square $PQRS$.

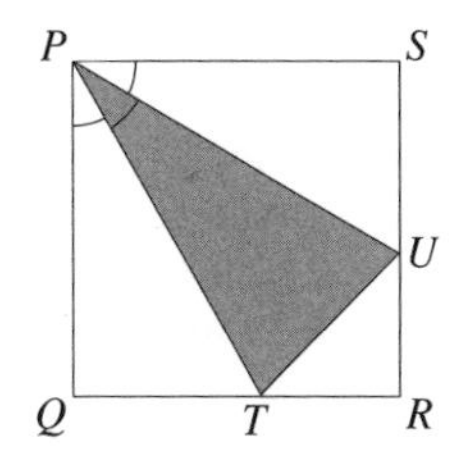

6. Two different cuboids are placed together, face-to-face, to form a large cuboid.

   The surface area of the large cuboid is $\frac{3}{4}$ of the total surface area of the original two cuboids.

   Prove that the lengths of the edges of the large cuboid may be labelled x, y and z, where

$$\frac{2}{z} = \frac{1}{x} + \frac{1}{y}.$$

2009 Olympiad Maclaurin Paper

All candidates must be in *School Year 11* (England and Wales), *S4* (Scotland), or *School Year 12* (Northern Ireland).

1. Five numbers are arranged in increasing order. As they get larger the difference between adjacent numbers doubles.

   The average of the five numbers is 11 more than the middle number. The sum of the second and fourth numbers is equal to the largest number.

   What is the largest number?

2. Miko always remembers his four-digit PIN (personal identification number) because
   - (a) it is a perfect square, and
   - (b) it has the property that, when it is divided by 2, or 3, or 4, or 5, or 6, or 7, or 8, or 9, there is always a remainder of 1.

   What is Miko's PIN?

3. Solve the simultaneous equations

$$\frac{5xy}{x+y} = 6$$

$$\frac{4xz}{x+z} = 3$$

$$\frac{3yz}{y+z} = 2.$$

4. In a trapezium $ABCD$ the sides AB and DC are parallel and $\angle BAD = \angle ABC < 90°$.

   Point P lies on AB with $\angle CPD = \angle BAD$.

   Prove that $PC^2 + PD^2 = AB \times DC$.

5. A lottery involves five balls being selected from a drum. Each ball has a different positive integer printed on it.

   Show that, whichever five balls are selected, it is always possible to choose three of them so that the sum of the numbers on these three balls is a multiple of 3.

6. In the figure, p, q, r and s are the lengths of four arcs which together form the circumference of the circle.

   Find, in simplified form, an expression for s in terms of p, q and r.

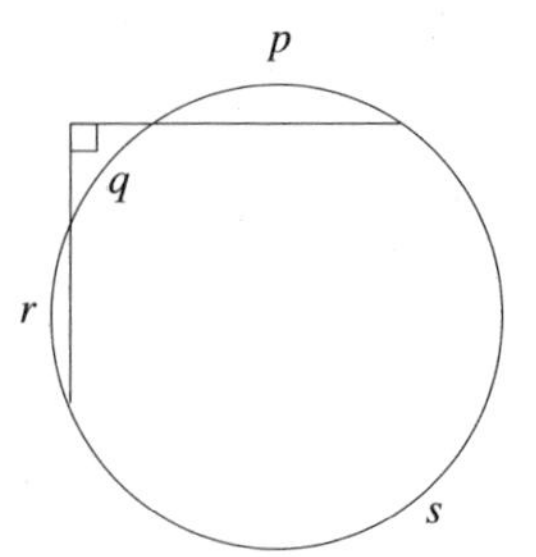

Solutions to the 2009 Olympiad Cayley Paper

1. An aquarium contains 280 tropical fish of various kinds. If 60 more clownfish were added to the aquarium, the proportion of clownfish would be doubled.
   How many clownfish are in the aquarium?

   Solution

   Let there be x clownfish in the aquarium.

   If 60 clownfish are added there are $x + 60$ clownfish and 340 tropical fish in total.

   Since the proportion of clownfish is then doubled, we have

$$2 \times \frac{x}{280} = \frac{x + 60}{340}.$$

   Multiplying both sides by 20 we get

$$\frac{x}{7} = \frac{x + 60}{17}$$

   and hence

$$17x = 7(x + 60).$$

   It follows that $x = 42$ and thus there are 42 clownfish in the aquarium.

2. The boundary of the shaded figure consists of four semicircular arcs whose radii are all different. The centre of each arc lies on the line AB, which is 10 cm long.
   What is the length of the perimeter of the figure?

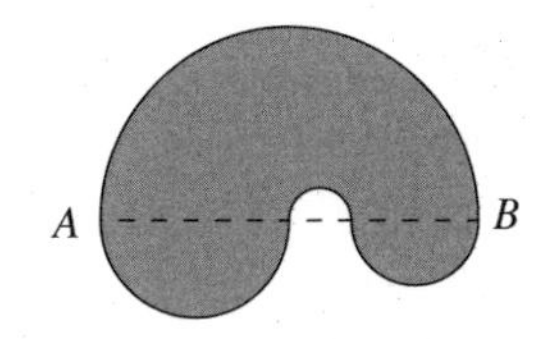

   Solution

   The centre of the large semicircular arc lies on AB, so we know that AB is a diameter of the large semicircle. But AB is 10 cm long, so the radius of the large semicircle is 5 cm.

   Let the radii of the other three semicircles be r_1 cm, r_2 cm and r_3 cm. The centres of these arcs also lie on AB, so the sum of their diameters is equal to the length of AB. It follows that $2r_1 + 2r_2 + 2r_3 = 10$ and hence $r_1 + r_2 + r_3 = 5$.

   Now the lengths, in cm, of the semicircular arcs are 5π, πr_1, πr_2 and πr_3. Therefore the perimeter of the figure has length, in cm,

$$\begin{aligned} 5\pi + \pi r_1 + \pi r_2 + \pi r_3 &= \pi(5 + r_1 + r_2 + r_3) \\ &= \pi(5 + 5) \\ &= 10\pi. \end{aligned}$$

   Hence the perimeter of the figure has length 10π cm.

3. Two different rectangles are placed together, edge-to-edge, to form a large rectangle. The length of the perimeter of the large rectangle is $\frac{2}{3}$ of the total perimeter of the original two rectangles.

Prove that the final rectangle is in fact a square.

First solution

Since the smaller rectangles are placed together edge-to-edge, they have a side length in common. Let this side have length y and let the other sides have lengths x_1 and x_2 as shown.

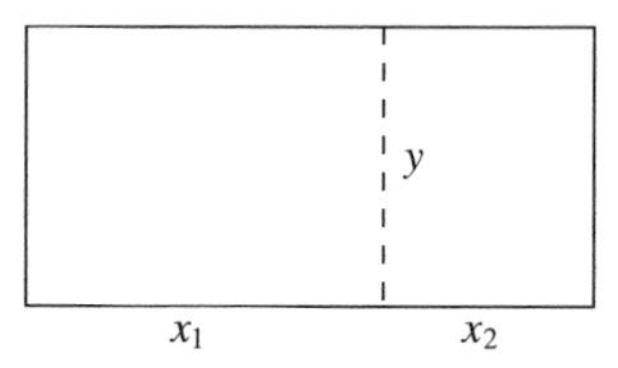

The perimeters of the smaller rectangles are $2x_1 + 2y$ and $2x_2 + 2y$, so the total perimeter of the two smaller rectangles is $2x_1 + 2x_2 + 4y$.
The perimeter of the large rectangle is $2(x_1 + x_2) + 2y = 2x_1 + 2x_2 + 2y$.
We are given that the length of the perimeter of the large rectangle is $\frac{2}{3}$ of the total perimeter of the two original rectangles. Hence we may form the equation

$$2x_1 + 2x_2 + 2y = \tfrac{2}{3}(2x_1 + 2x_2 + 4y).$$

We may simplify this equation by multiplying both sides by 3 and expanding the brackets, to obtain

$$6x_1 + 6x_2 + 6y = 4x_1 + 4x_2 + 8y,$$

which simplifies to

$$x_1 + x_2 = y.$$

This means that the length and width of the large rectangle are the same. In other words, the rectangle is actually a square.

Second solution

The total perimeter length P of the original two rectangles is equal to the perimeter length of the large rectangle added to the lengths of the two edges which are joined together.

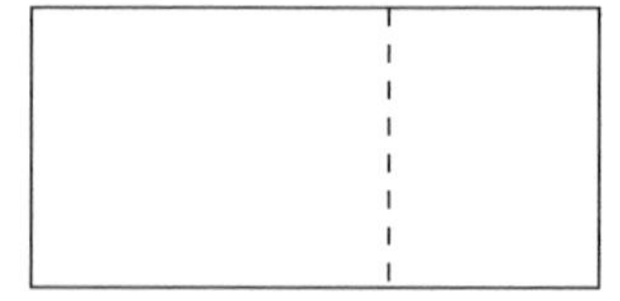

But the perimeter length of the large rectangle is $\frac{2}{3}P$ and hence the two edges which are joined together have total length $\frac{1}{3}P$.
However, the two edges which are joined together are parallel to two sides of the large rectangle and have the same length as them. Hence these two sides of the large rectangle have total length $\frac{1}{3}P$.
Since the perimeter length of the large rectangle is $\frac{2}{3}P$, the other two sides of the large rectangle also have total length $\frac{1}{3}P$. It follows that all the sides of the rectangle are equal in length, in other words, the rectangle is a square.

4. In the rectangle $ABCD$, the side AB has length $\sqrt{2}$ and the side AD has length 1. Let the circle with centre B and passing through C meet AB at X.

   Find $\angle ADX$ (in degrees).

   Solution
   We begin with a diagram showing the information given in the question. We have used the fact that $ABCD$ is a rectangle, so that $BC = AD = 1$ and $DC = AB = \sqrt{2}$, and angles ABC, BCD and CDA are right angles.

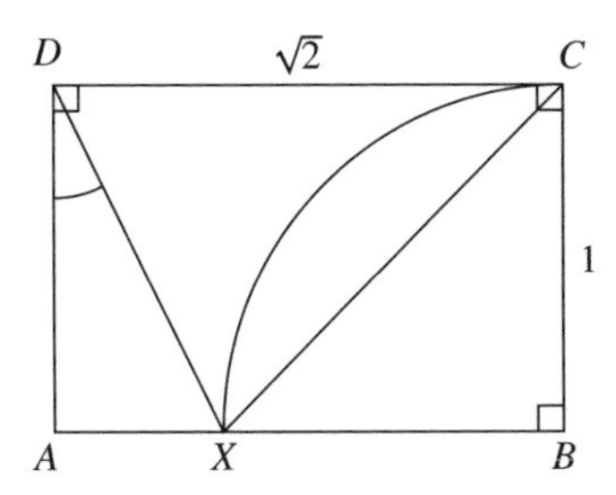

Since BX and BC are both radii of the circle, BX also has length 1. This means that triangle XBC is isosceles and so $\angle BXC = \angle BCX$.
Furthermore, since $\angle ABC$ is a right angle, $\angle BXC$ and $\angle BCX$ are both equal to 45°.
From the fact that $\angle BCD$ is a right angle, it follows that $\angle XCD = 90° - 45° = 45°$.
We may use Pythagoras' theorem in triangle XBC to obtain

$$\begin{aligned} XC^2 &= BX^2 + BC^2 \\ &= 1^2 + 1^2 \\ &= 2 \end{aligned}$$

and so $XC = \sqrt{2}$.
We are given that DC also has length $\sqrt{2}$ and so triangle XCD is isosceles. This means that $\angle CXD$ and $\angle CDX$ are equal, and so each is equal to $(180° - 45°) \div 2 = 67\frac{1}{2}°$.
Lastly, we use the fact that $\angle CDA$ is a right angle to conclude that $\angle ADX = 90° - 67\frac{1}{2}° = 22\frac{1}{2}°$.

5. Two candles are the same height. The first takes 10 hours to burn completely whilst the second takes 8 hours to burn completely.

   Both candles are lit at midday. At what time is the height of the first candle twice the height of the second candle?

   Solution

   Let the initial height of each candle be h cm. In one hour the first candle will burn $\frac{h}{10}$ cm and the second candle will burn $\frac{h}{8}$ cm. Thus in t hours, the candles will burn

$$\frac{ht}{10}\text{ cm} \qquad \text{and} \qquad \frac{ht}{8}\text{ cm},$$

   respectively.

   If both candles are lit at midday, then t hours after midday the heights of the first and second candles will be

$$\left(h - \frac{ht}{10}\right)\text{ cm} \qquad \text{and} \qquad \left(h - \frac{ht}{8}\right)\text{ cm},$$

   respectively.

   We are asked to find the time at which the height of the first candle is twice the height of the second candle. We therefore need to find the value of t such that

$$h - \frac{ht}{10} = 2\left(h - \frac{ht}{8}\right).$$

   We may divide every term by h, since we know that h is not zero, and expand the brackets to obtain the equation

$$1 - \frac{t}{10} = 2 - \frac{t}{4}.$$

   Multiplying both sides by 20, we get

$$20 - 2t = 40 - 5t,$$

   and so

$$t = \frac{20}{3}$$

$$= 6\tfrac{2}{3}.$$

   Hence the height of the first candle is twice that of the second after 6 hours and 40 minutes, in other words, this happens at 18:40.

6. Teams A, B, C and D competed against each other once. The results table was as follows:

Team	Win	Draw	Loss	Goals for	Goals against
A	3	0	0	5	1
B	1	1	1	2	2
C	0	2	1	5	6
D	0	1	2	3	6

(a) Find (with proof) which team won in each of the six matches.

(b) Find (with proof) the scores in each of the six matches.

Solution

(a) Team A won all three games and so beat teams B, C and D.

Of the three games that team C played, the one that was lost can only have been against team A. Therefore team C drew against teams B and D.

If we consider the three games that team B played, the game against team A was lost, the game against team C was a draw and so the remaining game, that team B won, was against team D.

In summary:

A beat B, A beat C, A beat D;

B drew with C, B beat D; and

C drew with D.

(b) Consider the following table in which the rows give the number of goals scored *for* each team and the columns give the number of goals *against* each team.

		Goals against				
		A	B	C	D	All
	A	–		$z + 1$		5
Goals	B		–	x	t	2
for	C	z	x	–	y	5
	D			y	–	3
	All	1	2	6	6	15

We have let the number of goals scored by team C against team B be x, so that the number of goals scored by team B against team C is also x, since their match was a draw. Similarly, we have let the number of goals scored by team C against team D be y, so that this is also the number scored by team D against team C.

Furthermore, we have let the number of goals scored by team C against team A be z, so that the number of goals scored by team A against team C is $z + 1$ since the difference between the number of goals scored and conceded by team C is 1.

Finally, we have let the number of goals scored by team B against team D be t. Then t is at least 1 since team B beat team D.

We observe that the row for C now means that $x + y + z = 5$ (which agrees with the column for C).

From the column for A we see that z is at most 1, since the total in that column is 1. Similarly, from the row for D, we see that y is at most 3, and from the row for B we see that x is at most 1 since t is at least 1.

But we have $x + y + z = 5$, so that the only possibilities are $x = 1$, $y = 3$ and $z = 1$. It follows that $t = 1$.

Therefore the table is:

Goals against

		A	B	C	D	All
	A	–		2		5
Goals	B		–	1	1	2
for	C	1	1	–	3	5
	D			3	–	3
	All	1	2	6	6	15

We may now complete the table by, for example, first noting that all other entries in the column for A are 0, and then filling in the rows from the bottom.

Goals against

		A	B	C	D	All
	A	–	1	2	2	5
Goals	B	0	–	1	1	2
for	C	1	1	–	3	5
	D	0	0	3	–	3
	All	1	2	6	6	15

In summary, the scores in each match were as follows:

A beat B	1 – 0
A beat C	2 – 1
A beat D	2 – 0
B drew with C	1 – 1
B beat D	1 – 0
C drew with D	3 – 3

Solutions to the 2009 Olympiad Hamilton Paper

1. An aquarium contains 280 tropical fish of various kinds. If 60 more clownfish were added to the aquarium, the proportion of clownfish would be doubled.

   How many clownfish are in the aquarium?

   Solution

   Let there be x clownfish in the aquarium.

   If 60 clownfish are added there are $x + 60$ clownfish and 340 tropical fish in total.

   Since the proportion of clownfish is then doubled, we have

$$2 \times \frac{x}{280} = \frac{x + 60}{340}.$$

   Multiplying both sides by 20, we get

$$\frac{x}{7} = \frac{x + 60}{17}$$

   and hence

$$17x = 7(x + 60).$$

   It follows that $x = 42$ and thus there are 42 clownfish in the aquarium.

2. Find the possible values of the digits p and q, given that the five-digit number '$p543q$' is a multiple of 36.

   Solution

   Since '$p543q$' is a multiple of 36 it is a multiple of both 9 and 4.

   The sum of the digits of a multiple of 9 is also a multiple of 9, hence $p + 5 + 4 + 3 + q$ is a multiple of 9. But $5 + 4 + 3 = 12$ and each of p and q is a single digit, so that $p + q = 6$ and $p + q = 15$ are the only possibilities.

   Since '$p543q$' is a multiple of 4 and '$p5400$' is always divisible by 4, it follows that '$3q$' is divisible by 4. The only possible values for '$3q$' are 32 and 36, so that $q = 2$ or $q = 6$.

   If $q = 2$, then $p + q = 15$ is not possible since p is a single digit. Hence $p + q = 6$ and so $p = 4$.

   If $q = 6$, then $p + q = 6$ is not possible since '$p543q$' is a five-digit number and therefore the digit p cannot be zero. Hence $p + q = 15$ and so $p = 9$.

   Therefore $p = 4$, $q = 2$ and $p = 9$, $q = 6$ are the only possible values of the digits p and q.

3. In the diagram, $ABCD$ is a rectangle with $AB = 16$ cm and $BC = 12$ cm. Points E and F lie on sides AB and CD so that $AECF$ is a rhombus.

   What is the length of EF?

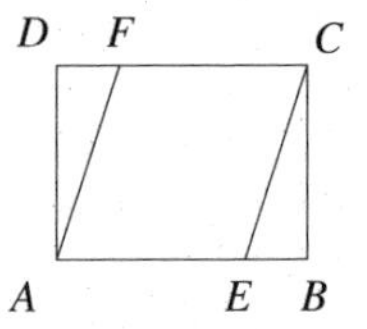

Solution

Let the sides of the rhombus $AECF$ have length x cm. Hence $AE = x$ and $EB = 16 - x$. Since $ABCD$ is a rectangle, angle EBC is a right angle.

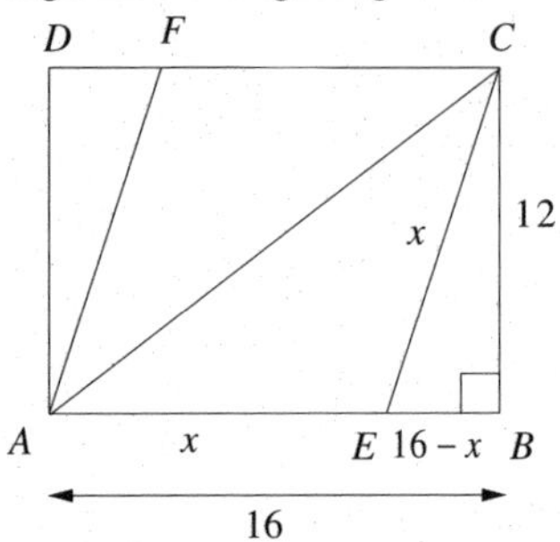

Using Pythagoras' theorem in triangle ABC, we have $AC^2 = 16^2 + 12^2 = 400$, so that $AC = 20$ cm.

Using Pythagoras' theorem in triangle EBC, we have

$$EC^2 = CB^2 + EB^2$$

and hence

$$x^2 = 12^2 + (16 - x)^2,$$

which can be rearranged to give

$$x^2 = 144 + 256 - 32x + x^2.$$

It follows that

$$32x = 400$$

and so

$$x = \frac{25}{2}.$$

We may now proceed in various ways; we show two different methods.

First method

Let M be the point of intersection of the diagonals AC and EF of $AECF$. Since $AECF$ is a rhombus, angle FMC is a right angle and M is the mid-point of both AC and EF.

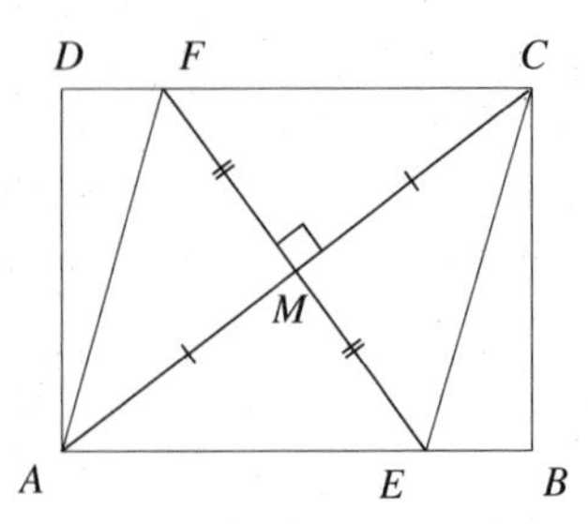

Using Pythagoras' theorem in triangle FMC, we have

$$CF^2 = (\tfrac{1}{2}AC)^2 + (\tfrac{1}{2}EF)^2$$

and hence

$$\left(\frac{25}{2}\right)^2 = 10^2 + (\tfrac{1}{2}EF)^2.$$

It follows that

$$625 = 400 + EF^2$$

and so

$$EF = 15.$$

Therefore the length of EF is 15 cm.

Second method

We make use of the fact that

area of rhombus $AECF$ = area of rectangle $ABCD - 2 \times$ area of triangle EBC.

Now the area of a rhombus is half the product of its diagonals. Also, the area of triangle EBC is $\tfrac{1}{2}EB \times BC$ and $EB = 16 - \tfrac{25}{2} = \tfrac{7}{2}$. We therefore have

$$\tfrac{1}{2}AC \times EF = 16 \times 12 - \tfrac{7}{2} \times 12.$$

Hence

$$10 \times EF = 192 - 42 = 150$$

and so

$$EF = 15.$$

Therefore the length of EF is 15 cm.

Remark

Another method uses Pythagoras' theorem in the right-angled triangle ENF shown below.

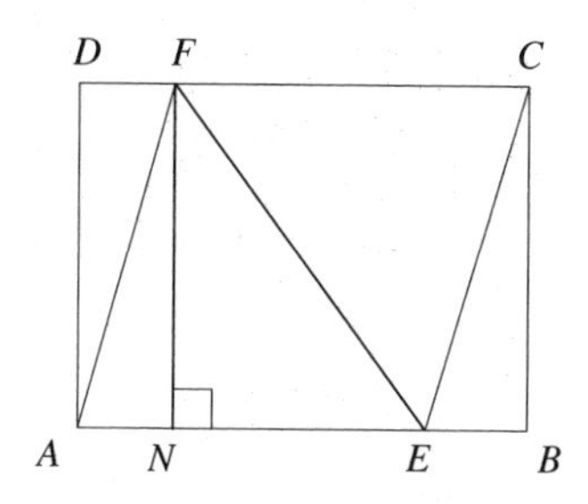

4. Four positive integers a, b, c and d are such that:

   the sum of a and b is half the sum of c and d;

   the sum of a and c is twice the sum of b and d;

   the sum of a and d is one and a half times the sum of b and c.

   What is the smallest possible value of $a + b + c + d$?

   Solution

   There are three equations here but four unknown values, a, b, c and d. Thus it is not possible just to solve the equations to find the values of a, b, c and d. What we can do is to find relationships between them and then deduce possible values of a, b, c and d.

   From the given information,

$$a + b = \tfrac{1}{2}(c + d) \tag{1}$$

$$a + c = 2(b + d) \tag{2}$$

$$a + d = \tfrac{3}{2}(b + c). \tag{3}$$

   We may proceed in various ways; we show two methods, substitution and elimination.

   First method: substitution

   From (1), we have

$$a = -b + \tfrac{1}{2}(c + d). \tag{4}$$

   Substituting in (2), we get

$$-b + \tfrac{1}{2}(c + d) + c = 2(b + d)$$

   and hence

$$\tfrac{3}{2}c - \tfrac{3}{2}d = 3b,$$

   that is,

$$c - d = 2b. \tag{5}$$

   Substituting from (4) in (3), we get

$$-b + \tfrac{1}{2}(c + d) + d = \tfrac{3}{2}(b + c)$$

   so that

$$-c + \tfrac{3}{2}d = \tfrac{5}{2}b. \tag{6}$$

   Now adding (5) and (6) we obtain

$$\tfrac{1}{2}d = \tfrac{9}{2}b,$$

   and hence

$$d = 9b.$$

Once we have minimised $b + d$, then we automatically minimise $a + c$, because of equation (2), and hence minimise the sum we are interested in.

Since b and d are positive integers, $b = 1$ and $d = 9$ are the smallest possible values with $d = 9b$. From (5) and (4), we see that the corresponding values of c and a are $c = 11$ and $a = 9$, both of which are also positive integers, as required.

Checking these values in equations (1) to (3), we confirm that they are valid solutions of the given equations.

Hence the smallest possible value of $a + b + c + d$ is 30.

Second method: elimination

We may rearrange the three equations (1), (2) and (3) to give

$$2a + 2b = c + d \tag{7}$$

$$a + c = 2b + 2d \tag{8}$$

$$2a + 2d = 3b + 3c. \tag{9}$$

Adding (7) and (8), we get

$$3a + 2b + c = 2b + c + 3d$$

and hence

$$a = d.$$

Then (7) and (9) may be rewritten

$$2b - c + d = 0. \tag{10}$$

and

$$3b + 3c - 4d = 0. \tag{11}$$

Now adding $3 \times$ (10) and (11), we obtain

$$9b - d = 0$$

and hence

$$d = 9b.$$

The solution now proceeds in the same way as the first method.

5. The diagram shows a triangle PTU inscribed in a square $PQRS$. Each of the marked angles at P is equal to 30°.

   Prove that the area of the triangle PTU is one third of the area of the square $PQRS$.

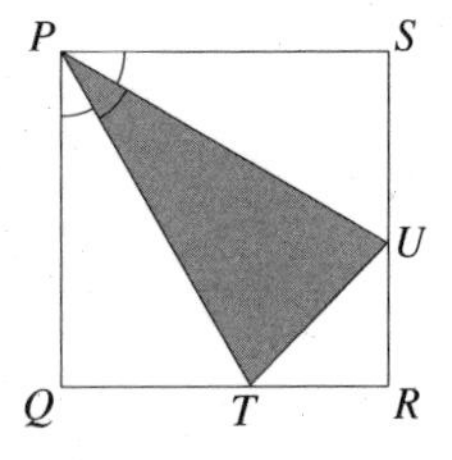

First solution

Let $QT = x$, so that $PT = 2x$, since triangle PTQ is half an equilateral triangle.

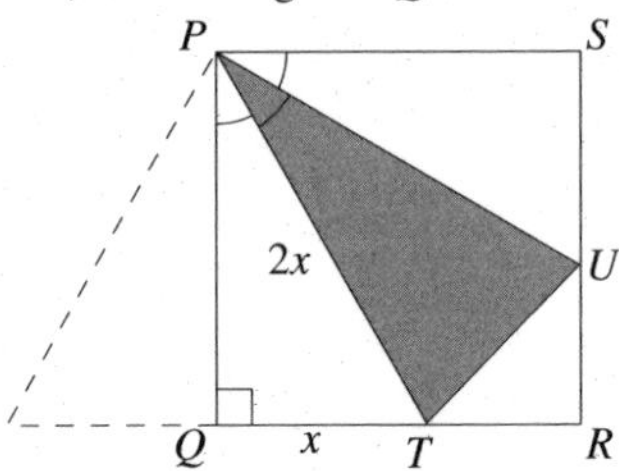

Using Pythagoras' theorem in triangle PTQ, we get

$$\begin{aligned} PQ^2 &= PT^2 - QT^2 \\ &= (2x)^2 - x^2 \\ &= 3x^2 \end{aligned}$$

and hence

$$PQ = \sqrt{3}x.$$

We can now find the areas of the three unshaded right-angled triangles.

$$\begin{aligned} \text{Area of triangle } PQT &= \tfrac{1}{2} \times x \times \sqrt{3}x \\ &= \frac{\sqrt{3}}{2}x^2. \end{aligned}$$

Similarly,

$$\text{area of triangle } PSU = \frac{\sqrt{3}}{2}x^2.$$

Finally,

$$\begin{aligned} \text{area of triangle } TRU &= \tfrac{1}{2} \times (\sqrt{3}x - x) \times (\sqrt{3}x - x) \\ &= \tfrac{1}{2}(3x^2 - 2\sqrt{3}x^2 + x^2) \\ &= 2x^2 - \sqrt{3}x^2. \end{aligned}$$

Therefore the total unshaded area is

$$\frac{\sqrt{3}}{2}x^2 + \frac{\sqrt{3}}{2}x^2 + 2x^2 - \sqrt{3}x^2 = 2x^2.$$

However, the area of the square $PQRS$ is $(\sqrt{3}x)^2 = 3x^2$. It follows that the shaded area is x^2, which is one third of the area of the square.

Second solution

Let the sides of the square $PQRS$ have length x.

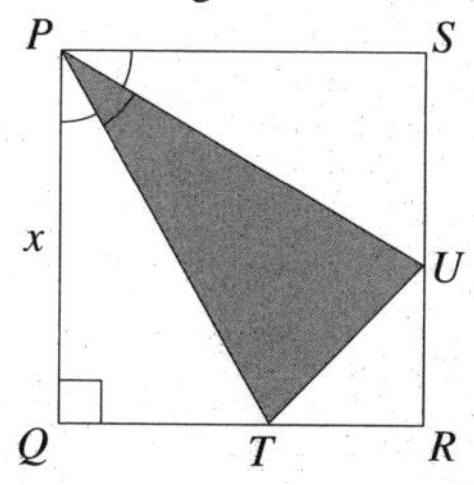

Then in triangle PQT we have

$$\cos 30° = \frac{x}{PT},$$

and hence

$$PT = \frac{x}{\cos 30°}.$$

Now by symmetry $PU = PT$ so that

$$\begin{aligned}\text{area of triangle } PTU &= \tfrac{1}{2}PT \times PU \sin \angle TPU \\ &= \tfrac{1}{2}x^2 \frac{\sin 30°}{\cos^2 30°}.\end{aligned}$$

Now $\cos 30° = \frac{\sqrt{3}}{2}$ and $\sin 30° = \frac{1}{2}$. Therefore

$$\begin{aligned}\text{area of triangle } PTU &= \tfrac{1}{2}x^2 \times \frac{\frac{1}{2}}{\frac{3}{4}} \\ &= \tfrac{1}{3}x^2.\end{aligned}$$

Hence the area of the triangle PTU is one third of the area of the square $PQRS$.

6. Two different cuboids are placed together, face-to-face, to form a large cuboid.
   The surface area of the large cuboid is $\frac{3}{4}$ of the total surface area of the original two cuboids.
   Prove that the lengths of the edges of the large cuboid may be labelled x, y and z, where

$$\frac{2}{z} = \frac{1}{x} + \frac{1}{y}.$$

First solution

Since the two cuboids are placed together, face-to-face, to form a large cuboid, two of the edges have the same lengths. Let these common lengths be x and y, and let the other edges of the two cuboids have lengths z_1 and z_2, as shown.

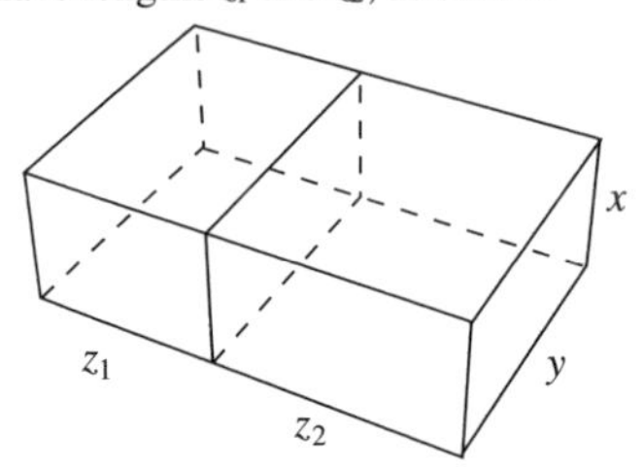

Now the surface area of the large cuboid is $\frac{3}{4}$ of the total surface area of the original two cuboids. Therefore

$$2\left[xy + x(z_1 + z_2) + y(z_1 + z_2)\right] = \tfrac{3}{4}\left[2(xy + z_1x + z_1y) + 2(xy + z_2x + z_2y)\right]$$

so that

$$4\left[xy + x(z_1 + z_2) + y(z_1 + z_2)\right] = 3\left[2xy + x(z_1 + z_2) + y(z_1 + z_2)\right]$$

and hence

$$2xy = x(z_1 + z_2) + y(z_1 + z_2),$$

that is,

$$2xy = (x + y)(z_1 + z_2).$$

Now $z_1 + z_2 = z$, where z is the edge length of the large cuboid. Therefore

$$2xy = (x + y)z$$

which may be rearranged to give

$$\frac{2}{z} = \frac{x + y}{xy} = \frac{1}{y} + \frac{1}{x}.$$

Hence the lengths of the edges of the large cuboid may be labelled x, y and z, where

$$\frac{2}{z} = \frac{1}{x} + \frac{1}{y}.$$

Second solution

Let the large cuboid have dimensions x, y and z, as shown.

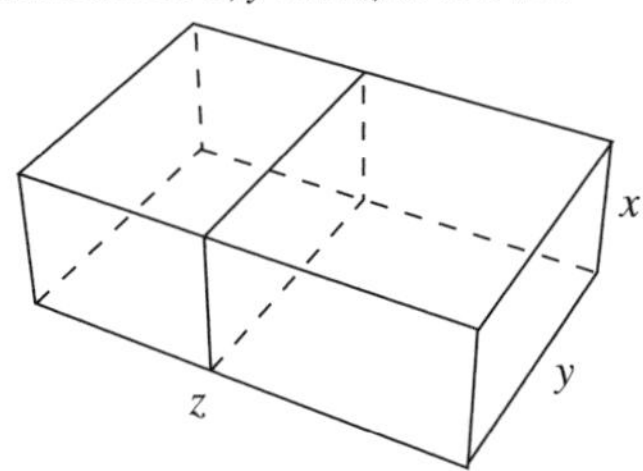

Now the total surface area T of the two original cuboids is equal to the surface area of the large cuboid added to the area of the two faces which are joined together. But the surface area of the large cuboid is $\frac{3}{4}T$, hence the area of the two faces which are joined together is $\frac{1}{4}T$, that is, $\frac{1}{3}$ of the surface area of the large cuboid.

Therefore

$$2xy = \tfrac{1}{3}(2xy + 2yz + 2zx)$$

so that

$$6xy = 2xy + 2yz + 2zx$$

and hence

$$2xy = yz + zx.$$

Dividing by xyz, we obtain, as required,

$$\frac{2}{z} = \frac{1}{x} + \frac{1}{y}.$$

Solutions to the 2009 Olympiad Maclaurin Paper

1. Five numbers are arranged in increasing order. As they get larger the difference between adjacent numbers doubles.

   The average of the five numbers is 11 more than the middle number. The sum of the second and fourth numbers is equal to the largest number.

   What is the largest number?

   Solution

   Let a be the smallest number and d be the difference between the first and second numbers. Then the other differences are $2d$, $4d$ and $8d$, so the five numbers are a, $a + d$, $a + 3d$, $a + 7d$ and $a + 15d$.

   The condition that 'the average of the five numbers is 11 more than the middle number' gives

   $$\frac{5a + 26d}{5} = a + 3d + 11,$$

   which means that $d = 5$.

   The condition that 'the sum of the second and fourth numbers is equal to the largest number' now gives

   $$2a + 8d = a + 15d$$

   and hence $a = 35$.

   So the five numbers are 35, 40, 50, 70 and 110. Hence the largest number is 110.

   Remark

   Slightly neater algebra is obtained if instead we define a and d so that the numbers are represented as $a - 3d$, $a - 2d$, a, $a + 4d$ and $a + 12d$.

2. Miko always remembers his four-digit PIN (personal identification number) because

   (a) it is a perfect square, and

   (b) it has the property that, when it is divided by 2, or 3, or 4, or 5, or 6, or 7, or 8, or 9, there is always a remainder of 1.

   What is Miko's PIN?

   Solution

   Since the required number has four digits, it is between 1000 and 9999.

   Let the number be N. We know that N is a perfect square, and also that $N - 1$ is divisible by 2, 3, 4, 5, 6, 7, 8 and 9. Hence $N - 1$ is divisible by the lowest common multiple of these numbers, which is $8 \times 9 \times 5 \times 7 = 2520$.

   There are therefore only three possible values for N in the range, namely 2521, 5041 and 7561, and of these only the middle one is a perfect square, being 71^2. Hence Miko's PIN is 5041.

   Remark

   It would be possible to start by listing all the four-digit perfect squares, and then checking them one by one for the condition (b) concerning remainders. This is, however, not a very efficient method, since there are 68 numbers to check. If a method like this is used, it must be made very clear that the check is done properly in every case. For example, one might exclude 5929 by showing that it is a multiple of 7 and thus has remainder 0. It would not be enough simply to claim that this check had been made without giving details in each case.

The task can be reduced by, for instance, excluding the even squares, leaving only 34 numbers to check, or realising that the number has to end in a 1 to satisfy the conditions for divisibility by 2 and 5. However, by the time you are applying this logic, you might as well go the whole way and use the method given above.

3. Solve the simultaneous equations

$$\frac{5xy}{x + y} = 6$$

$$\frac{4xz}{x + z} = 3$$

$$\frac{3yz}{y + z} = 2.$$

Solutions

It is worth beginning with the observation that none of x, y or z can be zero, since that would immediately invalidate the equations. This allows us, in subsequent work, to cancel a factor of x, y or z from both sides of an equation. Note also that we should not assume that x, y or z are whole numbers.

First solution

Label the equations as follows:

$$\frac{5xy}{x + y} = 6 \qquad (1)$$

$$\frac{4xz}{x + z} = 3 \qquad (2)$$

$$\frac{3yz}{y + z} = 2. \qquad (3)$$

From (1),

$$5xy = 6x + 6y$$

and from (2),

$$8xz = 6x + 6z,$$

so

$$5xy - 8xz = 6y - 6z. \qquad (4)$$

We can, however, also deduce from (1) and (2) that

$$\frac{5xy}{x + y} = \frac{8xz}{x + z},$$

so, cancelling x,

$$5y(x + z) = 8z(x + y)$$

and therefore

$$5xy - 8xz = 3yz. \tag{5}$$

But, from (3),

$$3yz = 2y + 2z. \tag{6}$$

Putting (4), (5) and (6) together, we have

$$6y - 6z = 2y + 2z$$

and so

$$y = 2z.$$

Now, substituting $y = 2z$ in (3) and cancelling z, we have

$$\frac{6z}{3} = 2,$$

so $z = 1$ and $y = 2$. Then $x = 3$, by using (5), for example.

Note that it is now necessary to check that this triple of values works for all the equations. All we have shown so far is that, if the equations are true, then the only possible values of x, y and z are 3, 2 and 1; this does not mean that, if x, y and z are 3, 2 and 1, then the equations are true—for example, the equations may have *no* solutions.

Second solution

Since none of x, y or z is zero, we can define

$$a = \frac{1}{x}, \ b = \frac{1}{y} \text{ and } c = \frac{1}{z}.$$

By taking the reciprocals of each side of the three equations, we obtain

$$b + a = \frac{5}{6}$$

$$a + c = \frac{4}{3}$$

$$c + b = \frac{3}{2}.$$

Hence, by adding, we deduce that

$$a + b + c = \frac{11}{6},$$

so $c = 1$, $b = \frac{1}{2}$ and $a = \frac{1}{3}$. Therefore $x = 3$, $y = 2$ and $z = 1$.

Again we should check these values satisfy the original equations, or show that our logic is reversible.

4. In a trapezium $ABCD$ the sides AB and DC are parallel and $\angle BAD = \angle ABC < 90°$.
   Point P lies on AB with $\angle CPD = \angle BAD$.
   Prove that $PC^2 + PD^2 = AB \times DC$.

Solutions

We begin with a diagram showing the information given in the question. The three marked angles are equal.

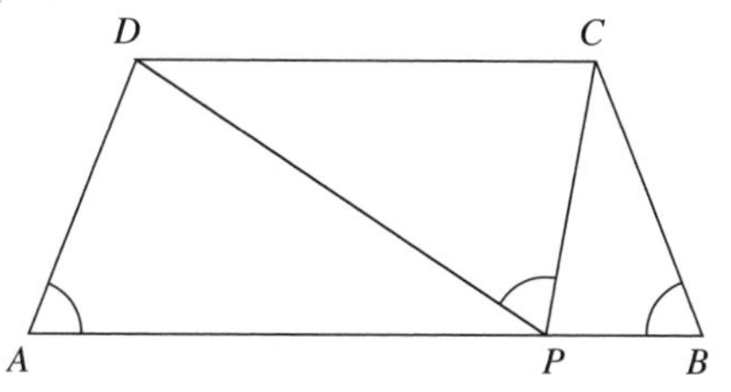

First solution

Since AB is parallel to DC, the alternate angles $\angle DCP$ and $\angle CPB$ are equal. Hence the two triangles ΔCDP and ΔPCB are similar.

Exactly the same argument shows that ΔDPA is also similar to ΔCDP. We therefore have three similar triangles. Notice that we have been careful to describe the triangles in the correct order of vertices, so that the ratios of sides can now be read off conveniently.

Now corresponding sides are in the same ratio, so we have

$$\frac{PB}{PC} = \frac{PC}{DC} \quad \text{and} \quad \frac{AP}{PD} = \frac{PD}{DC},$$

and it follows that

$$PC^2 = PB \times DC \quad \text{and} \quad PD^2 = AP \times DC.$$

Adding these two equations, we obtain

$$\begin{aligned} PC^2 + PD^2 &= (AP + PB) \times DC \\ &= AB \times DC. \end{aligned}$$

Second solution

This proof starts by using the converse of the alternate segment theorem. Because $\angle DAB = \angle CPD$ it follows that CP is a tangent at P to the circumcircle of ΔDAP.

Similarly, DP is a tangent at P to the circumcircle of ΔBCP.

Let DC (extended) meet the two circles at X and Y, as shown.

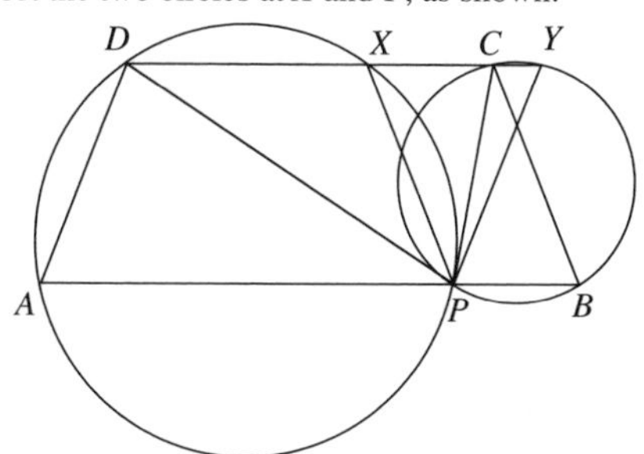

Now $\angle CXP = \angle DAP$, by the external angle of a cyclic quadrilateral, and also $\angle CXP = \angle XPA$, by alternate angles. Hence $\angle XPA = \angle DAP = \angle CBP$ and so XP is parallel to CB and $PBCX$ is a parallelogram. Similarly, $APYD$ is a parallelogram. In particular, $CX = PB$ and $DY = AP$.

Now we use the tangent-secant theorem for each circle. This gives

$$\begin{aligned} CP^2 &= CX \times CD \\ &= PB \times CD \end{aligned}$$

and

$$\begin{aligned} DP^2 &= DC \times DY \\ &= DC \times AP. \end{aligned}$$

The last stage of the proof proceeds in the same way as the first solution.

Remark

When the three marked angles are right angles the result reduces to Pythagoras' theorem.

5. A lottery involves five balls being selected from a drum. Each ball has a different positive integer printed on it.

   Show that, whichever five balls are selected, it is always possible to choose three of them so that the sum of the numbers on these three balls is a multiple of 3.

Solution

It is worth observing that, for the purposes of this question, we can replace the numbers on the balls by their remainders when they are divided by 3. This is because, for any two numbers a and b, their sum $a + b$ is a multiple of 3 if, and only if, the sum of their remainders is divisible by 3. To prove this, suppose that, when divided by 3, a has remainder r and b has remainder s. Then we can write $a = 3m + r$ and $b = 3n + s$, for some integers m and n. Therefore $a + b = 3m + 3n + r + s = 3(m + n) + r + s$ and this is divisible by 3 if, and only if, $r + s$ is divisible by 3.

Using this idea, any selection of five balls will result in a set of five numbers, each of which is 0 or 1 or 2.

If three of the balls have the same number, then their sum will be divisible by 3, and we are done.

If not, then there is one pair of numbers equal to x, another pair equal to y and a fifth number equal to z, where x, y and z are 0, 1 and 2, in some order. This means that there are three balls numbered 0, 1 and 2, and the sum of these numbers is divisible by 3.

Hence, in either case, we have a choice of three of the five balls whose sum is a multiple of 3.

6. In the figure, p, q, r and s are the lengths of four arcs which together form the circumference of the circle.
   Find, in simplified form, an expression for s in terms of p, q and r.

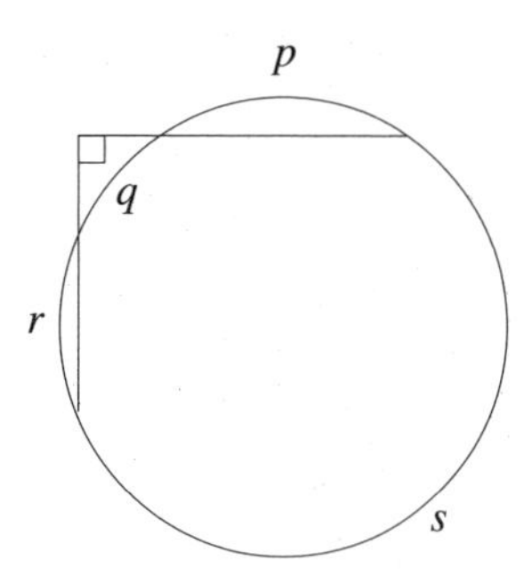

First solution

First note that the length of an arc of a circle is proportional to the angle subtended at the centre. Hence, by appropriate choice of radius, we can arrange that the arc lengths are actually equal to these angles. (If this is not done, the calculation proceeds in the same way, but there is some cancelling to do at the end.)

The diagram shows these four angles at the centre of the circle.

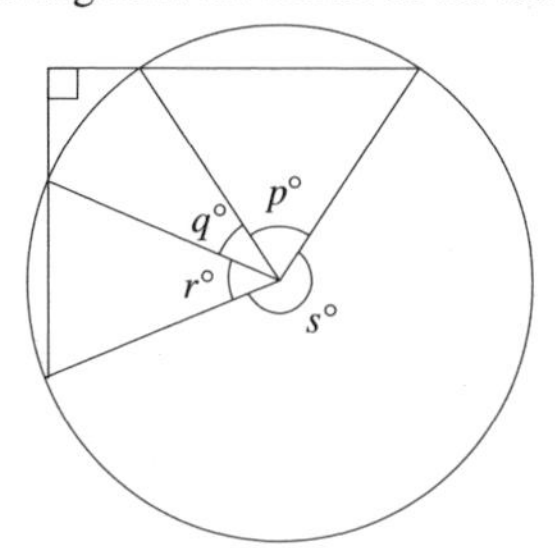

Now there are two relationships between p, q, r and s. First there is the obvious one

$$p + q + r + s = 360. \tag{1}$$

We also have the angle sum of a quadrilateral; one of the angles is 90°, one is $(p + q + r)°$, and the others can be calculated in terms of p and r using the fact that there are two isosceles triangles. This gives

$$(p + q + r) + (90 - \tfrac{1}{2}p) + 90 + (90 - \tfrac{1}{2}r) = 360$$

and so

$$p + 2q + r = 180.$$

Hence, from (1),

$$p + q + r + s = 2p + 4q + 2r$$

and so

$$s = p + 3q + r.$$

Second solution

We construct the two radii perpendicular to the two given chords, as shown in the diagram.

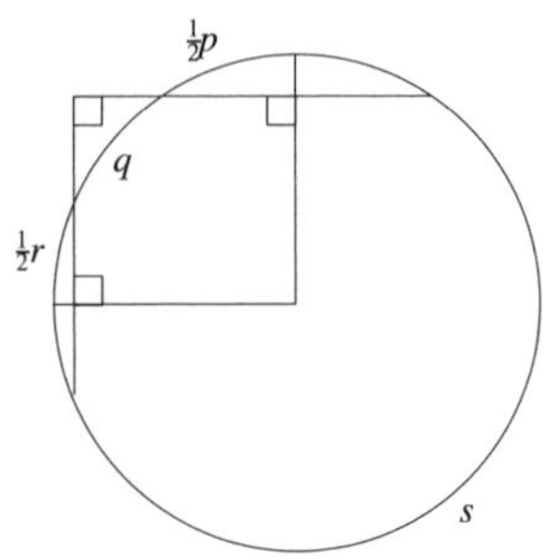

Since a radius perpendicular to a chord bisects the chord, it also bisects the corresponding arc. So we have arcs of length $\frac{1}{2}p$ and $\frac{1}{2}r$, as shown.

Now the diagram contains a quadrilateral with three right angles, so the fourth angle is also a right angle and therefore the two radii are perpendicular. Hence the radii determine a quarter of the circle, and so

$$p + q + r + s = 4 \times \left(\tfrac{1}{2}p + q + \tfrac{1}{2}r\right),$$

which gives

$$s = p + 3q + r.$$

Comments on the IMOK Olympiad Papers and Scripts

General comments (Gerry Leversha)

Both candidates and their teachers will find it helpful to know something of the general principles involved in marking Olympiad-type papers. The preliminary paragraphs therefore serve as an exposition of the 'philosophy' which has guided both the setting and marking of all such papers at all age levels, both nationally and internationally.

What we are looking for, essentially, is solutions to problems. This approach is therefore rather different from what happens in public examinations such as GCSE, AS and A level, where credit is given for the ability to carry out individual techniques regardless of how these techniques fit into a protracted argument. Such marking is cumulative; a candidate may gain 60% of the available marks without necessarily having a clue about how to solve the final problem. Indeed, the questions are generally structured in such a way as to facilitate this approach, divided into many parts and not requiring an overall strategy for tackling a multistage argument.

In contrast to this, Olympiad-style problems are marked by looking at each question synoptically and deciding whether the candidate has some sort of overall strategy or not. An answer which is essentially a solution, but might contain either errors of calculation, flaws in logic, omission of cases or technical faults, will be marked on a '10 minus' basis. One question we often ask is: if we were to have the benefit of a 2 minute interview with this candidate, could they correct the error or fill the gap? On the other hand, an answer which shows no sign of being a genuine solution is marked on a '0-plus' basis; up to 3 marks might be awarded for particular cases or insights. It is therefore important that candidates taking these papers realise the importance of the rubric about trying to finish whole questions rather than attempting lots of disconnected parts.

We are particularly strict about logical clarity. It is very important to distinguish an argument which proceeds from A to B from one which goes in the opposite direction (or, indeed, to recognise an 'if and only if' argument for what it is.) For instance, we are quite harsh on candidates who begin with a stated relationship and deduce something like '0 = 0'. We emphasise the need to begin with what you know and deduce what you are asked to prove. Another issue concerns the difference between looking at individual cases and proving something in general. In Maclaurin question 4, you must begin with a general isosceles trapezium, rather than, say, one composed of three equilateral triangles, and in Maclaurin question 5, you cannot conclude anything from special cases. Usually such simplifying assumptions will result in no marks at all for a question.

Cayley paper (comments from James Cranch)

The essence of a good Olympiad question is a genuine *problem*: even in questions that require calculation, a successful candidate will have to find strategies to make their calculations manageable. As a result, we are unable to give many marks to solutions in which the final answer appears as from nowhere. In order to make this possible, the rubric asks for full and reasoned solutions, and with them we are almost always able to determine if they truly understood the processes that led to the answer.

In particular, a solution which more-or-less fully describes a valid process leading to the final answer will receive at least 7 marks, while a solution which doesn't will usually receive at most 3 (and so marks of 4, 5 or 6 are fairly uncommon).

Doing this fairly can be particularly difficult with Year 9 students, as often their mathematical ingenuity far exceeds their powers of clear explanation. Nevertheless, some simple advice can be given to explain how to maximise a score.

Questions 1 and 5 both admit solutions by trial and improvement. It is quite important to avoid the temptation to do this, however, for several reasons:

- Trial and improvement intrinsically depends on calculating a large number of specific cases. Complete accuracy is too much to expect under exam conditions. But if an arithmetic slip causes one calculation to go wrong, the whole process is derailed. It requires considerable astuteness to recognise that the later results are inconsistent, and is very hard to patch.
- Trial and improvement, since it consists only of calculation, is hard to document. Sometimes a solution is found fortuitously, and it is hard to persuade the marker that the method which obtained it was a valid general approach.
- Trial and improvement tends to obscure any necessary understanding of the structure of the problem. For example, in question 5, it is not hard to see that, since one candle is burning down faster than the other, it will overtake the other in at most a single place while burning. This is implicit in any sophisticated approach, but isn't implicit in trial and error. Many marks will usually be lost in overlooking points such as this.

The best insurance against these is simply to avoid trial and improvement. Of course, the best approach to both questions 1 and 5 is to use algebra: wherever we identify certain quantities as important, we should label them with a variable, and then carefully explain how we can describe the situation using equations in those variables. In both cases these are not difficult to solve, and the resulting solutions suffer from none of the three deficiencies above.

One common cause of minor mark deductions in Question 5 was poorly explained choices of units. Many candidates said things like 'we assume the candles are 80cm tall'. This assumption can in fact be made without loss of generality, but candidates are rare at Year 9 who can explain this properly in words. Again, the easiest solution is to use algebraic notation. If the height of a candle be called h cm, then equations involving h can be formed, and the h can visibly be cancelled without thought.

In Question 2, as well, it was much better to use algebra than to provide a vague explanation of why the arc lengths of the smaller semicircles sum to 5π. After all, the vague explanation would merely be purporting to describe the phenomenon of linearity, which is manifest in the algebra.

Unfortunately, the biggest source of problems in Question 3 was simply misreading the question. The configuration described two different rectangles, and many candidates considered only two identical rectangles. Beyond that, two logical slips had to be avoided. One was the slip of proving the converse (the statement that, if you take a square and cut it across, then the perimeters have the given relationship). The other was the temptation to use the statement that the students were trying to prove. In detail, naming the common long side of the rectangles a and the short sides b and c, candidates often observed that the criterion for the resulting rectangle to be square was $a = b + c$. Unfortunately, having written this down, many candidates did not realise that they were banned from using it while attempting to derive it.

Question 4 was found to be the hardest on the paper. Those who know trigonometry were able to characterise the angle as $\arctan\left(\sqrt{2} - 1\right)$ without much difficulty. Unfortunately, the question asks for a number in degrees, and it is unfeasibly di cult to calculate this arctangent. Ideas from pure geometry are the only sensible way to proceed.

The difficulty of question 6 is of a similar type to the difficulty of describing angle-chasing arguments in geometry. In the former, one has a results chart, and in the latter a diagram. The difficulty is that of transcribing arguments which go back and forth, cross-referencing facts in di erent places, and writing it as a coherent trail which can be read top-to-bottom without difficulty.

Some advice for people looking to do this runs as follows:

- Use distinct words for distinct ideas, and parallel words for parallel ideas, so the reader can correctly sense whether you are doing something novel or not.
- It certainly helps to be familiar with the vocabulary of sport: good use of terms like 'goal difference' and 'goals conceded' is helpful.
- Write a list of deductions, not a single long paragraph.

- Refer constantly to other deductions, and to the given data. It is better to make too many references than too few, as good references are easy to ignore.
- The biggest single logical error was a false dichotomy. The team B had scored two and conceded two, while winning, losing and drawing one match. Many candidates asserted they must either have won 1–0, drawn 1–1, and lost 0–1, or won 2–0, drawn 0–0, and lost 0–2. Unfortunately, this is quite wrong: *prima facie* they could also have won 2–1, drawn 0–0 and lost 0–1, or won 1–0, drawn 0–0, and lost 1–2. A style of proof which admits errors like this is not optimal; it is much better to adopt a less enumerative style and deduce exactly what is needed.

Hamilton Paper (comments from Dean Bunnell)

The paper was very accessible to all candidates and there was no indication that they had not been able to engage in any of the questions. The high scores attained in the paper reflected this.

1. Candidates performed well on what was a very popular question. Setting up the equation

$$2 \times \frac{x}{280} = \frac{x + 60}{340}$$

was essential in order to make significant progress. Some candidates mixed up the proportion of clownfish getting

$$\frac{x}{280} = 2 \times \frac{x + 60}{340}$$

This earned three marks out of ten. The use of algebra was required and not just arithmetic reasoning. The answer only earned 1 mark. An answer of 102 clownfish was allowed as long as it was clear when this would occur.

2. Candidates scored well on this question. The most common approach was to use the fact that the sum of the digits of a multiple of 9 is also a multiple of 9, leading to $p + q = 6$ or 15. Divisibility by 4 resulted in the conclusion that $3q$ was divisible by 4 hence $q = 2$ or 6. Combining these conclusions gave $p + q = 6$ when $q = 2$ and $p + q = 15$ when $q = 6$. Candidates giving $p = 0$, $q = 6$ as a solution lost one mark. Other approaches were:

   (a) to observe q was even and try values for q of 0, 2, 4, 6 and 8;

   (b) to work using 6 as a factor of '$p543q$'.

   Answers only scored 1 mark.

3. There were many innovative methods used by candidates here. Using Pythagoras' Theorem to calculate that the side of the rhombus $AECF$ is $12\frac{1}{2}$ cm, also that $AC = 20$ cm, was often followed by one of the following:
   (a) Using $(12\frac{1}{2})^2 = (\frac{1}{2}AC)^2 + (\frac{1}{2}EF)^2$ hence $(12\frac{1}{2})^2 = 10^2 + (\frac{1}{2}EF)^2$;
   (b) Taking the area of triangles ADF and CEB away from the area of rectangle $ABCD$ produced the area of the rhombus $AECF = 12 \times 16 - 2 \times \frac{1}{2} \times 12 \times 3\frac{1}{2}$. Hence $\frac{1}{2}AC \times EF = 12 \times 16 - 12 \times 3\frac{1}{2}$ and hence $10 \times EF = 192 - 42$.
   (c) Drawing a perpendicular from F onto AB at point G, say, and deducing that $EG = 9$ gave $EF^2 = 9^2 + 12^2$,

4. The two main approaches were substitution and elimination. The initial equations formed from the information given were well set up but proceeding to establish two different equations in two variables proved to be more difficult. Getting to this stage was essential in order to progress further. Some candidates obtained the correct answer but failed to establish that this was the smallest possible value of $a + b + c + d$. This lost a mark.

5. The key point was how the candidate dealt with the 30° angles. Different options used were:
   (a) Finding the length of PT or PU and then using the values of $\sin 30°$ and $\cos 30°$ to find the area of triangle $PTU = \frac{1}{2}PT \times PU \sin 30°$.
   (b) The use of Pythagoras' Theorem, several times, enabled candidates to make good progress but then a 30° angle had to be incorporated in order to progress further.
   (c) An elegant method was to reflect the side PT in the line PQ to form an equilateral triangle. The problem could then be solved without the use of trigonometry.

6. Candidates approached this question by either considering the two cuboids separately, forming the equation
$$2xy = x(z_1 + z_2) + y(z_1 + z_2)$$
or by considering the large cuboid and forming the equation
$$2xy = \tfrac{1}{3}(2xy + 2yz + 2zx).$$
The equation $2xy = z(x + y)$ was derived from these two equations. Division by xyz was shown clearly in most cases. Similar to question 1, 3 marks were given for $\frac{3}{4}$ being on the wrong side of the equation.

Maclaurin Paper (comments from Gerry Leversha)

1. This is a fairly straightforward question where a sensible allocation of variables and formation of equations should lead quickly to the solution. You must not assume that the numbers are integers or resort to a 'trial and improvement' approach. Several candidates misread the condition about the differences and they consequently lost most of the available credit. Be sure that you have understood the question properly.

2. Questions like this allow a choice between analytical and enumeration methods. The former recognise that a crucial step is the calculation of the LCM of 2, 3, 4, 6, 7, 8 and 9, which is 2520, so the PIN can only be one of 2521, 5041 or 7561. Now we have a list of three possible PINs and each one must be examined to see if it is a perfect square.

   An enumeration or 'search' approach begins by making a list of possibilities and eliminating them one by one. If you opt for this, it is essential that you make the search process quite explicit. Do not expect the examiner to take on trust the fact that you really have looked at all the cases. In this problem, enumeration methods form a spectrum from the very crude to the quite sophisticated. The most tedious approach is to begin with all 68 four-digit perfect squares; it was gratifying to see that virtually nobody did this. A better model is to realise that the number has to be odd; this cuts the list down to 34 candidates. Other versions omitted multiples of 3, 5 or 7 (but, oddly, not many thought about 9). Probably the most sophisticated search model decided that it was only worth looking at squares of prime numbers. In order for this to be justified, it was necessary to explain why primes such as 11 and 13 were not considered; had the PIN contained five digits, it would have been necessary to think about these. A popular approach was to show why the PIN had to end in the digit 1, but a common error was to say that the square root also had to end in 1, forgetting the possibility of 9. One interesting fact that emerged was the common belief that 91 is prime! Even the 'recommended' approach has a search element in the final step, and it was important to show that 2521 and 7561 were not squares and that 5041 was. Incidentally, there was no mark for the statement of the solution.

   The setters can perhaps be criticised for a lack of clarity. The intention was that the solution was a four-digit number (and hence between 1000 and 9999). It is possible, of course, for a PIN to begin with a zero, leading to the trivial solution of 0001. Candidates who gave this as the solution were perhaps a little optimistic in underestimating the difficulty of Maclaurin problems. A further criticism is that the question might be taken to imply that there is a unique solution, so there is no need to continue searching after 5041 has been discovered or indeed to check 5041 after all alternatives have been eliminated. It is a common feature of problems set in these competitions that you should show that your answer is unique.

3. There are a number of good approaches to this algebra question. What we were looking for was the ability to manipulate the given equations so as to produce either a single equation in one variable or simultaneous linear equations in two. A favoured method was to change the subject of two of the given equations to x, y or z and then use the third to generate a quadratic equation. A problem that arises with something like $x = \dfrac{6y}{5y - 6}$ is the assumption that $y \neq \frac{6}{5}$; in fact, similar conditions are really necessary in the very statement of the problem on the question paper. Nearly all solutions required consideration of zero values, and it was deemed necessary to show that these are impossible (by reference to the original equations).

   A further requirement (a commonplace for algebraic problems in Olympiads) is that the solution needs to be *checked*. In normal school algebra (quadratics, linear equations, and the like) one is using an implicit existence theorem: if the argument produces a 'solution', then the solution does indeed satisfy the equations. The argument has actually shown that, if certain equations are true, then the solution can only be a member of a particular set. This does not establish that every member of that set is a solution to the equations. Consider, for example, four linear equations in three variables: three of them might imply a unique solution, but this might not be a solution to the fourth. Similar considerations apply to equations of the type $\sqrt{\ldots} + \sqrt{\ldots} = \sqrt{\ldots}$ which involve square roots. The normal solving procedure involves squaring both sides, perhaps twice, but as a result solutions to other equations, such as $\sqrt{\ldots} + \sqrt{\ldots} = \sqrt{\ldots}$, are discovered, so it is essential to check that any solutions you have found apply to the equation you began with. Equivalently, it would be sufficient to check that the argument used in producing the solutions is reversible—but even if this is so, it is a good habit to carry out the check as a matter of course. Candidates for competitions such as Maclaurin should recognise the need for checking in any but the most straightforward cases. (We did not, for instance, require a check in question 1, since this involved two equations in two unknowns.) However, in this problem, only one mark was deducted even if a candidate had omitted both to check and to deal with zero values of the variables.

4. This was a very straightforward problem on similar triangles, and produced a disappointing response. It might be that students are really only able to deal with similar triangles when the triangles are in the same orientation or not part of the same figure.

5. This involves two ideas. One is that the sum of three numbers is divisible by 3 if, and only if, they all have the same residue modulo 3 or they all have different residues. The other is that one of these two cases must obtain if five numbers are selected; this is essentially an application of the pigeonhole principle. To reach the threshold of a good mark, candidates had to appreciate both elements of the argument, and to attain a perfect mark, the second argument had to be spelt out very clearly.

6. This is an elegant problem and produced a better response than expected. A popular method was to 'complete the rectangle' either by reflecting the given diagram in perpendicular diameters or by adding various lines at right angles. Most of the resulting diagrams then relied on 'look and see' arguments (or appeals to symmetry) rather than precise Euclidean demonstrations; these were penalised, but not heavily. It is, of course, helpful to know that the length of an arc is proportional to the angle subtended at the centre (or circumference).

Marking

The marking was carried out on the weekend of 28th and 29th March in Leeds. There were three marking groups led by James Cranch, Dean Bunnell and Gerry Leversha. The other markers were:

Anne Andrews; Ann Ault; Philip Coggins; David Crawford; Mary Teresa Fyfe; James Gazet; Mark Harwood; Rita Holland; Ina Hughes; Carl James; Andrew Jobbings; Calum Kilgour; Nick Lord; Sam Maltby; Holly McLean; Linda Moon; Philip Moon; Peter Neumann; Sylvia Neumann; Stephen Power; Jenny Ramsden; Mary Read; Chris Robson; Paul Russell; John Slater; Jon Stone; Alex Voice; Christopher Walker; Jerome Watson; James Welham and Brian Wilson.

IMOK certificates

All participating students were awarded a certificate. Certificates came in three varieties: Participation, Merit and Distinction.

THE UKMT INTERMEDIATE MATHEMATICAL OLYMPIAD AND KANGAROO

In recognition of previous high performance in the UK Intermediate Mathematical Challenge, the top pupils in School Year 11 or below in England, S4 or below in Scotland and School Year 12 or below in Northern Ireland are invited to take part in one of the two strands of this follow-on competition.

The top-scoring pupils in each year are invited to sit the Olympiad, a two-hour examination which includes six demanding questions requiring full written solutions. The problems are designed to include interesting and attractive mathematics and may involve knowledge or understanding beyond the range of normal school work.

Other high-scoring pupils in each year-group are invited to enter the European Kangaroo. In 2009 the 'Kangourou sans Frontières' was taken by students in over forty countries in Europe and beyond. The multiple-choice questions involve amusing and thought-provoking situations which require the use of logic as well as mathematical understanding.

Further information on the UKMT and its activities can be found at www.ukmt.org.uk

IMOK Olympiad awards

As in recent years, medals were awarded in the Intermediate Mathematical Olympiad. Names of medal winners are listed below. Book prizes were still awarded to the top 50 or so pupils in each year group. The Cayley book prize was *Sacred Geometry* and *Sacred Number* by Miranda Lundy, the Hamilton book prize was *How to cut a cake* by Ian Stewart and the Maclaurin book prize was *Fallacies in Mathematics* by EA Maxwell. In addition, key fobs with a related design as shown were awarded to all IMOK participants.

In area, the central square is two-fifths of the whole square. What fraction are the shaded triangles?

IMOK medal winners

Cayley

Sinan Adibelli	Ozel Izmir Amerikan Lisesi, Turkey
Freddie Alford	Bromsgrove School, Worcestershire
Keith Barker	Wilson's School, Wallington, Surrey
Charles Barton	Westminster School, London
Isar Bhattacharjee	St Paul's School, Barnes, London
Anthony Boyle	Hampton School, Hampton, Middlesex
Sam Brennan	Northgate High School, Ipswich, Suffolk
Louie Brookgandy	King's College School, London
Leonardo Buizza	St Paul's School, Barnes, London
Edward Burns	King Edward's School, Birmingham
Andrew Carlotti	Sir Roger Manwood's School, Kent
William Chang	Ysgol Friars, Bangor, Gwynedd
Pawit Chantaworakit	Bangkok Patana School, Bangkok
Toby Chelton	St Paul's School, Barnes, London
Andrey Cherenkov	Loughborough GS, Leicestershire
Samuel Cheshire	Clifton Comp. School, Rotherham
Jaehoon Cho	Mayflower CHS, Billericay, Essex
Jake Cohen-Setton	St Paul's School, Barnes, London
Alexander Cooke	South Island School, Hong Kong
James Coxon	St Paul's School, Barnes, London

Alex Duncan	Aberdeen Grammar School
Edward Elcock	Shrewsbury School
Stuart Emmerson	Reading School, Berkshire
James Fage	Westminster School, London
Yi Fan	Watford GS for Girls, Hertfordshire
Noah Fechtorpradine	British School of Boston, Boston
Oliver Feng	Olchfa Comprehensive School, Swansea
Andrew Fernandes	Saffron Walden CHS, Saffron Walden
George Fortune	Altrincham GS for Boys, Cheshire
Michael French	Judd School, Tonbridge, Kent
Humphrey Galbraith	Winchester College, Hampshire
Bahar Gaser	Ozel Izmir Amerikan Lisesi, Turkey
Peter Gerlagh	Altrincham GS for Boys, Cheshire
Jenie Han	Redland High School, Redland, Bristol
Jamesy Han	Overseas Family School, Singapore
Zoe Harris	Stockport Grammar School, Cheshire
Daniel Heydecker	St Albans School, Hertfordshire
Eleanor Holderness	Latymer Upper School, London
Riki Houlden	Westminster School, London
Daniel Hu	City of London School, London
Liam Hughes	Welland Park Comm. Coll., Leicestershire
Freddie Illingworth	Dragon School, Oxford
Ben Jang	Caldicott School, Buckinghamshire
Matthew Jasper	St Crispin's School, Berkshire
Marc Jeffreys	Woodbridge School, Suffolk
Alex Jelicic	King's College School, London
Mark Jerjian	Westminster Under School, London
Hang bin Jo	Sir James Henderson School, Italy
Ralph Jordan	Bishops Stortford College, Hertfordshire
Soohee Kang	Frankfurt International School, Germany
Isaac Kang	Westminster School, London
Sahl Khan	St Paul's School, Barnes, London
Patrick Kidger	Torquay Boys' Grammar School, Devon
Minjung Kim	Badminton School, , Bristol

Seungwoo Ko	Ewell Castle School, Surrey
Yves Kwan	German Swiss Int. S, Hong Kong
Dabin Kwon	Badminton School, Bristol
Kai Laddiman	Heathfield Comm. Coll., East Sussex
Grace Lee	St Paul's Girls' School, London
Philip Leung	Harrow School, Middlesex
Baichuan Li	Highgate School, London
Harry Metrebian	Beacon School, Buckinghamshire
Tomoki Mineshima	Claremont High School, Harrow
Rana Mittra	King's School, Peterborough
Joe Moneim	Reading School, Berkshire
Hunsoo Na	Yew Chung Int. School of Bejing
Marcus Nielsen	Aylesbury Grammar S., Buckinghamshire
Eiki Norizuki	Fettes College, Edinburgh
Alistair O'Neill	St Olave's Grammar School, Kent
Liyang Pan	Royal Grammar School, High Wycombe
Katya Richards	School of St Helen and St Katharine, Abingdon, Oxfordshire
Bryony Richards	South Wiltshire Grammar S., Salisbury
Jack Robinson	Caistor Grammar School, Lincolnshire
Hannah Robson	Harrogate GS, North Yorkshire
Alex Ruff	Ashcroft Technology Academy, London
Sreya Saha	Altrincham Girls' GS, Cheshire
Nigethan Sathiyalingam	Queen Elizabeth's School, Hertfordshire
Saravana Sathyanandha	Haberdashers' Aske's Sch. for Boys, Elstree
Rowan Schrecker	Sandhurst School, Berks
Dylon Sivam	Haberdashers' Aske's Sch. for Boys, Elstree
Choi Soohyun	Bromsgrove International School, Minburi
Jeremy Soper	Taunton School, Somerset
Siddhart Swaroop	King's College School, London
Thierry Tan	Alice Smith School, Seri Kembangan
Joe Tomkinson	Harry Carlton School, Loughborough
Vincent Wang	West Island School (ESF), Hong Kong
Hanxi Wang	Watford Grammar School for Girls
Philip Warren	Sutton Grammar School for Boys, Surrey

Joanna Wu	North London Collegiate Sch., Middlesex
Minjin Yang	Richard Challoner School, Surrey
Chuyi Yang	King Edward VI Camp Hill Girls' School
Christopher Ying	Sevenoaks School, Kent
Paul Yoon	Cheltenham College, Gloucestershire
Teresa Yoon	Cranleigh School, Surrey
Ru Young	Summer Fields School, Oxford
Changmin Yun	Oundle School, Oundle
Linan Zhang	Millfield School, Somerset

Hamilton

James Aaronson	St Paul's School, Barnes, London
Iman Ahmedani	St Paul's Girls' School, London
Michael Alishaw	Latymer Upper School, London
Nirmala Arulampalam	King Henry VIII School, Coventry
Nant Arunyawongsako	Shrewsbury Int. Sch., Bangkok
Ian Baldwin	Forest School, London
Paras Bavisha	Merchant Taylors' School, Middlesex
Max Baxter-Allen	Millfield School, Somerset
Frank Bloomfield	Colchester Royal Grammar School, Essex
Callum Bungey	Westminster School, London
Sam Capplemanlynes	Shebbear College, Beaworthy, Devon
Rachel Carrington	St Alban's Catholic High School, Ipswich
Dickson Chan	Winchester College, Hampshire
Qiyang Chen	Queen Elizabeth's GS, Blackburn
Hugo Cheng	Sevenoaks School, Kent
Haydn Child	Westminster School, London
Wanyeung Chui	West Island School (ESF), Hong Kong
Matthew Colbrook	The King's School, Witney
Jennifer Collister	Oxford High School, Oxford
James Dixon	King Edward VI GS, Chelmsford, Essex
Bell Duncan	St Olave's Grammar School, Orpington
Jonathan Dungay	Steyning Grammar School, Steyning
Michael Dunngoekjian	Winchester College, Hampshire
Takehiro Fujita	Harrow School, Middlesex
Cosmos Fung	Tonbridge School, Kent

Sarah Gait	Queen Elizabeth GS, Penrith
Lee George	Lancaster Royal Grammar School
Adam Goucher	Heritage School, Chesterfield
Mark Green	Katharine Lady Berkeleys School, Glos
James Hall	Watford Grammar School for Boys, Herts
Eigen Horsfield	Tapton School, Sheffield
Chou-Ling Hsieh	Concord College, Shrewsbury, Shropshire
Xufu Huang	Bell Bedgebury Int. Sch., Goudhurst, Kent
Sun Hugo	Warwick School, Warwick
Daniel Hunt	Wilson's School, Wallington, Surrey
Joshua Hunt	Bryn Celynnog Comprehensive, Pontypridd
Raphael Hwang	Winchester College, Hampshire
Joshua Inoue	Queen Elizabeth's Hospital, Bristol
Akash Jain	Wellington College, Berkshire
Oliver Jia	West Buckland School, Barnstaple, Devon
Yibo Jin	Christ's College, East Finchley, London
Junho Kim	Frankfurt International School, Germany
Anant Kothari	Bangkok Patana School, Bangkok
Naomi Kraushar	Tiferes High School, London
Hazal Kurtcu	Rossall School, Fleetwood, Lancashire
Michelle Kwok	Headington School, Oxford
Frank Lam	Oundle School, Oundle
Joshua Lam	Leys School, Cambridge
Gregory Law	German Swiss Int. Sch., Hong Kong
Matthew Lee	Sir Roger Manwood's School, Kent
Jihoon Lee	Kingston Grammar School, Surrey
Jonathan Leung	German Swiss Int. Sch., Hong Kong
Christopher Lewis Brown	Holy Trinity School, Crawley, W. Sussex
Shuqing Lian	Caterham School, Surrey
Tom Lilburn	King Edward's, Birmingham
Andrew MacArthur	King Edward's School, Birmingham
Aidan McClure	Boston Grammar School, Lincolnshire
Ella Mi	King's School, Peterborough
Emma Mi	King's School, Peterborough
Michael Minshall	Robert May's School, Odiham, Hampshire
Natalia Mole	Sheffield High School, Sheffield
Theo Morrisclarke	Westminster School, London

Jananan Nathan	Merchant Taylors' School, Middlesex
James Nicholls	Oakham School, Rutland
Edward O'Brien	Abingdon School, Oxfordshire
Stephani Oyang	Taipei European School, Taipei
Dongsung Park	ACS International School, Cobham
Junhyung Park	Fulford School, York
Richard Parkinson	Reading School, Berkshire
Vishal Patil	King Edward's School, Birmingham
Kathryn Poole	Nelson Thomlinson School, Wigton
Thomas Rychlik	All Saint's RC School, York
Kshitij Sabnis	Westminster School, London
Aseem Sharma	Wisbech Grammar School, Cambridgeshire
Emma Shillam	St Paul's Girls' School, London
Serge Simakov	Dulwich College, London
Sheila Subbiah	City of London Girls' School, London
Wilson Suen	Ardingly College, West Sussex
Jeffrey Sun	West Island School, Hong Kong
Shuhan Sun	Wallington County GS, Surrey
Andrey Sushko	Dr Challoner's Grammar School, Bucks
Terence Tang Tsz Long	German Swiss Int. Sch., Hong Kong
Yinglun Teng	St John's College, Old St Mellons, Cardiff
Richard Thorburn	Lingfield Notre Dame School, Surrey
Samuel Tickle	Cartmel Priory CE School, Cumbria
Cumar Vasudeva	City of London School, London
Eric Wieser	Bottisham Village College, Cambridge
Chris Williamson	Ysgol Gyfun Gwynllyw, Torfaen
Arthur Wolstenholme	Dulwich College, London
Clement Woo	Harrow School, Middlesex
Robert Wright	Clitheroe Royal GS, Lancashire
Chengran Xie	Reading School, Berkshire
Lawrence Xu	Merchant Taylors' School, Middlesex
Catherine Xu	Sevenoaks School, Kent
Colman Yau	Dauntsey's School, Wiltshire
Ronald Yip	South Island School, Hong Kong
Youngtaek Yu	St Bede's College, Manchester
Tim Yung	Winchester College, Hampshire
James Zhao	Haberdashers' Aske's School for Boys, Herts

Maclaurin

Luke Abraham	St Olave's Grammar School, Orpington
Jacob Ader	St Paul's School, London
Ardavan Afshar	Winchester College, Hampshire
Alice Ahn	Glasgow Academy, Glasgow
Harry Alexander	Royal Grammar School, High Wycombe
Jack Atack	King Edward VI Camp Hill Boys' School, Kings Heath, Birmingham
Siobhan Barnard	King's School, Chester
Tom Baston	Kings School, Macclesfield
Archie Bott	Winchester College, Hampshire
Alice Brown	School of St Helen and St Katharine, Abingdon, Oxfordshire
Jack Buckingham	Marlwood School, Bristol
Douglas Buisson	Comberton Village College, Cambridge
Gaby Chan	King Edward VI HS for Girls, Birmingham
Martin Chan	Westminster School, London
Mark Chapman	Kingswinford School, West Midlands
Si Chen	St Paul's Girls' School, London
Dixin Chen	Kelly College, Devon
Derek Cheng	South Island School, Hong Kong
Jonathan Chetwynddiggle	Lancaster Royal Grammar School
Joseph Child	Alleyn's School, London
Andrea Chlebikova	Dorothy Stringer High School, Brighton
Jennifer Minjeong Chun	Yew Chung Int. Sch. of Bejing, Bejing
Ben Comeau	Truro School, Cornwall
George Corfield	Tonbridge School, Kent
Mat Coulson	Bishop Wordsworth's School, Wiltshire
Richard Crichton	Walton High School, Stafford
Gene Day	Int. Coll. Sherborne School, Dorset
Adam Dougall	Wymondham High School, Norwich
David Edey	Alcester Grammar School, Warwickshire
Beni Egressy	Clitheroe Royal GS, Lancashire
Lauren Ellison	Red Maids School, Bristol
Walker Ferguson	Lancing College, West Sussex
Richard Freeland	The Cathedral School Llandaff, Cardiff
Diwen Gao	Concord College, Shrewsbury, Shropshire
Kurtis Gibson	Millfield School, Somerset
Benjamin Gill	Royal Grammar School, High Wycombe, Bucks

Edward Godfrey	Thomas Hardye School, Dorchester
Joshua Green	Purbrook Park School, Hants
Theodore Green	Roundwood Park School, Harpenden
Chris Han	Yew Chung Int. Sch. of Bejing, Beijing
Kit Harris	St Olave's Grammar School, Kent
Timothy Heelis	Hutcheson's Grammar School, Glasgow
Nick Hilton	King Edward VI GS, Chelmsford, Essex
Jack Hou	Harrow School, Middlesex
Christopher Hughes	Comberton Village College, Cambridge
Michael Jarman	King's School, Peterborough
Adam Kaye	Hemel Hempstead School, Hertfordshire
Hyunjik Kim	Hampton School, Middlesex
Joohi Kim	Frankfurt International School, Germany
Naoki Koguchi	Southbank International School, London
Junho Ku	Cheltenham College, Gloucestershire
Dakyung Kwon	Badminton School, Bristol
Chris Lambeth	Trinity School, Croydon, Surrey
Sooho Lee	Clifton College, Bristol
Alex Leung	Abingdon School, Oxfordshire
Dori Levy	Jews' Free School, Kenton
Beiming Liu	Bell Bedgebury Int. Sch., Goudhurst, Kent
Junfeng Liu	Winchester College, Hampshire
James Lo	Harrow School, Middlesex
Jason Long	Glasgow Academy, Glasgow
Ted Loveday	Latymer Upper School, London
Matthew Lubel	Merchant Taylors' School, Middlesex
Ewan Macaulay	Winchester College, Hampshire
Alex McMillan	Wilson's School, Wallington, Surrey
David Mecrow	Whitley Bay High School, Tyne and Wear
Jordan Millar	Regent House School, Newtownards,
Geonhong Min	Frankfurt International School, Germany
Abdul Mohamad	King Edward VI GS, Chelmsford, Essex
Jaehoon Moon	Overseas Family School, Singapore
Jonathan Moore	King's School Ely, Cambridgeshire
Elizabeth Morland	St Paul's Girls' School, London
Prasanna Nanayakkara	Haberdashers' Aske's School for Boys, Herts
Younus Porteous	Westminster School, London
Tanon Protpagorn	Winchester College, Hampshire
Ben Prudden	Beechen Cliff School, Bath

Sean Quah	St Paul's School, Barnes, London
Alexander Read	Westminster School, London
Anais Ross	Island School, Hong Kong
Benedikt Schoenhense	Frankfurt International School, Germany
Eshan Shah	St Paul's School, Barnes, London
Niral Shah	Merchant Taylors' School, Middlesex
Tim Shao	King Edward VI Camp Hill Boys' School, Kings Heath, Birmingham
George Shillam	Westminster School, London
Subon Sivananthan	Haberdashers' Aske's School for Boys, Herts
Adam Smith	Magdalen College School, Oxford
Blaise Sturley	Devonport HS for Boys, Plymouth, Devon
Dalraj Tamber	Nottingham High School, Nottingham
James Tan	St Paul's School, Barnes, London
Nelson Tang	Queen Elizabeth's School, Barnet
Abby Watson	Wallington HS for Girls, Surrey
Josh Wearing	King Edward's School, Birmingham
Jonathan Williams	Tiffin School, Surrey
Kelvin Wong	Bootham School, York
Yikuan Yao	Stretford Grammar School, Manchester
Simon Ying	Taunton School, Somerset
Samuel Young	Alleyn's School, Dulwich, London
Robin Younghusband	Rugby School, Warwickshire
Monica Zhang	Blundell's School, Tiverton, Devon
Yaolin Zheng	Oxford High School, Oxford
Gaziz Zhotabayev	Concord College, Shrewsbury, Shropshire
Rose Zhou	Windermere St Annes School, Windermere

National Mathematics Summer Schools
July 5th – 11th and July 12th – 17th, 2009

This year, as previously, we ran two Summer Schools, but the selection criteria were different. For one week, as previously, we selected about 40 youngsters based on performance in the Intermediate Mathematical Olympiad. For the other week, we selected students with high scores in the Intermediate Challenge, from schools which had not recently been represented at a Summer School. Both Summer Schools were held at Queen's College, Birmingham and were a great success. Reports follow from each of the directors.

Week 1

This Summer School had a happy atmosphere from the start with many parents and friends staying throughout the afternoon to chat together about the forthcoming week.

The timetable followed the usual format with morning masterclasses on symmetry and groups led by Alan Slomson. All participants enjoyed a thorough grounding on these topics and completed a fairly intensive course of study. Following the masterclass, teams took part in daily competitions. These have been completely revamped for this particular summer school over the past couple of years and the responses have noticeably improved. Although the basic rounds of individual, team and relay are named as before, the content has been considerably altered. The format of the relay round was also altered towards a team approach to enable the young mathematicians to have greater success. This change also engendered good camaraderie among the various teams. A new short afternoon session was also introduced to give feedback on issues arising from responses to the competition questions. As usual, Friday morning had a different character with Vinay Kathotia holding all spellbound explaining the power of two. The political correctness of his sponge sword thrilling the audience into submission. Andre Rzym then joined us to explain the importance of able young mathematicians to the banking and investment industry.

Afternoon sessions covered a great variety of topics such as inequalities, the pigeonhole principle, game theory, environmental mathematics, proof, how shapes fill space efficiently, geometry, modular arithmetic, practical mathematics and Pythagorean triples. The mixture of pure and applied mathematics was welcomed by all. Neill Cooper's introduction to the life of an applied mathematician working on weather systems gave us all a very different perspective on possible careers.

An area of concern to all staff was the noticeable reluctance by the young people to attempt to answer questions whether in the team competitions or the afternoon sessions using algebra. Through the week, the staff attempted to address this concern and encourage an understanding of the of the power of abstraction.

James Cranch led the young Cambridge cohort in giving the seniors morning sessions on similar topics as the juniors had studied but at a much more advanced level. Rachel, Rachael, Daniel, James, Dori and Todd return to school with a much deeper understanding of mathematics due to the hard work they put in every morning.

Evening sessions are always lighter in tone and this year was no exception. We had origami, Howard Grove's introduction to impartial games, further discussions on mentoring, Nrich and careers as well as a bowling excursion and an Evening Extravaganza of music, magic and dance in the complex plane. Of special note was the dance troupe, Perfect Symmetry (Alec Gower, Daniel Hughes, Chris Lambeth, Jack Rans, Harry Rout and Angus Taylor) providing a new perspective on groups and symmetry set to music. No doubt this is available to view on you tube and we are all grateful to Alan for providing such inspiration to some very athletic dancers.

In no time at all, Friday had come around and there were the usual tearful goodbyes and promises to keep in touch by email. Having been inspired by previous summer school attendees now returning as seniors, mentors and session providers, this year‹s cohort know that they will keep in touch in the coming years and may well help inspire other young people in the future.

We are very grateful to the staff of Queen's College, especially Rona, James and Daniel. There is no doubt that much of the success of the Summer School is down to their support and cheerful help throughout the week. This year we had the added pleasure of a visit from Rona's son who worked for us for a day in preparation for his own training as a teacher.

Mary Teresa Fyfe

In attendance in Week 1

Pupils

Frank Bloomfield	Colchester Royal Grammar School
John Brazier	Ampleforth College Senior School
Adam Clark	Queen Elizabeth High School
Ben Comeau	Truro School
Matthew Cottell	Arden School
Matthew Coulson	Bishop Wordsworth's School
Abigail Davies	Parkstone Grammar School
Rafi Dover	King David High School
Jade Flaherty	Belvedere Academy
Rebecca Floyd	Ashville College
Thomas Flynn	Devonport High School for Boys
Samantha Ford	Nailsea School
Charlotte Frost	Burgess Hill School
Alexander Gower	Ivybridge Community College
John Halstead	Stalham High School
Alice Haynes	Petersfield School

Alex Homer	Beckfoot School
Robert Howlett	Ashfield School
Daniel Hughes	RGS Worcester & The Alice Ottley School
Fergus Imrie	Charterhouse
Alistair Jones	Imberhorne School
Alex Keane	Chichester High School for Boys
Matthew Kesseler	Hinchingbrooke School
Jun Ho Ku	Cheltenham College
Chris Lambeth	Trinity School
Richard Mathers	Forest School
Lisa McCarthy	Brookfield School
Timothy Pearson	Glenalmond College
Jack Rans	Windsor Boys' School
Harry Rout	Charters School
Aseem Sharma	Wisbech Grammar School
Ben Smith	Lincoln Minster School
Adam Smith	Thomas Mills High School
Alix Snell	Tomlinscote School & Sixth Form College
Sonya Storer	Manning Comprehensive School
Duncan Strachan	High School of Dundee
Angus Taylor	George Watson's College
Peter Thorp	Dame Allan's Schools
Beverley Tsang	St Mary's School
Emily Waters	St James Senior Girls' School
Andrew Wills	Woodbridge School
Chloe Wong	Mill Hill School

Staff

Neill Cooper	Wilson's School
James Cranch	Universities of Leicester & Sheffield
Mary Fortune	Trinity College, Cambridge
Mary Teresa Fyfe	Hutchesons' Grammar School, Glasgow
Howard Groves	Royal Grammar School, Worcester
Jo Harbour	Wolvercote Primary School
Andrew Jobbings	Arbelos
Vinay Kathotia	The Royal Institution
Jonathan Lee	Trinity College, Cambridge

Tom Lovering	Trinity College, Cambridge
Vicky Neale	Trinity College, Cambridge
Martin Orr	Trinity College, Cambridge
Hannah Roberts	Trinity College, Cambridge
Andre Rzym	Man Investments
Alan Slomson	University of Leeds

Week 2

Forty-two pupils attended, very ably supported by a sextet of Seniors. The School Director was James Gazet and the Masterclasses were taken by Gerry Leversha.

After domestic arrangements had been sorted out and Sunday supper consumed, teams hurled themselves into a variety of 'ice-breaker' problems. Some cut-up arguments to be arranged in a logical order were a useful novelty in these activities. It was clear from the start of the competitions on Monday that all members of the Summer School had quickly identified with their teams. Throughout the week pupils worked hard, concentrated well through a lengthy daily programme and generated a particularly enthusiastic atmosphere.

Gerry Leversha's detailed morning Masterclasses on Deductive Geometry ran from Monday to Friday, culminating in a discussion of the nine-point circle. This year they were accompanied by copies of the UKMT publication *Crossing the Bridge* (Pathways Number One). From Monday to Thursday the Masterclass was followed by the team competitions: individual, team and relays. The competitive spirit mounted steadily during the week and overall the Eulerians were the winners. This year more of the Team Choice time was devoted to team discussion and it was apparent that most team members settled more easily into the individual part of their work. An innovation was a short post-competition session when points raised by the marking of the Team Choice solutions could be discussed. Afternoon classes were similarly followed by feed-back sessions on problems set during the morning Masterclass.

Participants were divided into two groups for the afternoon sessions on a wide variety of topics, as follows.

Anne Andrews	Colouring Problems
Robin Battacharyya	The Pigeonhole Principle
Michael Bradley	Pell Equations
Ceri Fiddes	Combinatorics
James Gazet	Invariance

Ina Hughes	Modular Arithmetic
Julia Robson	Inequalities
Alison Zhu	Circle Theorems in Geometry

This group of tutors includes former Summer School and Olympiad veterans, passing on the fruits of their experience, and current or recently retired schoolteachers with their perspectives on the teaching and learning of demanding but inspiring topics.

On Monday evening four visitors from UBS returned to the Summer School with their trading game, vigorously pursued and enjoyed. On Tuesday evening James Gazet presented some tips for problem-solving and the presentation of solutions. Then Michael Bradley discussed an approach to the solution of Conway's 'Soldiers' problem, introduced the previous evening.

Non-mathematical activities occupied the two remaining evenings. On Wednesday there was an enjoyable bowling trip (also involving an invigorating walk there and back). This was followed by the traditional 'Extravaganza of Entertainment'. As usual this was music-based with many enjoyable voice, piano and wind performances. The culminating rendition of 'The Complex Number Song' was this year preceded by an unforgettable dance number: 'Strangely Come Bhangra'. Finally, on Friday morning the Geometry Masterclass was followed by Gerry Leversha's ingenious quiz, in which apparently 'ordinary' questions turned out to be mathematically-related after all.

The exceptionally committed working atmosphere during the week owed a lot to the group of Seniors: Andrea, Jordan, Joseph, Rebecca, Sophie and Timothy. Special thanks are due to the contribution of Joseph (and his hat), now veterans of several Summer Schools. As well as overseeing their teams and helping to run the competitions, the Seniors also contributed to the social life of the School, organising games during breaks and generally keeping an eye on the Juniors. They had their own academic programme, with their own Number Theory Masterclasses, given by Paul Russell. These were followed by afternoon sessions given by other members of the staff team.

The Queen's Foundation administrative and domestic staff made us very welcome and many thanks are due to them for providing the meals, facilities and support that made a big contribution to the success of the School.

Pupils' contributions to the comments book, plus other responses, were exceptionally positive this year. The spirit of the Summer School can best be symbolised by the last remarkable event on Thursday evening. After pupils had been told to go to bed, staff were understandably surprised to see more than half of them proceeding in a party towards the dining-hall. When they emerged into the light it was seen that they were accompanying a beautiful, intricate and co-operatively made model (essentially an icosahedron) composed of ice-breaker-style indented cubes. It fully deserved the subsequent torrent of applause and photographs.

James Gazet

In attendance in Week 2

Pupils

Harry Alexander	Royal Grammar School, High Wycombe
Nirmala Arulampalam	King Henry VIII School, Coventry
Jack Atack	King Edward VI Camp Hill Boys' School
Duncan Bell	St Olave's Grammar School
Sam Cappleman-Lynes	Shebbear College
Rachel Carrington	St Alban's Catholic High School
Dickson Chan	Winchester College
Matthew Colbrook	The King's School (Seniors)
Jennifer Collister	Oxford High School
David Edey	Alcester Grammar School
Beni Egressy	Clitheroe Royal Grammar School
Takehiro Fujita	Harrow School
Sarah Gait	Queen Elizabeth Grammar School, Penrith
Edward Godfrey	Thomas Hardye School
Joshua Green	Purbrook Park School
Timothy Heelis	Hutcheson's Grammar School
Eigen Horsfield	Tapton School
Joshua Hunt	Bryn Celynnog Comprehensive
Gemma Izen	Haberdashers' Aske's School for Girls
Adam Kaye	Hemel Hempstead School
Hazal Kurtcu	Rossall School
Michelle Kwok	Headington School
Frank Lam	Oundle School
Matthew Lee	Sir Roger Manwood's School
Jihoon Lee	Kingston Grammar School
Jason Long	Glasgow Academy
Ted Loveday	Latymer Upper School
Emma Mi	King's School

Abdul Mohamad	King Edward VI Grammar School
Elizabeth Morland	St Paul's Girls' School
Junhyung Park	Fulford School
Vishal Patil	King Edward's School
Kathryn Poole	Nelson Thomlinson School
Anais Ross	Island School
Thomas Rychlik	All Saint's RC School
Kshitij Sabnis	Westminster School
Niral Shah	Merchant Taylors' School
Sheila Subbiah	City of London Girls' School
Dalraj Tamber	Nottingham High School
James Tan	St Paul's School
Abby Watson	Wallington High School for Girls
Catherine Xu	Sevenoaks School

Senior Mathematical Challenge and British Mathematical Olympiads

The Senior Challenge took place on Thursday 6th November 2008. Once again it, and also the BMO events, were sponsored by the Institute of Actuaries. There were 92,520 entries and around 1,200 took part in the next stage, British Mathematical Olympiad Round 1, held on Thursday 4th December 2008. BMO Round 1 was again held before Christmas to reduce clashes with A levels.

UK SENIOR MATHEMATICAL CHALLENGE

Thursday 6 November 2008

Organised by the **United Kingdom Mathematics Trust**

and supported by

The Actuarial Profession
making financial sense of the future

RULES AND GUIDELINES (to be read before starting)

1. Do not open the question paper until the invigilator tells you to do so.
2. **Use B or HB pencil only**. Mark *at most one* of the options A, B, C, D, E on the Answer Sheet for each question. Do not mark more than one option.
3. Time allowed: **90 minutes**.
   No answers or personal details may be entered on the Answer Sheet after the 90 minutes are over.
4. The use of rough paper is allowed.
   Calculators, measuring instruments and squared paper are forbidden.
5. Candidates must be full-time students at secondary school or FE college, and must be in Year 13 or below (England & Wales); S6 or below (Scotland); Year 14 or below (Northern Ireland).
6. There are twenty-five questions. Each question is followed by five options marked A, B, C, D, E. Only one of these is correct. Enter the letter A-E corresponding to the correct answer in the corresponding box on the Answer Sheet.
7. **Scoring rules**: all candidates start out with 25 marks;
   0 marks are awarded for each question left unanswered;
   4 marks are awarded for each correct answer;
   1 mark is deducted for each incorrect answer.
8. **Guessing**: Remember that there is a penalty for wrong answers. Note also that later questions are deliberately intended to be harder than earlier questions. You are thus advised to concentrate first on solving as many as possible of the first 15-20 questions. Only then should you try later questions.

The United Kingdom Mathematics Trust is a Registered Charity.

http://www.ukmt.org.uk

1. What is the value of $2 \times 2008 + 2008 \times 8$?

A 4016 B 16064 C 20080 D 64256 E 80020

2. A giant thresher shark weighing 1250 pounds, believed to be the heaviest ever caught, was landed by fisherman Roger Nowell off the Cornish coast in November 2007. The fish was sold by auction at Newlyn Fish Market for £255. Roughly, what was the cost per pound?

A 5p B 20p C 50p D £2 E £5

3. What is the value of $\sqrt{\frac{1}{2^6} + \frac{1}{6^2}}$?

A $\frac{1}{10}$ B $\frac{1}{9}$ C $\frac{1}{3}$ D $\frac{5}{24}$ E $\frac{7}{24}$

4. In this subtraction, P, Q, R and S are digits. What is the value of $P + Q + R + S$?

$$\begin{array}{r} 8\,Q\,0\,S \\ -\ P\,0\,R\,2 \\ \hline 2\,0\,0\,8 \end{array}$$

A 12 B 14 C 16 D 18 E 20

5. 200 T-shirts have been bought for a Fun Run at a cost of £400 plus VAT at $17\frac{1}{2}$%. The cost of entry for the run is £5 per person. What is the minimum number of entries needed in order to cover the total cost of the T-shirts?

A 40 B 47 C 80 D 84 E 94

6. It is required to shade at least one of the six small squares in the diagram on the right so that the resulting figure has exactly one axis of symmetry. In how many different ways can this be done?

A 6 B 9 C 10 D 12 E 15

7. A newspaper headline read 'Welsh tortoise recaptured 1.8 miles from home after 8 months on the run'. Assuming the tortoise travelled in a straight line, roughly how many minutes did the tortoise take on average to 'run' one foot?
[1 mile = 5280 feet]

A 3 B 9 C 16 D 36 E 60

8. In the figure shown, $AB = AF$ and ABC, AFD, BFE and CDE are all straight lines.
Which of the following expressions gives z in terms of x and y?

A
B
F
$x°$
$y°$
$z°$
C
D
E

A $\frac{y - x}{2}$ B $y - \frac{x}{2}$ C $\frac{y - x}{3}$ D $y - \frac{x}{3}$ E $y - x$

9. What is the remainder when the 2008-digit number 222 ... 22 is divided by 9?

A 8 B 6 C 4 D 2 E 0

10. Which one of the following rational numbers *cannot* be expressed as $\frac{1}{m} + \frac{1}{n}$ where m, n are different positive integers?

A $\frac{3}{4}$ B $\frac{3}{5}$ C $\frac{3}{6}$ D $\frac{3}{7}$ E $\frac{3}{8}$

11. The distance between two neighbouring dots in the dot lattice is 1 unit. What, in square units, is the area of the region where the two rectangles overlap?

A 6 B $6\frac{1}{4}$ C $6\frac{1}{2}$ D 7 E $7\frac{1}{2}$

12. Mr and Mrs Stevens were married on a Saturday in July 1948. On what day of the week did their diamond wedding anniversary fall this year?

A Monday B Tuesday C Thursday D Friday E Saturday

13. Positive integers m and n are such that $2^m + 2^n = 1280$. What is the value of $m + n$?

A 14 B 16 C 18 D 32 E 640

14. Five touching circles each have radius 1 and their centres are at the vertices of a regular pentagon. What is the radius of the circle through the points of contact P, Q, R, S and T?

A $\tan 18°$ B $\tan 36°$ C $\tan 45°$ D $\tan 54°$ E $\tan 72°$

15. A sequence of positive integers $t_1, t_2, t_3, t_4, \ldots$ is defined by:
$t_1 = 13$; $t_{n+1} = \frac{1}{2}t_n$ if t_n is even; $t_{n+1} = 3t_n + 1$ if t_n is odd.
What is the value of t_{2008}?

A 1 B 2 C 4 D 8 E None of these.

16. The numbers x, y and z satisfy the equations

$$x + y + 2z = 850, \qquad x + 2y + z = 950, \qquad 2x + y + z = 1200.$$

What is their mean?

A 250 B $\frac{1000}{3}$ C 750 D 1000 E More information is needed.

17. Andy and his younger cousin Alice both have their birthdays today. Remarkably, Andy is now the same age as the sum of the digits of the year of his birth and the same is true of Alice. How many years older than Alice is Andy?

A 10 B 12 C 14 D 16 E 18

18. The shaded square of the lattice shown has area 1. What is the area of the circle through the points X, Y and Z?

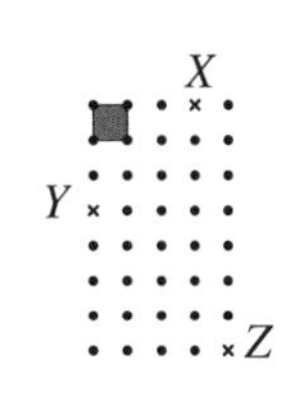

A $\frac{9\pi}{2}$ B 8π C $\frac{25\pi}{2}$ D 25π E 50π

19. How many prime numbers p are there such that $199p + 1$ is a perfect square?

A 0 B 1 C 2 D 4 E 8

20. The diagram shows four semicircles symmetrically placed between two circles. The shaded circle has area 4 and each semicircle has area 18. What is the area of the outer circle?

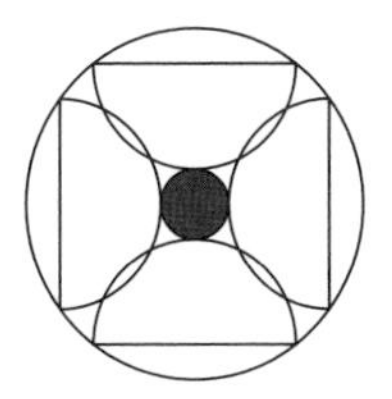

A $72\sqrt{2}$ B 100 C 98 D 96 E $32\sqrt{3}$

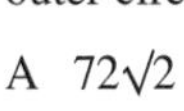

21. The fraction $\frac{2008}{1998}$ may be written in the form $a + \cfrac{1}{b + \cfrac{1}{c + \cfrac{1}{d}}}$ where a, b, c and d are positive integers. What is the value of d?

A 2 B 4 C 5 D 199 E 1998

22. A pentagon is made by attaching an equilateral triangle to a square with the same edge length. Four such pentagons are placed inside a rectangle, as shown.
What is the ratio of the length of the rectangle to its width?

A $\sqrt{3}:1$ B $2:1$ C $\sqrt{2}:1$ D $3:2$ E $4:\sqrt{3}$

23. How many pairs of real numbers (x, y) satisfy the equation $(x + y)^2 = (x + 3)(y - 3)$?

A 0 B 1 C 2 D 4 E infinitely many

24. The length of the hypotenuse of a particular right-angled triangle is given by $\sqrt{1 + 3 + 5 + 7 + \ldots + 25}$. The lengths of the other two sides are given by $\sqrt{1 + 3 + 5 + \ldots + x}$ and $\sqrt{1 + 3 + 5 + \ldots + y}$ where x and y are positive integers. What is the value of $x + y$?

A 12 B 17 C 24 D 28 E 32

25. What is the area of the polygon formed by all points (x, y) in the plane satisfying the inequality $\left||x| - 2\right| + \left||y| - 2\right| \leqslant 4$?

A 24 B 32 C 64 D 96 E 112

Further remarks

The 2008 paper was again marked by UKMT (in the same way as the Junior and Intermediate Challenges) rather than being marked in centres. This provided the full profile of marks and a valuable breakdown for the Problems Group. Schools were provided with the usual pupil answer sheet (shown below) and so could give the rapid feedback which is a feature of the Senior Challenge.

1.	
2.	
3.	
4.	
5.	
6.	
7.	
8.	
9.	
10.	
11.	
12.	
13.	
14.	
15.	
16.	
17.	
18.	
19.	
20.	
21.	
22.	
23.	
24.	
25.	

UK SENIOR MATHEMATICAL CHALLENGE

THURSDAY 6 NOVEMBER 2008

ANSWER SHEET

To be completed by the student

SCHOOL/COLLEGE NAME ....

UKMT CENTRE NUMBER ....

YOUR NAME ....

SCHOOL YEAR ....

MATHS SET/ TEACHER ....

Enter the option (A, B, C, D or E) which corresponds to the correct answer for each question in the box for that question.

To be completed by the teacher not by the student

Each question is worth *four* marks.

One mark is deducted for each wrong answer.

No marks are deducted for questions left unanswered.

The total score is calculated by taking four times the number of correct answers, subtracting the number of wrong answers, and then adding 25.

Number correct [ ] × 4 = [ ]

– Number wrong [ ]

Difference [ ]

\+ 25

Total score [ ]

NB: Blank papers score 25.

*Please do **NOT** return to UKMT*

The solutions are provided in a leaflet which is also set up to facilitate marking in centres who wished to continue to mark in house.

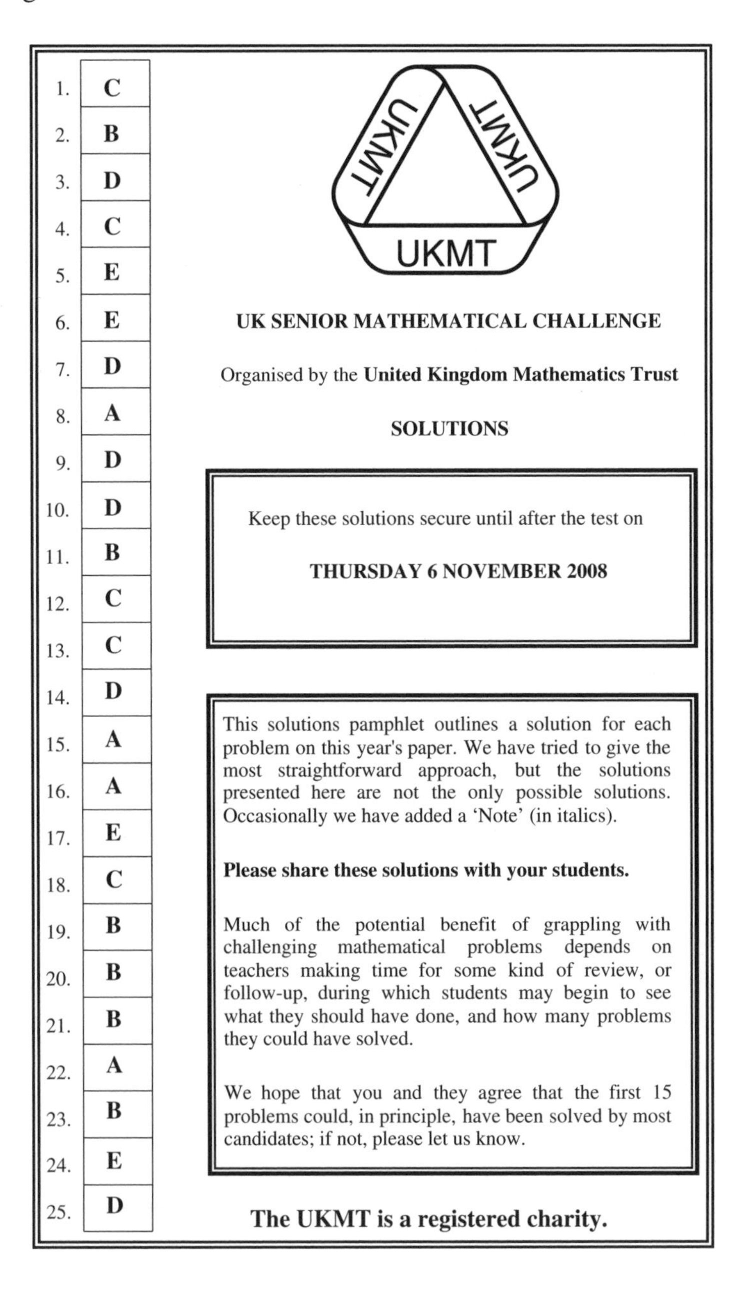

1.	C
2.	B
3.	D
4.	C
5.	E
6.	E
7.	D
8.	A
9.	D
10.	D
11.	B
12.	C
13.	C
14.	D
15.	A
16.	A
17.	E
18.	C
19.	B
20.	B
21.	B
22.	A
23.	B
24.	E
25.	D

UKMT UKMT UKMT

UK SENIOR MATHEMATICAL CHALLENGE

Organised by the **United Kingdom Mathematics Trust**

SOLUTIONS

Keep these solutions secure until after the test on

THURSDAY 6 NOVEMBER 2008

This solutions pamphlet outlines a solution for each problem on this year's paper. We have tried to give the most straightforward approach, but the solutions presented here are not the only possible solutions. Occasionally we have added a 'Note' (in italics).

Please share these solutions with your students.

Much of the potential benefit of grappling with challenging mathematical problems depends on teachers making time for some kind of review, or follow-up, during which students may begin to see what they should have done, and how many problems they could have solved.

We hope that you and they agree that the first 15 problems could, in principle, have been solved by most candidates; if not, please let us know.

The UKMT is a registered charity.

1. **C** $2 \times 2008 + 2008 \times 8 = 10 \times 2008 = 20080$.

2. **B** The cost per pound is $£\frac{255}{1250} \approx £\frac{1}{5} = 20$ p.

3. **D** $\frac{1}{2^6} + \frac{1}{6^2} = \frac{3^2 + 2^4}{2^6 \times 3^2} = \frac{25}{2^6 \times 3^2} = \frac{5^2}{(2^3 \times 3)^2}$. Hence the answer is $\frac{5}{2^3 \times 3} = \frac{5}{24}$.

4. **C** From the units column we see that $S = 0$. Then the tens column shows that $R = 9$, the hundreds column that $Q = 1$, and the thousands that $P = 6$. So $P + Q + R + S = 16$.

5. **E** Since 1% of £400 = £4, the total VAT charged was £4 × 17.5 = £70, giving a total cost of £400 + £70 = £470. Therefore the minimum number of entries needed is 94.

6. **E**

6
4 5
1 2 3

We number the squares to identify them. The only line of symmetry possible is the diagonal through 1 and 5. For a symmetric shading, if 4 is shaded, then so too must be 2; so either both are shaded or neither. Likewise 3 and 6 go together and provide 2 more choices. Whether 1 is shaded or not will not affect a symmetry, and this gives a further 2 choices; and the same applies to 5. Overall, therefore, there are $2^4 = 16$ choices. However, one of these is the choice to shade no squares, which is excluded by the question.

7. **D** In 1.8 miles there are 1.8×5280 feet $= 18 \times 528$ feet, while in 8 months there are roughly $8 \times 30 \times 24 \times 60$ minutes. Hence the time to 'run' one foot in minutes is roughly $\frac{10 \times 30 \times 20 \times 60}{20 \times 500} = 36$ minutes.

8. **A** In triangle ACD, $\angle CAD = (180 - x - y)°$. As $AB = AF$, triangle ABF is isosceles hence $\angle ABF = \angle AFB = \frac{1}{2}(x + y)°$. Thus $\angle DFE = \angle AFB = \frac{1}{2}(x + y)°$ (vertically opposite angles). Now in triangle DFE, $\angle FDE = (180 - y)°$. Hence $z° = 180° - \angle DFE - \angle FDE = \frac{1}{2}(y - x)°$.

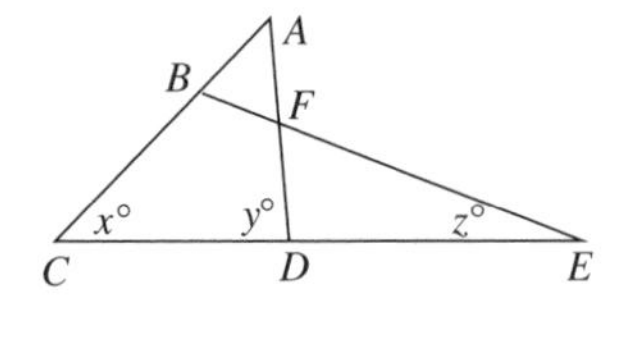

9. **D** A number is divisible by 9 if, and only if, the sum of its digits is divisible by 9. The given number is $N + 2$, where $N = 222\ldots 220$ has 2007 2s. Since $2007 = 223 \times 9$, N is divisible by 9 and the required remainder is therefore 2.

10. **D** By inspection

$$\frac{3}{4} = \frac{1}{2} + \frac{1}{4}; \quad \frac{3}{5} = \frac{1}{2} + \frac{1}{10}; \quad \frac{3}{6} = \frac{1}{3} + \frac{1}{6}; \quad \frac{3}{8} = \frac{1}{4} + \frac{1}{8}.$$

However $\frac{3}{7} \neq \frac{1}{m} + \frac{1}{n}$. [To see why, suppose that $\frac{3}{7} = \frac{1}{m} + \frac{1}{n}$ and note that $\frac{1}{m} > \frac{1}{n}$ or vice versa. We will suppose the former. Then $\frac{1}{m} \geqslant \frac{3}{14} > \frac{3}{15}$ and so $\frac{1}{m} > \frac{1}{5}$ and $m < 5$. Also $\frac{1}{m} < \frac{3}{7}$ and so $3m > 7$. Hence $m \geqslant 3$. So $m = 4$ or $m = 3$. However $\frac{3}{7} - \frac{1}{4} = \frac{5}{28}$ and $\frac{3}{7} - \frac{1}{3} = \frac{2}{21}$ neither of which has the form $\frac{1}{n}$.]

11. **B** Let the six points where lines meet on the dot lattice be A, B, C, D, E, F as shown and let the other two points of intersection be P (where AC and BF meet) and Q (where CE and DF meet).
Triangles APB and CPF are similar with base lengths in the ratio 3:5. Hence triangle CPF has height $\frac{5}{8} \times 2 = \frac{5}{4}$ units and base length 5 units so that its area is $\frac{1}{2} \times \frac{5}{4} \times 5$ square units. Since the same is true of triangle CQF, the required area is $\frac{5}{4} \times 5 = 6\frac{1}{4}$ square units.

12. **C** There are 365 days in a normal year and 366 in a leap year. Apart from certain exceptions (none of which occurs in this period) a leap year occurs every 4 years. Now $365 = 7 \times 52 + 1$ and $366 = 7 \times 52 + 2$. Hence each date moves on by 5 days every 4 years. So in 60 years, it moves on 75 days. Since $75 = 7 \times 10 + 5$, that means it moves on to a Thursday.

13. **C** Since $1280 = 2^8 \times 5 = 2^8(2^0 + 2^2) = 2^8 + 2^{10}$, we may take m=8 and $n = 10$ (or vice versa) to get $m + n = 8 + 10 = 18$. It is easy to check that there are no other possibilities.

14. **D** The internal angle of a regular pentagon is 108°. Let A be the centre of a touching circle, as shown. Since OA bisects $\angle RAQ$, $\angle OAQ = 54°$. Also, triangle OAQ is right-angled at Q (radius perpendicular to tangent). Since $AQ = 1$, $OQ = \tan 54°$.

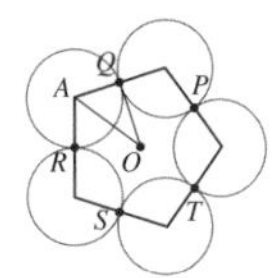

15. **A** The sequence proceeds as follows: 13, 40, 20, 10, 5, 16, 8, 4, 2, 1, 4, 2, 1 … . The block 4, 2, 1 repeats *ad infinitum* starting after t_7. But $2008 - 7 = 2001$ and $2001 = 3 \times 667$. Hence t_{2008} is the third term in the 667th such block and is therefore 1.

16. **A** Adding the three given equations gives $4(x + y + z) = 3000$. Therefore $x + y + z = 750$. So the mean is $\frac{750}{3} = 250$.

17. **E** Let 'X' be a single digit. If $2008 - 200X = 2 + 0 + 0 + X$ then $8 - X = 2 + X$ so $X = 3$. So Alice (being the younger) could have been born in 2003. Next if $2008 - 199X = 1 + 9 + 9 + X$ then $18 - X = 19 + X$, which is impossible. Similarly if $2008 - 198X = 1 + 9 + 8 + X$ then $28 - X = 18 + X$, so $X = 5$. Thus Alice or Andy could have been born in 1985. Finally if $2008 - 19YX = 1 + 9 + X + Y$ for some digit $Y \leqslant 7$, then $108 - YX = 10 + Y + X$. Hence $98 = YX + Y + X$ which is impossible, since $YX + Y + X$ is at most $79 + 7 + 9 = 95$. Hence there are no more possible dates and so Andy was born in 1985 and Alice in 2003.

18. **C** Since $XY^2 = 18$, $YZ^2 = 32$ and $XZ^2 = 50$, we have $XZ^2 = XY^2 + YZ^2$. Hence by the converse of Pythagoras' Theorem, $\angle XYZ = 90°$. Since the angle in a semi-circle is 90° the segment XZ is the diameter of the specified circle. Hence the radius is $\frac{1}{2}\sqrt{50}$ and the area of the circle is $\dfrac{50\pi}{4} = \dfrac{25\pi}{2}$.

19. **B** Let $199p + 1 = X^2$. Then $199p = X^2 - 1 = (X + 1)(X - 1)$. Note that 197 is prime. If p is also to be prime then **either** $X + 1 = 199$, in which case $X - 1 = 197$, **or** $X - 1 = 199$, in which case $X + 1 = 201$ (and $201 = 3 \times 67$ is not prime). Note that $X - 1 = 1, X + 1 = 199p$ is impossible. Hence $p = 197$ is the only possibility.

20. **B** Let r_1, r_2 and r_3 be the radii of the shaded circle, semicircles and outer circle respectively. A right-angled triangle can be formed with sides r_3, $(r_1 + r_2)$ and r_2.
Hence, by Pythagoras' Theorem, $r_3^2 = (r_1 + r_2)^2 + r_2^2$.
Now $\pi r_1^2 = 4$, hence $r_1 = 2/\sqrt{\pi}$. Likewise $r_2 = 6/\sqrt{\pi}$.
Hence $r_2 = 3r_1$ so that $r_3^2 = (r_1 + 3r_1)^2 + (3r_1)^2 = 25r_1^2$. Thus the required area is $25 \times 4 = 100$.

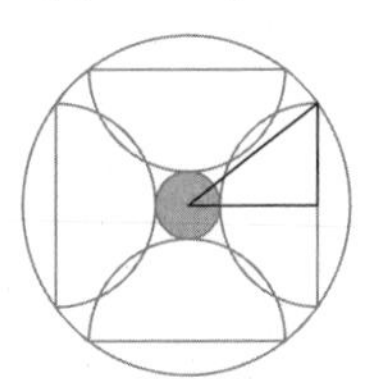

21. B Since 2008/1998 lies between 1 and 2, $a = 1$. Subtracting 1 and inverting gives $b + 1/(c + 1/d) = 1998/10 = 199 + 4/5$ so that $b = 199$. Then $1/(c + 1/d) = 4/5$ so that $c + 1/d = 5/4$ and this gives $c = 1$ and $d = 4$.
{*Note : This is an example of a continued fraction.*}

22. A Let r be the length of a side of the equilateral triangle.
Hence the width of the rectangle is $r \sin 60° + r + r \sin 60° =$
$r(1 + 2 \sin 60°) = r(1 + \sqrt{3})$ and its length is $3r + 2r \sin 60° = r(3 + \sqrt{3})$.
So the ratio of the length to the width is

$$(3 + \sqrt{3}) : (1 + \sqrt{3}) = \sqrt{3}(1 + \sqrt{3}) : (1 + \sqrt{3}) = \sqrt{3} : 1.$$

23. B Let $X = x + 3$ and $Y = y - 3$. Then the given equation becomes $(X + Y)^2 = XY$. So $X^2 + XY + Y^2 = 0$. However X^2, Y^2 and $XY \left(= (X + Y)^2\right)$ are non-negative. Hence $X = Y = 0$; so $x = -3$ and $y = 3$ is the only solution.

24. E $1 + 3 + 5 + 7 + \ldots + (2n + 1) = (n + 1)^2$. The n in the three cases given is 12, $\frac{1}{2}(x - 1)$ and $\frac{1}{2}(y - 1)$. So, the triangle has sides of length $12 + 1$, $\frac{1}{2}(x - 1) + 1$ and $\frac{1}{2}(y - 1) + 1$. However the only right-angled triangle having sides of whole number length with hypotenuse 13 is the (5, 12, 13) triangle. So $x = 9$ and $y = 23$ (or vice versa). Hence $x + y = 32$.

25. D To work out the area of $\left||x| - 2\right| + \left||y| - 2\right| \leqslant 4$, we first consider the region $|x| + |y| \leqslant 4$ which is shown in (a). This region is then translated to give $|x - 2| + |y - 2| \leqslant 4$ as shown in (b).
By properties of the modulus, if the point (x, y) lies in the polygon, then so do $(x, -y)$, $(-x, y)$ and $(-x, -y)$. Thus $\left||x| - 2\right| + \left||y| - 2\right| \leqslant 4$ can be obtained from (b) by reflecting in the axes and the origin, as shown in (c).

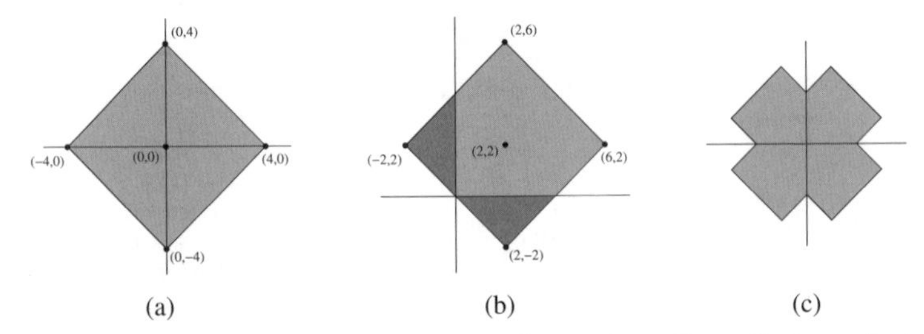

(a) (b) (c)

Hence the required area is 4 times the area in the first quadrant. From (b), the required area in the first quadrant is the area of a square of side $4\sqrt{2}$ minus two triangles (cut off by the axes) which, combined, make up a square of side $2\sqrt{2}$. So the area in the first quadrant is $(4\sqrt{2})^2 - (2\sqrt{2})^2 = 32 - 8 = 24$.
Hence the area of the polygon is $4 \times 24 = 96$ square units.

The answers

The table below shows the proportion of pupils' choices. The correct answer is shown in bold. [The percentages are rounded to the nearest whole number.]

Qn	A	B	C	D	E	Blank
1	0	3	**90**	6	0	1
2	7	**61**	5	2	22	2
3	12	3	4	**31**	34	15
4	5	8	**73**	3	1	9
5	1	1	4	5	**86**	2
6	21	15	8	17	**21**	17
7	18	9	8	**42**	8	15
8	**24**	9	5	4	13	45
9	9	11	20	**24**	10	25
10	4	10	11	**44**	2	28
11	22	**37**	10	5	7	19
12	9	14	**26**	11	11	29
13	4	7	**59**	6	3	20
14	4	9	9	**14**	15	48
15	**11**	4	5	2	32	44
16	**33**	8	5	7	12	36
17	6	5	4	4	**32**	49
18	5	6	**13**	8	3	65
19	13	**6**	3	3	2	72
20	7	**5**	3	6	4	75
21	3	**8**	3	3	4	78
22	**7**	7	3	5	6	72
23	11	**8**	5	2	7	67
24	2	5	5	3	**9**	74
25	2	4	4	**3**	1	86

SMC 2008: Some comments on the pupils' choice of answers as sent to schools in the letter with the results

The Problems Group aims to set a paper in which the earlier questions are accessible to most pupils, while the last few questions are really challenging. The 2007 average score was significantly lower than that of 2006, and so we tried to set a slightly easier paper this year. We did not succeed. The average after 42 653 scripts had been processed was 48.5, just below than last year's average of 48.6.

The students got off to a good start with 90% getting the first question correct, but the number of correct answers to the next two 'easy' questions was disappointing. If your students' results were at, or even below, the national average for these questions, please discuss these problems with them. For question 2, as many as 22% of the students chose the answer £5. Did they divide 1250 by 255, rather than the other way round? However, if number of pounds weight of the shark is more than the selling price in pounds sterling, the cost per pound must be less than £1. A simple check of this kind will often save your students from blunders.

Things were worse in question 3, where only 31% chose the right answer $\frac{5}{24}$, while 34% selected the answer $\frac{7}{24}$. Some of these wrong answers may have been wild guesses, but the most likely explanation is that pupils made use of the false 'result' that $\sqrt{x} + \sqrt{y}$ is always equal to $\sqrt{x + y}$, and hence calculated the answer as $\sqrt{\frac{1}{64}} + \sqrt{\frac{1}{36}} = \frac{1}{8} + \frac{1}{6}$. If this 'method' was popular with your students, please emphasise that it only works if x or y is 0. It may help to make a connection with Pythagoras' Theorem, since if $\sqrt{a^2 + b^2}$ were equal to $\sqrt{a^2} + \sqrt{b^2}$, Pythagoras' Theorem would imply that in a right-angled triangle the length of the hypotenuse was the sum of the lengths of the other two sides, and this is something we hope your pupils would realise must be false.

The later questions are intended to be very challenging. This is to help us identify students who might make it to the International Mathematical Olympiad. This year all the questions from 19 onwards fell into this category, and anyone who solved more than one of them correctly should feel very pleased with themselves.

The SMC marks

As the papers are now marked centrally, the full profile of the marks is available and this is shown below.

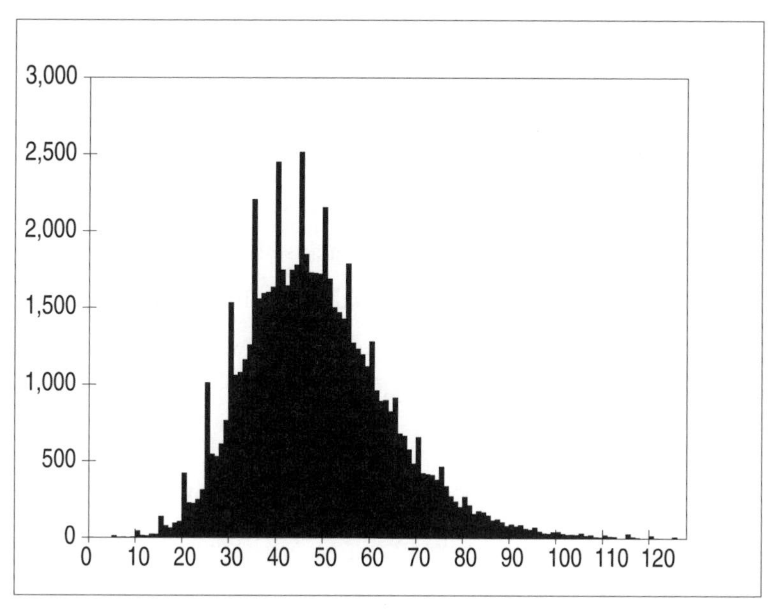

Bar chart showing the actual frequencies in the 2008 SMC

Overall, the paper was slightly harder than in 2007 so the cut-offs were lowered accordingly. On the basis of the standard proportions used by the UKMT, the cut-off marks were set at

GOLD – 74 or over SILVER – 61 to 73 BRONZE – 51 to 60

List of high scorers in the 2008 UK Senior Mathematical Challenge

125	Alex Barrell	Wilson's School, Wallington, Surrey
	Chris Bellin	Queen Mary's Grammar School, Walsall
	Joseph Briggs	Kennet School, Thatcham, Berkshire
	Peter Bullock	RGS Worcester & The Alice Ottley School
	Tim Hennock	Christ's Hospital, Horsham, West Sussex
	Andrew Hyer	Westminster School, London
	Preeyan Parmar	Eton College, Berks
	David Phillips	St Albans School, Hertfordshire
	Andrew Sluman	Wilson's School, Wallington, Surrey
	Wei Yue	Dulwich College, Dulwich Common, London
121	Woojin Chae	Eton College, Berks
	Kshitij Sabnis	Westminster School, London
120	Jim Ashworth	Trinity School, Croydon, Surrey
	Luke Betts	Hills Road VI Form College, Cambridge
	Martin Chan	Westminster School, London
	John Corke	Queen Elizabeth's Grammar School, Horncastle
	Oscar Cunningham	Portsmouth Grammar School, Hants
	Jonathan Flint	Aylesbury Grammar School, Buckinghamshire
	Ruth Franklin	Manchester High School for Girls, Manchester
	Jacob Hilton	Queen Elizabeth's School, Barnet, Hertfordshire
	Viktor Konstantinov	Concord College, Shrewsbury, Shropshire
	Peter Leach	Monkton Combe School, Bath
	Keren Ma	Tonbridge School, Tonbridge, Kent
	Joseph May	Royal Grammar School, High Wycombe
	Ben Millwood	Graveney School, Tooting, London
	Lingrui Xiang	Cambridge Tutors College, Croydon, Surrey
	Vincent Yu	Sha Tin College, Sha Tin, Hong Kong
	Hotin Yuen	Abingdon School, Oxfordshire

	Yue Zhao	Abbey College, Cambridge
	Mengqing Zou	Concord College, Shrewsbury, Shropshire
117	Sadegh Khoshzaban	Canons High School, Edgware
	Khalid Musenor	Rosedale College, Hayes, Middlesex
	Jack Smith	King's School, Grantham, Lincolnshire
	Chris Stokes	Chester Catholic High School, Handbridge
	Wilf Wilson	Perth Academy, Perth
116	Alex Cutbill	Trinity School, Croydon, Surrey
	Dohyun Kwak	MPW College, London
	James Male	Westminster School, London
	Yuming Mei	Hills Road VI Form College, Cambridge
	Kenan Wang	Hurtwood House School, Dorking, Surrey
	Tracy Wang	St Francis' College, Letchworth, Hertfordshire
	Jordan Watts	Henley College, Henley-on-Thames, Oxon
	Di Wu	John Leggott VI Form College, Scunthorpe, Lincs
	Taekwan Yoon	Anglo-American School of Moscow
115	Joseph Bailey	Torquay Boys' Grammar School, Shiphay, Devon
	Andrew Carlotti	Sir Roger Manwood's School, Sandwich, Kent
	Ben Challen	Winchester College, Hampshire
	Thomas Chambers	Lancaster Royal Grammar School, Lancaster
	Iqbal Chandan	Rosedale College, Hayes, Middlesex
	Nanyu Chen	Woodbridge School, Suffolk
	Bryan Chu	Charterhouse, Godalming, Surrey
	Edward Cree	Carre's Grammar School, Sleaford, Lincolnshire
	Guy Emerson	St Paul's School, London
	Xiao Fan	Winchester College, Hampshire
	Alex Gordon-Brown	Winchester College, Hampshire
	Yunqing Guan	Woodhouse College, London
	Andrew Hardt	American School in London, London

130		
	Lingchen Kong	Brentwood School, Brentwood, Essex
	Samuel Kwong	Colchester Royal Grammar School, Essex
	Victor Lam	Colchester Royal Grammar School, Essex
	Hans Larsen	Westminster School, London
	Han chao Li	Colchester Sixth Form College, Essex
	Benedict Lo	Reading School, Berkshire
	Simon Morris	Elizabeth College, St Peter Port, Guernsey
	Zhuyuan Ni	Cambridge Tutors College, Croydon, Surrey
	Sergei Patiakin	Dame Alice Owen's School, Hertfordshire
	Aaron Pereira	King Edward VI Camp Hill Boys' School, Birmingham
	Julian Ryan	Eton College, Berks
	Ram Sarujan	Dr Challoner's Grammar School, Amersham
	Arthur Wong	Tonbridge School, Kent
	We Wu	Brittin College, Torquay
	Long Zhang	Oundle School, Oundle
	Tianbo Zhqu	Pangbourne College, Berkshire
112	Zhonghao Chen	Rendcomb College, Cirencester
	Yanqing Cheng	Devonport High School for Girls, Plymouth
	Alex Dawes	King Edward's School, Birmingham
	Michael Heaton	Tiffin School, Kingston-upon-Thames, Surrey
	Nicholas Hill	Forest School, Nr Snaresbrook, London
	Augustus Lonergan	Tadcaster Grammar School, North Yorkshire
	Jamie Mcneill	King Edward VI Five Ways School, Birmingham
	Jordan Millar	Regent House School, Newtownards, Co Down
	Nevin Nirsimloo	Whitgift School, South Croydon, Surrey
	Daniel Williams	Belper School, Belper
	Yisheng Xu	Lawrence Sheriff School, Rugby, Warwickshire

A sample of one of the certificates is shown below.

UKMT

UK SENIOR MATHEMATICAL CHALLENGE
2008

of

received a

BRONZE CERTIFICATE

The Actuarial Profession
making financial sense of the future

Bernard Silverman
Chairman, United Kingdom Mathematics Trust

THE UNITED KINGDOM SENIOR MATHEMATICAL CHALLENGE

The UK SMC encourages mathematical reasoning, precision of thought, and fluency in using basic mathematical techniques to solve non-standard problems. It is targeted at sixteen to eighteen year olds with a genuine interest in mathematics.

The problems on the UK SMC are designed to make students think, and sometimes smile. Most are accessible to younger students, yet still challenge those with more experience; they are also meant to be memorable and enjoyable.

Mathematics controls more aspects of the modern world than most people realise — from CDs, cash machines, telecommunications and airline booking systems to production processes in engineering, efficient distribution and stock-holding, investment strategies and 'whispering' jet engines. The scientific and industrial revolutions flowed from the realisation that mathematics was both the language of nature, and also a way of analysing — and hence controlling — our environment. In the last fifty years old and new applications of mathematical ideas have transformed the way we live.

All these developments depend on mathematical thinking — a mode of thought whose essential style is far more permanent than the wave of technological change which it has made possible. The problems on the UK SMC reflect this style, which pervades all mathematics, by challenging students to think clearly about simple, yet unfamiliar problems.

The UK SMC was established as the National Mathematics Contest in 1961. In 2007 there were over 87,000 entries from 1932 schools and colleges. Certificates are awarded to the highest scoring 40% of candidates (6% Gold, 13% Silver, 21% Bronze).

Further information on the UKMT and its activities can be found at www.ukmt.org.uk

The next stage

Subject to certain conditions, candidates who obtained a score of 87 or over in the 2008 Senior Mathematical Challenge were invited to take the British Mathematical Olympiad Round One. Within the UKMT, the British Mathematical Olympiad Subtrust has control of the papers and everything pertaining to them. The BMOS produces an annual account of its events which, for 2008-2009, was edited by James Cranch (University of Sheffield) and Jack Shotton (Trinity College, Cambridge). Much of this report is included in the following pages.

United Kingdom Mathematics Trust

British Mathematical Olympiad

Round 1 : Thursday, 4 December 2008

Time allowed *Three and a half hours.*

Instructions

- *Full written solutions – not just answers – are required, with complete proofs of any assertions you may make. Marks awarded will depend on the clarity of your mathematical presentation. Work in rough first, and then write up your best attempt.*

  Do not hand in rough work.

- *One* **complete** *solution will gain more credit than several unfinished attempts. It is more important to complete a small number of questions than to try all the problems.*
- *Each question carries 10 marks. However, earlier questions tend to be easier. In general you are advised to concentrate on these problems first.*
- *The use of rulers and compasses is allowed, but calculators and protractors are forbidden.*
- *Start each question on a fresh sheet of paper. Write on one side of the paper only. On each sheet of working write the number of the question in the top* left-*hand corner and your name, initials and school in the top* **right**-*hand corner.*
- *Complete the cover sheet provided and attach it to the front of your script, followed by your solutions in question number order.*
- *Staple all the pages neatly together in the top* **left**-*hand corner.*

Do not turn over until told to do so.

United Kingdom Mathematics Trust

2008/9 British Mathematical Olympiad
Round 1: Thursday, 4 December 2008

1. Consider a standard 8×8 chessboard consisting of 64 small squares coloured in the usual pattern, so 32 are black and 32 are white. A zig-zag path across the board is a collection of eight white squares, one in each row, which meet at their corners. How many zig-zag paths are there?

2. Find all real values of x, y and z such that

$$(x+1)yz = 12, \qquad (y+1)zx = 4 \qquad \text{and} \qquad (z+1)xy = 4.$$

3. Let $ABPC$ be a parallelogram such that ABC is an acute-angled triangle. The circumcircle of triangle ABC meets the line CP again at Q. Prove that $PQ = AC$ if, and only if, $\angle BAC = 60°$.

The circumcircle of a triangle is the circle which passes through its vertices.

4. Find all positive integers n such that $n + 2008$ divides $n^2 + 2008$ **and** $n + 2009$ divides $n^2 + 2009$.

5. Determine the sequences $a_0, a_1, a_2, \ldots$ which satisfy all of the following conditions:

   a) $a_{n+1} = 2a_n^2 - 1$ for every integer $n \geqslant 0$,

   b) a_0 is a rational number, and

   c) $a_i = a_j$ for some i, j with $i \neq j$.

6. The obtuse-angled triangle ABC has sides of length a, b and c opposite the angles $\angle A$, $\angle B$ and $\angle C$ respectively. Prove that

$$a^3 \cos A + b^3 \cos B + c^3 \cos C < abc.$$

The British Mathematical Olympiad 2008-2009

The paper was marked by volunteers in December. Although difficult, the paper still allowed many candidates to display great skill and knowledge and they deserve much commendation for their efforts. Below is a list of the prize winners from Round 1.

Round 1 Prize Winners

The following contestants were awarded prizes:

Gold

Chris Bellin	Queen Mary's Grammar School, Walsall
Joseph Briggs	Kennet School, Berkshire
Andrew Carlotti	Sir Roger Manwood's School, Kent
Ruth Franklin	Manchester High School for Girls
Alex Gordon-Brown	Winchester College
Tim Hennock	Christ's Hospital, West Sussex
Henry Husband	Lycée Français Charles de Gaulle, London
Andrew Hyer	Westminster School
Lincheng Kong	Brentwood School, Essex
Peter Leach	Monkton Combe School, Bath
Jiawei Min	Abbey College, London
Preeyan Parmar	Eton College, Berkshire
Sergei Patiakin	Dame Alice Owen's School, Hertfordshire
Michal Sosnowski	Dulwich College, London
James Taylor	Judd School, Kent
James Zou	Concord College, Shropshire

Silver

James Aaronson	St Paul's School, London
Thomas Anthony	Hampton School, Middlesex
Benjamin Barrett	Cardiff High School
Luke Betts	Hills Road VI Form College, Cambridge
Nathan Brown	King Edward VI Camp Hill, Birmingham
Martin Chan	Westminster School
Chen Chen	Bellerbys College, London
Oscar Cunningham	Portsmouth Grammar School
Minh Trang Duong	Cambridge Tutors College
Ben Elliott	Frensham Heights School, Surrey
Guy Emerson	St Paul's School, London
Noah Fechtor-Pradines	British School of Boston
Richard Freeland	The Cathedral School, Llandaff

Yuhan Gao	Loughborough Grammar School
Zizheng Huang	Oundle School, Peterborough
Adil Zhan Ismailov	Abbey College, London
Mark Lewis	Royal Latin School, Buckingham
Augustus Lonergan	Tadcaster Grammar School, North Yorkshire
David Mestel	Hills Road VI Form College, Cambridge
Wesley Mok	Tonbridge School, Kent
Sean Moss	Havering Sixth Form College, London
Hieu Trong Nguyen	Rossall School, Lancashire
Aaron Pereira	King Edward VI Camp Hill, Birmingham
David Phillips	St Albans School
Alex Potts	Winchester College
Leo Shine	Reading School
Elliot Spragg	St Paul's School, London
Nguyen Hoang Tung	Bosworth College, Leicester
Carl Turner	Gorseinon College, Swansea
Aled Walker	King Edward VI Camp Hill, Birmingham
Wei Yue	Dulwich College, London
Jason Zhang	Queen Mary's Grammar School, Walsall
Yaoyu Zhu	King's School, Oxford

Bronze

Joseph Bailey	Torquay Boys' Grammar School
Neeloy Banerjee	Haberdashers' Aske's School for Boys, Herts
Alex Barrell	Wilson's School, London
Guy Bartlett	St Paul's School, London
Peter Bullock	RGS Worcester & The Alice Ottley School
Thomas Chambers	Lancaster Royal Grammar School
Luke Chapman	King Edward VI Community College, Devon
Nanyu Chen	Woodbridge School, Suffolk
Andrea Chlebikova	Dorothy Stringer High School, Brighton
Tin Yan Choi	Caterham School, Surrey
Edward Cree	Carre's Grammar School, Lincolnshire
Nhan Hie Danjnguen	Albion College, London
Adam Dougall	Wymondham High School, Norfolk
Christopher Elsby	Winchester College
Jonathan Flint	Aylesbury Grammar School
Rebecca Hann	Judd School, Kent
Jacob Hilton	Queen Elizabeth's School, Barnet, Hertfordshire
Keyang Hu	Caterham School, Surrey
Mark Jackson	Hills Road VI Form College, Cambridge

Alex Jeffreys	Haberdashers' Aske's Hatcham College, London
Mikhail Kartashov	St Clare's, Oxford
Sahl Khan	St Paul's School, London
Viktor Konstantinov	Concord College, Shropshire
Samuel Kwong	Colchester Royal Grammar School
Howon Lee	Whitgift School, Croydon
Jihoon Lee	Kingston Grammar School, London
Philipp Legner	Shrewsbury School
Keren Ma	Tonbridge School, Kent
Joseph May	Royal Grammar School, High Wycombe
David McLeod	St Albans School
Jordan Millar	Regent House School, County Down
Craig Newbold	Whitley Bay High School, North Tyneside
Huu Duc Nguyen	Cambridge Tutors College
Julian Parmar	Haberdashers' Aske's School for Boys, Herts
Barnaby Roberts	Farlingaye High School, Suffolk
Benedict Scholl	St Paul's School, London
Charles Shen	Aylesbury Grammar School
Stephen Smith	King's College School, London
Jack Smith	King's School, Grantham, Lincolnshire
Kingston Tam	Eton College, Berkshire
Thi Hai Yen Vu	Abbey College, Cambridge
Danny Wang	Bellerbys College, London
Zhe Wang	Roedean School, Brighton
Kenan Wang	Hurtwood House School, Surrey
Thomas Warrener	Tonbridge School, Kent
Benjamin Windsor	Lawrence Sheriff School, Rugby
Lingrui Xiang	Cambridge Tutors College
Niannan Xue	Teesside High School
Xin Zhang	Bellerbys College, London
Tom Zhang	Oundle School, Peterborough
Chuwei Zhang	Ruthin School, Denbighshire
Xinlin Zhao	Royal Russell School, Croydon

United Kingdom Mathematics Trust

British Mathematical Olympiad

Round 2 : Thursday, 29 January 2009

Time allowed *Three and a half hours.*

Each question is worth 10 marks.

Instructions

- *Full written solutions – not just answers – are required, with complete proofs of any assertions you may make. Marks awarded will depend on the clarity of your mathematical presentation. Work in rough first, and then draft your final version carefully before writing up your best attempt.*

  Rough work should *be handed in, but should be clearly marked.*
- *One or two* complete *solutions will gain far more credit than partial attempts at all four problems.*
- *The use of rulers and compasses is allowed, but calculators and protractors are forbidden.*
- *Staple all the pages neatly together in the top* left-*hand corner, with questions 1, 2, 3, 4 in order, and the cover sheet at the front.*

In early March, twenty students eligible to represent the UK at the International Mathematical Olympiad will be invited to attend the training session to be held at Trinity College, Cambridge (2-6 April). At the training session, students sit a pair of IMO-style papers and 8 students will be selected for further training. Those selected will be expected to participate in further correspondence work and to attend further training sessions. The UK Team of six for this summer's International Mathematical Olympiad (to be held in Bremen, Germany 13-22 July) will then be chosen.

Do not turn over until **told to do so**.

UKMT

United Kingdom Mathematics Trust

2008/9 British Mathematical Olympiad
Round 2: Thursday, 29 January 2009

1. Find all solutions in non-negative integers a, b to $\sqrt{a} + \sqrt{b} = \sqrt{2009}$.

2. Let ABC be an acute-angled triangle with $\angle B = \angle C$. Let the circumcentre be O and the orthocentre be H. Prove that the centre of the circle BOH lies on the line AB.

   The circumcentre of a triangle is the centre of its circumcircle. The orthocentre of a triangle is the point where its three altitudes meet.

3. Find all functions f from the real numbers to the real numbers which satisfy

$$f(x^3) + f(y^3) = (x + y)(f(x^2) + f(y^2) - f(xy))$$

   for all real numbers x and y.

4. Given a positive integer n, let $b(n)$ denote the number of positive integers whose binary representations occur as blocks of consecutive integers in the binary expansion of n. For example, $b(13) = 6$ because $13 = 1101_2$, which contains as consecutive blocks the binary representations of $13 = 1101_2$, $6 = 110_2$, $5 = 101_2$, $3 = 11_2$, $2 = 10_2$ and $1 = 1_2$.

   Show that if $n \leqslant 2500$, then $b(n) \leqslant 39$, and determine the values of n for which equality holds.

The British Mathematical Olympiad 2008-2009
Round 2

The second round of the British Mathematical Olympiad was held on Thursday 29th January 2009. Some of the top scorers from this round were invited to a residential course at Trinity College, Cambridge.

Leading Scores

Score	Name	School
40	Tim Hennock	Christ's Hospital, West Sussex
39	Nathan Brown	King Edward VI Camp Hill, Birmingham
	Peter Leach	Monkton Combe School, Bath
	Craig Newbold	Whitley Bay High School, North Tyneside
38	Andrew Hyer	Westminster School
	Luke Betts	Hills Road VI Form College, Cambridge
35	Michal Sosnowski	Dulwich College, London
33	Preeyan Parmar	Eton College, Berkshire
32	Sean Moss	Havering Sixth Form College, London
30	Geoffrey Penington	Abingdon School, Oxford
	Jordan Millar	Regent House School, County Down
	Joseph Briggs	Kennet School, Berkshire
29	Jaiwei Min	Abbey College, London
	Hieu Trong Nguyen	Rossall School, Lancashire
	Sahl Khan	St Paul's School, London
28	Wesley Mok	Tonbridge School, Kent
	Alex Gordon-Brown	Winchester College
27	James Zou	Concord College, Shropshire
26	Martin Chan	Westminster School
25	Chris Bellin	Queen Mary's Grammar School, Walsall
	Leo Shine	Reading School
22	Jiwei Fu	Concord College, Shropshire
	Sophie Kneller	Prior Park College, Bath
	Yuhan Gao	Loughborough Grammar School
	Julian Parmar	Haberdashers' Aske's School for Boys, Herts
	Jack Smith	King's School, Grantham, Lincolnshire
	Oscar Cunningham	Portsmouth Grammar School
	Minh Trang Duong	Cambridge Tutors College
21	Keren Ma	Tonbridge School, Kent
	Augustus Lonergan	Tadcaster Grammar School, North Yorkshire
	Christopher Elsby	Winchester College
	Mikhail Kartashov	St. Clare's, Oxford

IMO 2009

The 2009 International Mathematical Olympiad took place in Bremen, Germany from the 10th to the 22nd of July. The Team Leader was Geoff Smith and the Deputy Leader was Vesna Kadelburg. A full account of the 2009 IMO and the UK preparation for it appears later in this book.

The UK team was: Chris Bellin; Luke Betts; Tim Hennock; Peter Leach; Sean Moss and Preeyan Parmar. The reserves were: Craig Newbold; Nathan Brown and Andrew Hyer.

Introduction to the BMO problems and full solutions

The ‘official’ solutions are the result of many hours of work by a large number of people, and have been subjected to many drafts and revisions. The contestants’ solutions included here will also have been redrafted several times by the contestants themselves, and also shortened and cleaned up somewhat by the editors. As such, they do not resemble the first jottings, failed ideas and discarded pages of rough work with which any solution is started.

Before looking at the solutions, pupils (and teachers) are encouraged to make a concerted effort to attack the problems themselves. Only by doing so is it possible to develop a feel for the question, to understand where the difficulties lie and why one method of attack is successful while others may fail. Problem solving is a skill that can only be learnt by practice; going straight to the solutions is unlikely to be of any benefit.

It is also important to bear in mind that solutions to Olympiad problems are not marked for elegance. A solution that is completely valid will receive a full score, no matter how long and tortuous it may be. However, elegance has been an important factor influencing our selection of contestants' answers.

BMO Round 1 – Questions and Solutions

1. Consider a standard 8×8 chessboard consisting of 64 small squares coloured in the usual pattern, so 32 are black and 32 are white. A zig-zag path across the board is a collection of eight white squares, one in each row, which meet at their corners. How many zig-zag paths are there?

(*Proposer: Geoff Smith, University of Bath*)

Solution by the editors

We can calculate the number of paths to each white square, row-by-row.

In the first row, each white square can be reached from the first row in only one way. After that, each white square can be reached from the one or two white squares above it: the number of ways it can be reached is the sum of the numbers directly above. Calculating repeatedly, we produce the following diagram:

1		1		1		1	
	2		2		2		1
2		4		4		3	
	6		8		7		3
6		14		15		10	
	20		29		25		10
20		49		54		35	
	69		103		89		35

As can be seen, there are 35, 89, 103 and 69 ways of reaching the four white squares in the last row, respectively. Thus, in total, there are $35 + 89 + 103 + 69 = 296$ zig-zag paths.

2. Find all real values of x, y and z such that

$$(x+1)yz = 12, \qquad (y+1)zx = 4 \qquad \text{and} \qquad (z+1)xy = 4.$$

(Proposer: Christopher Bradley, formerly of Clifton College, Bristol)

Solution by Preeyan Parmar, Eton College, Berkshire

We number the equations:

$$(x+1)yz = 12, \qquad (1)$$
$$(y+1)zx = 4, \qquad (2)$$
$$(z+1)xy = 4. \qquad (3)$$

By subtracting the equations in pairs we obtain:

$$(2)-(1): \qquad z(x-y) = -8,$$
$$(3)-(2): \qquad x(y-z) = 0, \qquad (4)$$
$$(1)-(3): \qquad y(z-x) = 8.$$

Equation (4) implies that either $x = 0$ or $y = z$. However, if $x = 0$ then $(y+1)zx = 0$, contradicting equation (2). Hence $y = z$.

Now equations (1) and (2) become $(x+1)y^2 = 12$ and $(y+1)xy = 4$ respectively. We note that by (1) $y \neq 0$, and by (2) $y \neq -1$, which gives $x = \dfrac{4}{y(y+1)}$ and hence

$$x+1 = \frac{y^2+y+4}{y(y+1)}.$$

Combining these, we get

$$\frac{y^2+y+4}{y(y+1)}y^2 = 12,$$

giving $$y^4 + y^3 + 4y^2 = 12y^2 + 12y$$

and so $$y^4 + y^3 - 8y^2 - 12y = 0$$

and so $$y(y+2)^2(y-3) = 0.$$

Thus $y = 0$, $y = -2$ or $y = 3$.

But if $y = 0$, then $(x+1)y^2 = 0$, which contradicts equation (1).

If $y = z = -2$ then $x + 1 = 12/y^2 = 3$ so $x = 2$. This gives the solution $(x, y, z) = (2, -2, -2)$, which is easily checked to be valid.

If $y = z = 3$ then $x + 1 = 12/y^2 = 4/3$ so $x = \frac{1}{3}$. This gives the solution $(x, y, z) = \left(\frac{1}{3}, 3, 3\right)$, which is also easily checked to be valid.

3. Let $ABPC$ be a parallelogram such that ABC is an acute-angled triangle. The circumcircle of triangle ABC meets the line CP again at Q. Prove that $PQ = AC$ if, and only if, $\angle BAC = 60°$.

   The circumcircle of a triangle is the circle which passes through its vertices.

   (*Proposer: David Monk, formerly of Edinburgh University*)

Solution by David Phillips, St. Albans School

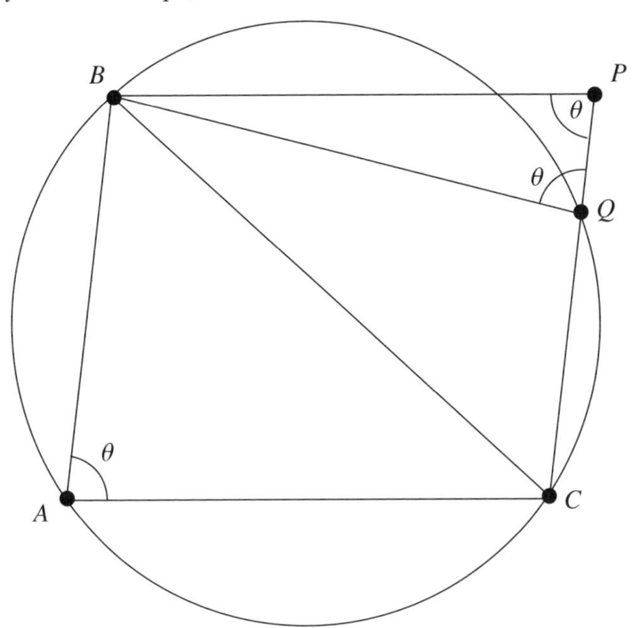

Let $\angle BAC = \theta$. Opposite angles in a cyclic quadrilateral add up to 180°, so $\angle BQC = 180° - \theta$ and $\angle BQP = \theta$.

Opposite angles in a parallelogram are equal, and so $\angle BPQ = \theta$. Hence BPQ is isosceles and $BP = BQ$. Also, opposite sides of a parallelogram are equal, so that $BP = AC$.

Therefore $AC = PQ$ if, and only if, $BP = BQ = PQ$, which occurs if, and only if, BPQ is equilateral.

Therefore $PQ = AC$ if, and only if, $\theta = 60°$, as required.

4. Find all positive integers n such that $n + 2008$ divides $n^2 + 2008$ **and** $n + 2009$ divides $n^2 + 2009$.

(Proposer: Jeremy King, Tonbridge School, Kent)

Solution by Carl Turner, Gorseinon College

We can write $n^2 + 2008 = m(n + 2008)$ and $n^2 + 2009 = l(n + 2009)$ for some positive integers l and m.

Subtracting these, we get

$$(m - l)n + 2008m - 2009l = -1$$

which rearranges to

$$(m - l)(n + 2008) = l - 1.$$

We could have $m = l$ and then $l - 1 = 0$. This means we have $n^2 + 2008 = n + 2008$ and $n^2 + 2009 = n + 2009$, so $n^2 = n$, and we get the solution $n = 1$ (as 0 is not positive). This is indeed a solution, as can easily be checked.

If however $m \neq l$ then $n + 2008 = \frac{l - 1}{m - 1}$. We must have $(m - l)$ positive, since $n + 2008$ and $l - 1$ are both positive. (Note that $l - 1 \neq 0$.)

Thus

$$n + 2008 = (l - 1)/(m - l) \leqslant l - 1. \qquad (1)$$

But $n^2 - ln - 2009(l - 1) = 0$, and so

$$n = \frac{l \pm \sqrt{l^2 + 4 \times 2009(l - 1)}}{2}.$$

However $l^2 + 4 \times 2009(l - 1) \geqslant l^2$. So either $n < 0$ (which is not permitted) or $n > l$ (which contradicts (1)).

Hence $n = 1$ is the only solution.

5. Determine the sequences $a_0, a_1, a_2, \ldots$ which satisfy all of the following conditions:

   a) $a_{n+1} = 2a_n^2 - 1$ for every integer $n \geqslant 0$,

   b) a_0 is a rational number, and

   c) $a_i = a_j$ for some i, j with $i \neq j$.

(Proposer: Paul Jefferys, UBS)

Solution by Peter Leach, Monkton Combe School, Bath

Assume $a_k = p/q$, where the greatest common divisor $(p, q) = 1$.

Then $a_{k+1} = (2p^2 - q^2)/q^2$.

Since $(p, q) = 1$, we have $(2p^2 - q^2, q^2) = (2p^2, q^2) = (2, q^2)$, which is either 1 or 2.

If $q > 2$, then the denominator of a_{k+1} is strictly greater than the denominator of a_k. The sequence of denominators will be strictly increasing, and we cannot have equality.

Furthermore, if $|a_k| > 1$ then, writing $|a_k| = 1 + e$, where $e > 0$, we have $a_{k+1} = 1 + 4e + 2e^2 > |a_k|$. So this will give a strictly increasing sequence.

So in order for terms to repeat, our starting value must have denominator at most 2, and must lie between −1 and 1 inclusive. This gives only five values to test:

- $a_0 = -1$ gives the sequence −1, 1, 1, 1, …, which is a solution.
- $a_0 = -1/2$ gives the sequence −1/2, −1/2, −1/2, …, which is a solution.
- $a_0 = 0$ gives the sequence 0, −1, 1, 1, 1, …, which is a solution.
- $a_0 = 1/2$ gives the sequence 1/2, −1/2, −1/2, −1/2, …, which is a solution.
- $a_0 = 1$ gives the sequence 1, 1, 1, …, which is a solution.

6. The obtuse-angled triangle ABC has sides of length a, b and c opposite the angles $\angle A$, $\angle B$ and $\angle C$ respectively. Prove that

$$a^3 \cos A + b^3 \cos B + c^3 \cos C < abc.$$

(*Proposer: David Monk, formerly of University of Edinburgh*)

Solution by Tim Hennock, Christ's Hospital

From the cosine rule, $a^2 + b^2 - c^2 = 2ab \cos C$ is negative if, and only if, $\angle C$ is obtuse. Exactly one of $\angle A$, $\angle B$, and $\angle C$ is obtuse, and so exactly one of $a^2 + b^2 - c^2$, $b^2 + c^2 - a^2$ and $c^2 + a^2 - b^2$ is negative.

It follows that

$$(a^2 + b^2 - c^2)(b^2 + c^2 - a^2)(c^2 + a^2 - b^2) < 0$$

which rearranges to

$$-a^6 - b^6 - c^6 + a^4b^2 + a^2b^4 + b^4c^2 + b^2c^4 + c^4a^2 + c^2a^4 < 2a^2b^2c^2.$$

We may divide by $2abc$, which is positive, and group terms cunningly to obtain

$$a^3\frac{(b^2 + c^2 - a^2)}{2bc} + b^3\frac{(c^2 + a^2 - b^2)}{2ca} + c^3\frac{(a^2 + b^2 - c^2)}{2ab} < abc,$$

and so, on applying the cosine rule we have proved the inequality in the question, i.e.

$$a^3 \cos A + b^3 \cos B + c^3 \cos C < abc.$$

BMO Round 2 – Questions and Solutions

1. Find all solutions in non-negative integers a, b to $\sqrt{a} + \sqrt{b} = \sqrt{2009}$.

(Proposer: Paul Jefferys, UBS)

Comment:

To solve this question, candidates needed to use the fact that if a is an integer such that $\sqrt{a}$ is rational, then $\sqrt{a}$ is an integer. No marks were deducted from candidates who assumed this without proof.

Solution by Sean Moss, Havering Sixth Form College

Rearrange the given equation:

$$\sqrt{a} + \sqrt{b} = \sqrt{2009} \qquad (1)$$

$$\sqrt{a} = \sqrt{2009} - \sqrt{b}.$$

Squaring and noting that $2009 = 7^2 \times 41$, we obtain

$$a = 2009 + b - 14\sqrt{41b}.$$

Since a, 2009 and b are integers, $\sqrt{41b}$ is rational. Therefore $\sqrt{41b}$ is an integer.

But 41 is prime, and so if $41b = B^2$, with B a non-negative integer, then $B = 41t$ for a non-negative integer t. Therefore $b = 41t^2$. By similar reasoning, $a = 41s^2$ for some non-negative integer s.

Equation (1) holds if, and only if, $(s + t)\sqrt{41} = 7\sqrt{41}$. The possible solution pairs (s, t) are $(0, 7), (1, 6), \ldots, (6, 1), (7, 0)$.

We therefore have a complete list of solutions (a, b):

$$(a, b) = (0,\ 2009), (41,\ 1476),\ (164,\ 1025),\ (369,\ 656)$$

$$(2009,\ 0),\ (1476,\ 41),\ (1025,\ 164),\ (656,\ 369).$$

2. Let ABC be an acute-angled triangle with $\angle B = \angle C$. Let the circumcentre be O and the orthocentre be H. Prove that the centre of the circle BOH lies on the line AB.

   The circumcentre of a triangle is the centre of its circumcircle. The orthocentre of a triangle is the point where its three altitudes meet.

   (*Proposer: Christopher Bradley, formerly of Clifton College, Bristol*)

Comment:

The solution given below represents one of many different ways to do this question. Some candidates noted that there is *diagram dependency*; in particular, O is closer to A than H if $\angle B > 60°$, but further away if $\angle B < 60°$; congratulations are due to them, although no marks were deducted for not considering the different cases.

The solution below is given for the case $\angle B > 60°$.

Solution by Preeyan Parmar, Eton College

Let AHD be the altitude from A. Since $\angle B = \angle C$, O lies on this altitude.

Since O is the centre of the circle through A, B and C, $\angle AOB = 2\angle ACB = 2\angle C$.

Let P be on AB such that $\angle BOP = \angle BAO$. Then since we also have $\angle OBP = \angle ABO$, the triangles BOP and BAO are similar. OA and OB are radii of circle ABC, and so are equal; therefore $PB = PO$. Now consider the circle centre P going through O and B. We would like to show that H lies on this circle; we would then have that the circumcentre of ΔBOH is P which lies on AB.

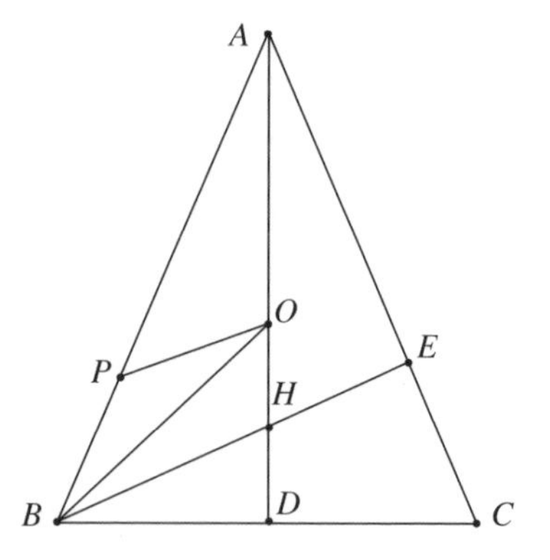

Because $\angle BPO = 2\angle C$, the chord BO subtends an angle of $\angle C$ at the circumference, on the same side of BO as P.

Therefore BO subtends an angle of $180° - \angle C$ at the circumference on the same side of BO as H (since for $\angle B > 60°$, H and P are on opposite sides of BO), and we only need show that $\angle BHO = 180° - \angle C$.

But $\angle BHO = \angle EHD$, and $HECD$ is cyclic because $\angle HEC = \angle HDC = 90°$. Therefore $\angle BHO = 180° - \angle ECD = 180° - \angle C$, as required.

3. Find all functions f from the real numbers to the real numbers which satisfy

$$f(x^3) + f(y^3) = (x + y)(f(x^2) + f(y^2) - f(xy))$$

for all real numbers x and y.

(Proposer: Tom Lovering, Trinity College, Cambridge)

Solution by Nathan Brown, King Edward VI Camp Hill Boys' School, Birmingham

If we set $x = y = 0$ then we get

$$f(0) + f(0) = 0(f(0) + f(0) - f(0)),$$

and so $f(0) = 0$.

If we substitute $y = -x$ then we get $f(x^3) + f(-x^3) = 0$. Since every real number has a real cube root, this implies that $f(-a) = -f(a)$ for all real a.

If we substitute $x = 0$, we get

$$f(0) + f(y^3) = y(f(0) + f(y^2) - f(0)).$$

This gives $f(y^3) = yf(y^2)$ for all real y.

Thus we have the following:

$$xf(x^2) + yf(y^2) = f(x^3) + f(y^3) = (x + y)(f(x^2) - f(xy) + f(y^2)) \qquad (1)$$

$$xf(x^2) - yf(y^2) = f(x^3) + f(-y^3) = (x - y)(f(x^2) - f(-xy) + f(y^2))$$

$$= (x - y)(f(x^2) + f(xy) + f(y^2)). \qquad (2)$$

Adding (1) and (2), we get

$$2xf(x^2) = 2xf(x^2) - 2yf(xy) + 2xf(y^2),$$

and thus $yf(xy) = xf(y^2)$. Setting $y = 1$, we get $f(x) = xf(1)$. Thus, writing k for $f(1)$, we have $f(x) = kx$ for all real x.

It is straightforward to check that $f(x) = kx$ gives a solution for any real k.

4. Given a positive integer n, let $b(n)$ denote the number of positive integers whose binary representations occur as blocks of consecutive integers in the binary expansion of n. For example, $b(13) = 6$ because $13 = 1101_2$, which contains as consecutive blocks the binary representations of $13 = 1101_2$, $6 = 110_2$, $5 = 101_2$, $3 = 11_2$, $2 = 10_2$ and $1 = 1_2$.

   Show that if $n \leqslant 2500$, then $b(n) \leqslant 39$, and determine the values of n for which equality holds.

   (Proposer: Adrian Sanders, formerly of Trinity College, Cambridge)

Solution by Craig Newbold, Whitley Bay High School

In this solution, all references to digits should be understood to mean in base 2. We write $l(n)$ to denote the number of digits in n. Since $2500 \leqslant 4096 = 2^{12}$, we have $l(n) \leqslant 12$ for all $n \leqslant 2500$.

We divide into cases according to the number $l(n)$.

Case 1: $l(n) = 12$

The first digit of n is 1 and (since $2500 < 2^{11} + 2^9$) the next two digits must be 0.

By a 'substring' of n, we mean a number that appears as a consecutive block in the base 2 representation of n. Clearly we can assume that a substring must start with a 1.

There is only one substring of length 12, one of length 11, and one of length 10 in n, since $l(n) = 12$, because such substrings cannot begin at the second or third digit. Similarly, there are at most two distinct substrings of length 9, at most three of length 8, and so on, up to at most seven of length 4.

Also, there are only 2^{k-1} different numbers of length k (since we must start with 1 and have $k - 1$ choices of 0 or 1 thereafter). So there is at most one distinct substring of length 1, at most two distinct substrings of length 2, and at most four of length 3.

Therefore, in the case $l(n) = 12$, we have (counting substrings of each possible length)

$$b(n) \leqslant 1 + 1 + 1 + 2 + 3 + 4 + 5 + 6 + 7 + 4 + 2 + 1 = 37 \leqslant 39.$$

Case 2: $l(n) \leqslant 10$

There is at most one substring of length 10, at most two of length 9, and so on. As before, there is at most one distinct substring of length 1, at most two distinct substrings of length 2, and at most four of length 3.

So, in this case,

$$b(n) \leqslant 1 + 2 + 3 + 4 + 5 + 6 + 7 + 4 + 2 + 1 = 35 \leqslant 39.$$

Case 3: $l(n) = 11$

For the final case, we use the estimates as before, which give

$$b(n) \leqslant 1 + 2 + 3 + 4 + 5 + 6 + 7 + 8 + 4 + 2 + 1 = 43.$$

However, if we have a zero as the d-th digit from the right, that reduces the maximum number of substrings of length e (for all $4 \leqslant e \leqslant d$) by 1.

Hence any zero in the leftmost four digits reduces the maximum number of substrings by at least 5 (and so $b(n) \leqslant 43 - 5 = 38$). Also, if there are three zeros among the leftmost eight digits of n, they reduce the bound by at least 6 (and so $b(n) \leqslant 43 - 6 = 37$). Further, any two zeros in the leftmost seven digits reduce it by at least 5 (and so $b(n) \leqslant 43 - 5 = 38$). In each case, we need look no further.

So, if $b(n) \geqslant 39$, the number n must look like $1111a_1a_2a_3b_1b_2b_3b_4$, where at most one of the a_i is zero. If $a_1 = a_2 = a_3 = 1$, then there are four identical substrings 1111 of length four, and three identical substrings 11111 of length five. This means there are at least five duplicates, so $b(n) < 39$.

If $a_1 = a_2 = 1$ and $a_3 = 0$, then having $a_3 = 0$ reduces the bound by two, and $a_1 = a_2 = 1$ causes two duplicates of 1111 and one duplicate of 11111 at the beginning. This reduces the bound by $2 + 2 + 1 = 5$, and so $b(n) < 39$.

If $a_1 = a_3 = 1$ and $a_2 = 0$, then having $a_2 = 0$ reduces the bound by three and $a_1 = 1$ causes a duplicate of 1111 at the beginning, meaning $b(n) \leqslant 39$.

If $a_2 = a_3 = 1$ and $a_1 = 0$, then having $a_1 = 0$ reduces the bound by four, meaning $b(n) \leqslant 39$.

In any case we have now proved $b(n) \leqslant 39$; we shall now investigate the cases of equality. These are the cases where a_1 or a_2 is zero. We must also have $b_1 = 1$ (or else it will reduce the bound by 1). So the number looks like $1111a_1a_211b_2b_3b_4$. However, if $a_1 = 0$ and $a_2 = 1$, we either have a duplicate of 1111 or of 1110. Thus $a_1 = 1$ and $a_2 = 0$, and the number looks like $11111011b_2b_3b_4$. However, if $b_2 = 1$, we shall again certainly get a duplicate of length 4.

So the number looks like $111110110b_3b_4$. If $b_3 = 1$, then 1101 is duplicated. So the only possibilities are

$$11111011000, \qquad \text{and} \tag{1}$$

$$11111011001.$$

We can tabulate the distinct substrings of each by length:

length	1	2	3	4	5	6	7	8	9	10	11	total
(1)	1	2	4	6	6	5	5	4	3	2	1	39
(2)	1	2	4	6	6	5	5	4	3	2	1	39

Hence these two (and only these two) give equality. Note that they are 2008 and 2009 (respectively) in base 10.

Olympiad Training

As usual the training programme for the academic year 2008-09 began with a training camp at Bath for students new to IMO preparation. There was the standard New Year training in Hungary while the highly successful camp at Trinity College, Cambridge took place at Easter and details of this follow.

The New Year Camp in Hungary was attended by 20 British and 20 Hungarian students. It was a 'proper cold weather camp'. As usual, the Hungarian IMO deputy, Sandor Dobos, was responsible for local arrangements. UK staff were Geoff Smith, Vesna Kadelburg and Jacqui Lewis. The UK students were: Chris Bellin, Luke Betts, Joseph Briggs, Nathan Brown, Andrew Carlotti, Ruth Franklin, Richard Freeland, Alex Gordon Brown, Tim Hennock, Henry Husband, Andrew Hyer, Peter Leach, Jordan Millar, Wesley Mok, Craig Newbold, Preeyan Parmar, Sergei Patiakin, Aaron Pereira, Jack Smith, Aled Walker.

Trinity College IMO camp, 2nd to 6th April 2009
Outline Programme

Twenty young UK mathematicians gathered in Cambridge for the Trinity College Training Session and IMO Squad selection exams. We were joined by three Hungarian students and their deputy leader.

The programme below outlines the main scheduled activities. This had a parallel structure with 'innocents' and 'experienced' (Mint and Used – in a philatelic sense) having sessions tailored to their needs.

Thursday 2nd April

14:00	Welcome and Introductions	(GCS)
14:15	Health and safety, camp rules	(VK)
15:00	Mint: Geometry 1	(VK)
	Used: Polynomials	(IL)
	Tea	
17:00	Mint: Geometry 2	(GL)
	Used: Combinatorics 1	(PAR)
18:00	Background Problems	
19:00	*Dinner followed by Mathematical Relays*	

Friday 3rd April

09:00	Mint: Geometric Inequalities	(SD)
	Used: Combinatorics 2	(JM)
	Tea	

11:00	Mint: Geometry 3	(GL)
	Used: Combinatorics 2	(JC)
13:00	*Lunch*	
14:00	Mint: Number Theory 1	(IL)
	Used: Inversion	(SD)
15:30	Mint: Combinatorics 1	(PAR)
	Used: Number Theory 1	(RB)
	Tea	
17:20	Mint: Polynomials	(JC)
	Used: Geometry 1	(TL)
19:00	*Dinner followed by Hungarian Event*	

Saturday 4th April

08:30	First Selection Test 1	
13:00	*Lunch*	
14:30	Presentation of cheques	(BB)
	Tea	
17:00	Areal co-ordinates and circles	(GCS)
19:00	*Dinner followed by Quiz*	

Sunday 5th April

09:00	Mint: Functional Equations	(EC)
	Used: Number Theory 2	(KB)
	Tea	
11:00	Mint: Number Theory 2	(RB)
	Used: Geometry 2	(TL)
13:00	*Lunch*	
14:00	Mint: Number Theory 3	(KB)
	Used: Geometry 3	(GCS)
15:30	Mint: Inequalities	(VK)
	Used: Functional Equations	(EC)
	Tea	
17:20	Mint: Combinatorics 2	(JM)
	Used: Number Theory 3	(KB)
19:00	*Dinner and social event*	

Monday 6th April

08:30	First Selection Test 2
13:00	*Lunch*
14:00	Background Problems
16:00	Tea and farewell

Participants

Luke Betts	Cottenham Village College, Cambridge
James Aaronson	St Paul's School
Chris Bellin	Queen Mary's Grammar School
Luke Betts	Hills Road Sixth Form College
Joseph Briggs	Kennet School
Nathan Brown	King Edward VI Camp Hill Boys' School
Ruth Franklin	Manchester High School for Girls
Yuhan Gao	Loughborough Grammar School
Alex Gordon-Brown	Winchester College
Tim Hennock	Christ's Hospital
Andrew Hyer	Westminster School
Sahl Kahn	St Paul's School
Sophie Kneller	Prior Park College
Peter Leach	Monkton Combe School
Jordan Millar	Regent House School
Wesley Mock	Tonbridge School
Sean Moss	Havering Sixth Form College
Craig Newbold	Whitley Bay High School
Preeyan Parmar	Eton College
Leo Shine	Reading School
Jack Smith	King's School

Staff

Richard Atkins	RA	Robin Bhattacharyya	RB	Bela Bollobas	BB
Kevin Buzzard	KB	James Cranch	JC	Edward Crane	EC
Sandor Dobos	SD	Vesna Kadelburg	VK	Gerry Leversha	GL
Imre Leader	IL	Tom Lovering	TL	Joseph Myers	JM
Paul Russell	PAR	Geoff Smith	GCS		

Lee Zhao was the local organizer and Jack Shotton was the catering officer.

Subsequent to this, the team plus reserves were selected. Final selection of the team was at Oundle school during the Spring half-term holiday.

The International Mathematical Olympiad

In many ways, a lot of the events and activities described earlier in this book relate to stages that UK IMO team members will go through before they attend an IMO. At this stage, it is worth explaining a little about the structure of the Olympiad, both for its own sake as well as to fit the following report into a wider context.

An IMO is a huge event and takes several years to plan and to execute. In 2009, teams from 104 countries went to Germany to participate. A team consists of six youngsters (although in some cases, a country may send fewer). The focus of an IMO is really the two days on which teams sit the contest papers. The papers are on consecutive days and each lasts $4\frac{1}{2}$ hours. Each paper consists of three problems, and each problem is worth 7 marks. Thus a perfect score for a student is 42/42. The students are ranked according to their personal scores, and the top half receive medals. These are distributed in the ratios gold:silver:bronze = 1:2:3. The host city of the IMO varies from year to year. Detailed contemporary and historical data can be found at

http://www.imo-official.org/

But, whilst these may be the focus, there are other essential stages, in particular the selection of the problems and, in due course, the co-ordination (marking) of scripts and awarding of medals.

As stated, an IMO team is built around the students but they are accompanied by two other very important people: the Team Leader and the Deputy Leader. (Many teams also take Observers who assist at the various stages. Some Observers may turn out to be future Leaders.) Some three or four days before the actual IMO examinations, the Team Leaders arrive in the host country to deal with the task of constructing the papers. Countries will have submitted questions for consideration over the preceding months and a short list of questions (and, eventually, solutions) are given to Team Leaders on arrival. The Team Leaders gather as a committee (in IMO parlance, the Jury) to select six of the short-listed questions. This can involve some very vigorous debate and pretty tough talking! But it has to be done. Once agreed, the questions are put into the papers and translations produced into as many languages as necessary, sometimes over 50.

At some stage, the students, accompanied by the Deputy Leader, arrive in the host country. As is obvious, there can be no contact with the Team Leader who, by then, has a good idea of the IMO papers! The Leaders and the students are housed in different locations to prevent any contact, casual or otherwise.

On the day before the first examination, there is an Opening Ceremony. This is attended by all those involved (with due regard to security). Immediately after the second day's paper, the marking can begin. It may seem strange that students' scripts are 'marked' by their own Leader and Deputy. In fact, no actual marks or comments of any kind are put on the scripts themselves. Instead, having looked at scripts and decided what marks they think should be awarded, the Leader and Deputy have to justify their claim to others, called co-ordinators, who are supplied by the host country. Once all the marks have been agreed, sometimes after extremely protracted negotiation, the Jury decides where the medal boundaries should go. Naturally, this is a crucial part of the procedure and results in many tears as well as cheers.

Whilst the co-ordination of marks is going on, the students have time to relax and recover. There are often organised activities and excursions and there is much interaction and getting to know like-minded individuals from all corners of the world.

The grand finale is always the closing ceremony which includes the awarding of medals as well as speeches and numerous items of entertainment – some planned but others accidental.

The 50th International Mathematical Olympiad Bremen and Bremerhaven, Germany 14th to 21st July 2009 Geoff Smith (UK IMO Team Leader)

The 50th International Mathematical Olympiad was held in July 2009 in Bremen and Bremerhaven, Germany. This is in the north-west corner of Germany, near its North Sea coast.

In 2009, the UK team was led by Dr Geoff Smith, University of Bath. The Deputy was Dr Vesna Kadelburg of Mander Portman Woodward, Cambridge. Observer with leader was Mr James Cranch, University of Leicester, and the Observer with students was Ms Jacqui Lewis of St Julian's International School, Carcavelos, Portugal. The UKMT executive director Mary Wimbury also made a short visit to study IMO procedures.

The UK team was:

Chris Bellin	Queen Mary's Grammar School, Walsall
Luke Betts	Hills Road Sixth Form College, Cambridge
Tim Hennock	Christ's Hospital, Horsham
Peter Leach	Monkton Combe School, Bath

Sean Moss	Havering Sixth Form College
Preeyan Parmar	Eton College

The three reserves were:

Nathan Brown	King Edward VI Camp Hill Boys School
Andrew Hyer	Westminster School
Craig Newbold	Whitley Bay High School

Each of the six questions is marked out of 7. The UK picked up marks on 5 of the 6 problems.

		P1	P2	P3	P4	P5	P6	Total	Medal
UNK1	Chris Bellin	7	7	1	4	1	0	20	Bronze
UNK2	Luke Betts	7	7	7	7	3	0	31	Silver
UNK3	Tim Hennock	7	7	7	7	4	0	32	Gold
UNK4	Peter Leach	7	3	1	7	7	0	25	Silver
UNK5	Sean Moss	7	7	0	0	7	0	21	Bronze
UNK6	Preeyan Parmar	6	7	1	7	7	0	28	Silver
		41	38	17	32	29	0	157	1G, 3S, 2B

The cut-offs were 32 for Gold, 24 for Silver and 14 for Bronze. The efficiency prize therefore goes to Tim Hennock who achieved his medal with no margin of safety whatever.

It was gratifying that all six British students received medals, and that Tim Hennock was awarded a gold. Luke Betts only missed a gold medal by 1 mark, and is determined to do even better next year. The rest of our team are ineligible because they are going to university in 2009. Our reserves Nathan Brown and Andrew Hyer will also be available next year. From the point of view of a coach, I was particularly pleased that the team scored nineteen 7s and only one 6. Our efforts to minimise the number of marks lost by careless writing-up have been almost completely effective.

In terms of the rank order, the UK was in the peloton as usual, on equal 19th with both Hungary and Bulgaria. The detailed statistics of IMO 2009 and all previous IMOs can be found at the excellent site:

http://www.imo-official.org/

Details of previous British performances at the IMO can be found at Joseph Myers's IMO register:

http://www.imo-register.org.uk/

As for international achievement, the leading performances of the 104 countries participating were: 1 People's Republic of China (221), 2 Japan (212), 3 Russian Federation (203), 4 Republic of Korea (188), 5

Democratic People's Republic of Korea (183), 6 United States of America (182), 7 Thailand (181), 8 Turkey (177), 9 Germany (171), 10 Belarus (167), 11= Taiwan, Italy (165), 13 Romania (163), 14 Ukraine (162), 15= Vietnam, Islamic Republic of Iran (161), 17 Brazil (160), 18 Canada (158), 19= United Kingdom, Bulgaria, Hungary (157), 22 Serbia (153), 23 Australia (151), 24 Peru (144), 25= Georgia, Poland (140). Here are some selected other performances of possible interest to Anglophones: 28 India (130), 29 Hong Kong (122), 30 Singapore (116), 31 France (112), 43 South Africa (84), 50 Sri Lanka (74), 58 Bangladesh (67), 66 New Zealand (53), 69 Cyprus (45), 75 Malaysia (31), 76 Trinidad and Tobago (28), 85 Pakistan (21), 89 Ireland (20), 90 Nigeria (17) and 100 Zimbabwe (5).

Of course China is to be congratulated as usual. This year's big surprise was the wonderful performance of the Japanese team. The two Koreas are establishing themselves as leading players. In the case of North Korea this is remarkable since they were absent from the IMO for many years. One expects Russia and the USA to be near the top, but this year there were excellent performances by Thailand and Turkey. After that comes a rush of nations on fairly similar scores, headed by Germany.

There were three exceptional individual performances, these being precisely the three students who solved problem 6 completely. They were: 1= Makoto Soejima, Japan (42), 1= Dongyi Wei, People's Republic of China (42) and 3 Lisa Sauermann, Germany (41). Of course the German media were very excited by Lisa's performance, but strangely enough she elected to have her medal presented to the German team's tiger mascot.

Another remarkable feature of this IMO was the participation of 11-year-old Raúl Chávez Sarmiento from Peru. He won a bronze medal, and a prolonged standing ovation at the medal ceremony. Under the leadership of Emilio Gonzaga Ramírez, Peru has become quite a force at recent IMOs. Our training partners from Australia obtained two good golds through Andrew Price (37) and Sampson Wong (34). There were 59 girls participating at the 50th IMO, breaking through the 10% barrier.

Here are the problems:

Day 1

Problem 1

Let n be a positive integer and let $a_1, \dots, a_k$ $(k \geqslant 2)$ be distinct integers in the set $\{1, \dots, n\}$ such that n divides $a_i(a_{i+1} - 1)$ for $i = 1, \dots, k - 1$. Prove that n does not divide $a_k(a_1 - 1)$.

Problem 2

Let ABC be a triangle with circumcentre O. The points P and Q are interior points of the sides CA and AB, respectively. Let K, L and M be the midpoints of the segments BP, CQ and PQ, respectively, and let Γ be the circle passing through K, L and M. Suppose that the line PQ is tangent to the circle Γ. Prove that $OP = OQ$.

Problem 3

Suppose that $s_1, s_2, s_3, \dots$ is a strictly increasing sequence of positive integers such that the subsequences

$$s_{s_1}, s_{s_2}, s_{s_3}, \dots \qquad \text{and} \qquad s_{s_1+1}, s_{s_2+1}, s_{s_3+1}, \dots$$

are both arithmetic progressions. Prove that the sequence $s_1, s_2, s_3, \dots$ is itself an arithmetic progression.

Day 2

Problem 4

Let ABC be a triangle with $AB = AC$. The angle bisectors of $\angle CAB$ and $\angle ABC$ meet the sides BC and CA at D and E, respectively. Let K be the incentre of triangle ADC. Suppose that $\angle BEK = 45°$. Find all possible values of $\angle CAB$.

Problem 5

Determine all functions f from the set of positive integers to the set of positive integers such that, for all positive integers a and b, there exists a non-degenerate triangle with sides of lengths

$$a, \qquad f(b) \qquad \text{and} \qquad f(b + f(a) - 1).$$

(A triangle is *non-degenerate* if its vertices are not collinear.)

Problem 6

Let $a_1, a_2, \dots, a_n$ be distinct positive integers and let M be a set of $n - 1$ positive integers not containing $s = a_1 + a_2 + \dots + a_n$. A grasshopper is to jump along the real axis, starting at the point 0 and making n jumps to the right with lengths $a_1, a_2, \dots, a_n$ in some order. Prove that the order can be chosen in such a way that the grasshopper never lands on any point in M.

The problems were submitted by Australia, Russia, USA, Belgium, France and Russia respectively.

Leader's Diary

The IMO of 2009 was exceptionally well organized and a great success. Nonetheless, this diary will inevitably focus on the things which went awry.

July 5–6 This year my IMO began on July 5th. We are having a joint pre-IMO camp with the Australian team, and they are due in at dawn at Heathrow.

I have ordered a minibus taxi to pick up the Australians from Heathrow, and it arrives just before the team enters the arrivals hall. The team leader is Angelo di Pasquale, and his able deputy is Ivan Guo. The travellers all look rather battered.

The taxi gets to Cambridge just in time for us to race to the Great Hall of Trinity College for breakfast. The UK pastoral person Jacqui Lewis is already there and, assisted by the local organizer Lee Zhao and the UK deputy leader Vesna Kadelburg, we sort things out. The Australians spend a gentle day reconstructing their personalities. The UK team arrives in time for supper, and old friendships are renewed and the endless round of card games begins.

July 7 Today we have our first practice exam. It is held in the Junior Parlour. This room is only just big enough to accommodate both teams, and overlooks a busy street where noise is generated. Thus the venue is not quite ideal, but after discussions with Angelo, we decide that it is good enough and that we will not have to switch locations for subsequent exams.

July 8 Today is tourism day. After breakfast we catch a train to London, and use the tube to get to Green Park and walk across to catch most of the changing of the guard at Buckingham Palace. We then stroll up The Mall, walk under Admiralty Arch, and then lounge around in Trafalgar Square for a while.

We walk up Whitehall, past many ministries, Downing Street and at length to Parliament Square. We purchase sandwiches and eat in Parliament Square. Then we look at the Parliament Buildings, and stroll west through Victoria Tower Gardens and cross the river over Lambeth Bridge. We then turned left, walking past Lambeth Palace, the residence of the Archbishop of Canterbury when he is in town, and back to the south end of Westminster Bridge. We arrived at the London Eye, a Ferris wheel of some note. We took a flight, and then boarded a boat trip. This took us under several of the well-known bridges, including Tower Bridge, and back again. The commentary was grotesque.

At length we escaped, and made our way by tube to Leicester Square, and a Japanese restaurant for dinner. That really was very good, and we made it back to Cambridge for plenty of sleep before the next day's exam.

July 9 The Mathematics Ashes is the trophy of the annual contest between the British and Australian IMO teams. The burnt remains of the scripts of the first exam are stored in a funerary urn. Today's exam will decide the Ashes. This year the result was very satisfactory from a northern hemispherical point of view, and the UK will hold the urn for at least the next 12 months. In the evening we have a celebratory dinner in hall (shirts, ties, shoes, the works). We are joined by the UK Observer A, James Cranch, who will accompany me to the IMO the next day.

July 10 The flight to Bremen is uneventful, and takes only 100 minutes. Careful readers of this diary series may recall problems with being greeted at IMO Spain in 2008 (but no problems at all in Vietnam 2007 where there was a dedicated IMO passport control).

James and I arrive in the Ryanair terminal. There is no-one to meet us. Eventually, after numerous phone calls, an IMO bus turns up at the advertised spot. Unfortunately this IMO-designated parking spot is in the strictly-forbidden parking spot category as far as the airport authorities are concerned, and the bus is chased off to a place several hundred metres away across a car park. News spreads among the leaders and their deputies and observers A.

It turns out that it was an IMO bus, but unfortunately not the *right* IMO bus. Eventually we board the bus, and are driven to the jury site at Bremerhaven. En route, I use my newly acquired IMO travel organizer's telephone number to place a call urging her to get someone competent to the airport pronto. It will later turn out that the situation for those arriving at the train station was also rather disorganised. However, by the time that the students started to arrive, these problems were sorted out.

After that start, things had to improve, and they did. We arrive at the Atlantic Hotel Sail City in Bremerhaven in time for lunch. I am based here and James is based nearby. We are given our copies of the shortlist, and set to work trying to solve some problems. The hotel is very luxurious, and by dinner most of the jury has arrived.

James and I decide to explore. My hotel is next to the estuary of the river Weser in the harbour area. There is a shopping mall which connects the hotel to the main street. Near the hotel, the outlets are expensive. At length we arrive at the main street. Here the shops are very familiar. We pick up supplies and return to the comfort of my hotel.

My room is one level up from ground level (so I sleep on what I call the first floor), handily positioned so that no lift journey is required to get to the restaurant, a 20 metre run. The jury area is on the ground floor, but when you arrive at the hotel the only way to get to the jury area is via the first floor, so you climb up and then down. You can see where you want to go through glass walls, but it is not a completely trivial matter.

July 11 James and I spend the day working on the shortlist problems. At 4pm we pick up the version of the shortlist which contains solutions, and carry on working during the evening. It is difficult to think of anything to say which might be entertaining, except of course to confess that we convinced ourselves that the grasshopper question, later to become Problem 6, had an easy solution.

July 12 The jury is chaired by Prof. Dr. Hans-Dietrich Gronau. He has a bell to keep us in order, and is an enthusiast for keeping to time. This is good news. The wonderful quality of the academic side of the administration was a particular feature of this IMO. There are very helpful jury guides. The hard-to-please UK observer James Cranch is satisfied by the arrangements.

The jury decides to select the so-called easy problems first, numbers 1 and 4, because there is a shortage of very accessible problems. By now the procedure is finely honed. First the jury conducts a paper vote called the *beauty contest*, where problems are rated for difficulty and beauty. The results are published, and then inform the selection of problems. Problem 1 will be N1, and Problem 4 will be G1, the questions which the Problem Selection Committee rank easiest among the shortlist problems in Number Theory and Geometry respectively. Selection is done via a 'devil take the hindmost' process, where a large number of pairs of so-called easy questions are considered, and pairs are eliminated by a long sequence of votes. Oh yes, and there are speeches.

Next, the jury selects the hard problems by similar means. The problems selected are A6 and C7. The first involves subsequences of a sequence, where you look only at those terms indexed by terms of the sequence, or one more than the terms of the sequence. Just the sort of convoluted mind-bending stuff that sits well at problem 3. Problem 6 concerns the ability of a grasshopper to do combinatorics, and will be fully solved by only 3 students. Thus it is worthy.

By now the jury is in ferment, because it has selected four problems and only one of them concerns geometry. Like a vampire after dusk, the jury has a thirst that must be slaked. It lunges for G2, the next best thing to G1. It is not enough. There is an inequality question which mentions triangles, and that is grabbed as a kind of 'geometry-lite' problem. We now have the medium problems. The jury is now in a blood-frenzy, and wants to select more geometry problems, but the chair points out that we are only allowed to choose six problems, and the jury reluctantly calms down.

In recent years it has become the usual practice for the English Language Committee to sort out both the English wording, and also the mathematical notation for the problems. This year the full jury works out the notation first, and then the ELC does its work on the wording.

July 13 Today is student arrival day, but we are cut off from all that. The Anglophones have some time to spare, as other language groups work on their exam papers. The co-ordinators draw up six marking schemes, and these are mostly accepted by the jury. There is a case where the jury feels that the proposed marking scheme is too loose, inviting lengthy performances by disputatious leaders. The jury advises the relevant Problem Captain to tighten up the scheme, and he does.

I and several colleagues have lunch with Hans van Duijn, Rector Magnificus of Technische Universiteit Eindhoven. He will play a major role in IMO 2011 in the Netherlands. Hans knows several of my colleagues in the maths department of the University of Bath, but even so, he seems very nice.

After lunch some of us decide to mount an expedition to a local attraction. Next to the shopping centre there is a museum of climate. It has recently been opened, so presumably it will be in excellent condition.

You may not have realised, but it turns out that much of the world is hot and some of it is hot and sticky. I don't care for it at all. Suddenly there is a rapid improvement. I go through an ice tunnel and enter an Alaskan winter. All sorts of tourists are wrapping themselves up against the cold, but this is ideal weather for an Englishman in shorts. I rest and relax, bringing my core body temperature down to an acceptable level. At last I continue the journey, and return to the outside world.

The translations of the paper have all been prepared by the time we return. This year there are 55 language versions. My efforts to persuade the Australian leader to construct his own version of the English language paper fall on deaf ears. The idea would be to replace the grasshopper by a kangaroo.

July 14 This the day of the opening ceremony. The jurors and students must not meet, so the logistics of this event are always challenging. The jury is driven to an industrial area of Bremen, and spills out of the coaches on to tarmac. We are led round a corner to what appears to be a giant industrial unit. We step inside and discover that it is a concert hall for rock music. Unusually, proceedings begin and end with a performance by a breakdancing troupe 'Breakmathix', with sonic accompaniment drawn from the beatbox genre, an aspect of soi-disant hip-hop culture. There are some well-judged short speeches by local and national politicians, a video address by Angela Merkel (who senses the mood rather better than George W. Bush did in 2001), and words of welcome from the Chair of the IMO advisory board, József Pelikán.

The teams parade across the stage. This year the UK students are not wearing Panama hats, but are carrying large numbers of UKMT frisbees which they hurl from the stage over the audience.

David Brindley, who produced the BBC film 'Beautiful Young Minds' is at the ceremony with the writer James Graham. That film was a 90-minute documentary on the build-up to IMO 2006 in Slovenia, including material on the IMO itself. It had great critical acclaim, receiving nominations for both BAFTA and RTS awards (the two most prestigious TV awards in the UK).

In the evening the hotel provides a themed German dinner, with various types of Wurst. I have never seen Paul Vaderlind, the Swedish leader, so happy. It was very good indeed.

July 15 Day 1 of the exams. The jury meets at 09:00 to consider its answers to questions of clarification. All three problems give rise to questions. Problem 1 involves a positive integer n which is at least 2. The wording does not state that it is at least 2, but this follows immediately from other information in the question. Nervous candidates seek reassurance. Problem 2 is a geometry problem which involves the interior point of a line segment. Various students want to know what this terminology means. Finally, problem 3 involves a subscripted subscript. This frightens the horses.

I am slightly baffled by the question from UNK3 who asks if he may use a geometrical instrument known as a set square (a transparent triangle) which is not marked with angles (so it is not a closet protractor). Protractors are banned from the IMO exam, along with squared paper, pocket calculating machines and similar instances of moral corruption. Set squares are standard items in British geometry sets, and their use has never been in question. I will return later to this important matter, the *Geodreieck scandal*, as it will henceforth be known.

In the evening the scripts arrive, and I am pleased that our students have written up their solutions very clearly, so that it is relatively easy to see what they have done. They have had a good day, especially Tim Hennock who has written a perfect paper, and walked out of the exam after just two and a half hours.

Later on there is a joint meeting of the IMO jury and the IMO Advisory Board.

July 16 Day 2 of the exams. Once again, all three of the problems attract questions of clarification from the candidates. As ever, there are students who do not know the definition of an incentre, a point which appears in problem 1. In problem 2, the vexed matter of degenerate triangles arises again. I am tempted to say that a degenerate triangle is one which is drawn on squared paper, or uses a protractor or a calculator. We give a more helpful answer involving collinear vertices. Problem 3 involves a grasshopper jumping to the right on the real line. Some students choose their real line to point vertically, so that jumping to the right takes the insect off the real line. The Netherlands leader successfully convinces me that it is Dutch national policy to have all real lines pointing vertically up, and that we have a real problem on our hands. Nice one Quintijn, a brilliant wind-up. My student UNK6 Preeyan Parmar asked the question 'what is a grasshopper?' Since this was frivolous, following the sensible warning of Finnish leader Matti Lehtinen, I wait until all serious questions had been dealt with before proposing an answer. 'A grasshopper is an insect of the suborder *Caelifera* in the order *Orthoptera*. It is modelled by a variable point on the real line.' The jury agreed that this answer be sent.

Later, I was to discover that the Geodreieck scandal had burst open on Day 2. A Geodreieck is a set square. Each juror was equipped with a wooden voting stick in the shape of an arrow, the arrowhead taking the form of a set square decorated with protractor markings rendering it IMO illegal. In IMO morality, a protractor is deemed even worse than odious areal co-ordinates and multivariate calculus methods for solving three variable symmetric inequalities. The fact that this taboo instrument featured so prominently on the voting sticks foreshadowed other problems.

Someone handed out a gift of real illegal Geodreiecke (with protractor markings!) to all competitors at the start of the IMO. A better informed fragment of the IMO organization then swung into action, issuing a Ukase prohibiting the use of this evil instrument in the IMO. On Day 2 of the IMO, matters came to a head.

Chief Invigilator Dierk Schleicher found that UNK3 Tim Hennock was about to use a set square, and ripped the offending instrument from Hennock's geometry set. Prof. Dr. Schleicher queried UNK3's use of his set square, and was satisfied when told that the jury had given explicit permission for it to be used.

After lunch the jury and their retinue transfers to the students' site, Jacobs University in Bremen. Rice University in Houston played a major role in creating Jacobs University. Leaders meet their teams and deputies, and listen eagerly to the students' sometimes fanciful tales of how they have performed on Day 2. We also get to meet the UK deputy Vesna Kadelburg, and our observer with students Jacqui Lewis. They recount their adventures, and give us a tutorial on living at Jacobs University. It all seems very straightforward. The way to find things out is to ask the guide of the Australian team. Now is the time to cut the students a little more slack, and this is very easy because the campus is such a safe environment. Jacqui co-ordinates by text messaging.

In the evening the scripts arrive, and we see that our team have gathered more marks. The performance is not so strong as that on Day 1, but it is not a disaster.

Walking into a crowded university cafeteria comes as quite a shock after the days of being spoiled at the Atlantic Hotel Sail City. The UK team stayed in Rice University, Houston on the way to IMO 2005 in Mexico. Jacobs University has some features which are improvements over Rice.

There is a little café tucked round the side of the porters' lodge. It serves good coffee, rolls and beer. It opens and closes at random, but seems to be able to read my mind. When I want to use it, it is almost always open.

July 17 Today is the first co-ordination day. The co-ordinators are the IMO police, and they will examine our marking of our students' papers, and make sure that our suggested scores conform to the various marking schemes.

An area of campus is coned off, and becomes forbidden ground to competitors. Inside the security zone are two buildings; East Hall and West Hall. Each contains the co-ordinators for three of the problems.

We begin with problem 1, for which we have six solutions, including fair wear and tear. The co-ordinators are happy to give 7 to four of the scripts, but argue for reductions to 6 for the two remaining ones. We adjourn for a brief discussion, and go back in to face them again. We put our hands up and agree that the case against Preeyan Parmar UNK6 is proved, and that he must drop to 6, but we argue carefully why the imperfection in the other script of Peter Leach UNK4 is much less, and ask for leniency. Now it is time for the co-ordinators to call a time out. They meet with their colleagues, and grant the 7. Well, 41/42 is a good start.

Next we have to co-ordinate problem 2. This is a geometry problem. We have five excellent and uncontroversial solutions, but Peter Leach UNK4 is in trouble. He has overlooked the straightforward solution, but has made a remark in pencil which indicates he sees how to clinch the argument. We go in ready to beg for 1 for this remark in rough. The co-ordinators, however, have different ideas. There is a new tradition (this is how a change of policy is described in IMO speak). We are apparently going to give non-trivial part marks for serious attempts at algebraic solutions. Now, UNK4's progressively more sordid calculations sprawl over many pages, accurate in all respects until the algebra explodes in a mess of errors at the end. For some reason the co-ordinators insist on giving 3 marks for this nonsense. We accept under protest.

Next we must co-ordinate problem 5. Mary Wimbury, the UKMT executive director, has arrived on a fact-finding mission. She goes in to observe James Cranch and Vesna Kadelburg do the talking. I am left pacing the corridor in expectant father mode until I am called in to sign off the marks. The negotiations go well. Attempts by James to point out one or two weaknesses in the solutions have been firmly over-ruled by the co-ordinators, and we have an attractive collection of marks.

By now we have discovered that there is a room near the leaders' hall where you can get coffee and cake, and watch partial IMO results projected on screens. There is also a timetable which allows you to read the co-ordination schedule. This is colour-coded, so it tells you which co-ordinations are happening, which are pending, and shows you when extended co-ordination meetings have been rescheduled. This is all magnificent, but we rapidly discover that the information is false. It depends on humans updating the system in real time, and you have no way of knowing whether or not the relevant human has gone to lunch, fallen asleep or worse. For example, we have a co-ordination scheduled at 18:00, but the display tells us that our table is queued up, and that there are a couple of nations in front of us. Vesna points out that the organizers said that they would keep to schedule. We walk 50 metres to see, and sure enough our co-ordinators are ready to start on time.

July 18 First thing, Vesna and James co-ordinate problem 3. It goes well. We have two certain 7s, and some scraps. We are hoping for more credit than we get for these fragments, but the marks are fair.

In the middle of the day, we co-ordinate problem 6. Here we are claiming five 0s and one script which might be worth something if you believe in fairies. The co-ordinators do not. Nonetheless, they are so bored with handing out 0s that they keep us talking about the non-empty script.

Finally we must co-ordinate problem 4, a geometry problem so I will lead. We have three uncontroversial 7s, one stone cold 0, and two scripts worth talking about. We begin with Chris Bellin's script. You are supposed to discover and verify two possible triangles. There is the main case, and a side case which using some methods is harder to spot. Now our UNK1 has turned the problem into trigonometry, and has then introduced a classic sign error but pressed on. His subsequent calculation involves the same bits of algebraic cunning as the correct solution, so it is clear that, had he not made this algebraic slip, he would have found both solutions. Unfortunately he does not make a serious attempt to verify the solutions, so that loses him 2 marks. I can see what is coming. Using the new tradition of awarding significant credit to incorrect solutions, he is going to get a good score. The co-ordinators try to get me to say how much I think it is worth. 'Not a lot' is what I am thinking, but I persuade them to declare first. They say it is worth 4 points. I say that in my judgement it is worth 2 points, but agree that they have to be consistent, so we are willing to accept the 4 points.

July 19 We have the final jury meeting first thing in the morning. The leader of Pakistan makes a forlorn bid to challenge a mark awarded on one of his scripts, but unless the case is overwhelming, the jury always sides with the co-ordinators. The medal boundaries are quickly agreed, and there are no delicate judgements to make. Luke Betts UNK2 has fallen one mark short of a gold medal. Thus we have GSSSBB. Our position is level with Bulgaria and Hungary in 19th place. As usual the rank statistic is very sensitive for those countries in the *peloton*. If one member of our team had solved an extra problem, we would be on 164 points and in 13th place, just behind Italy. On the other hand, if one of our students had solved one question fewer, then on 150 points the United Kingdom would have been in 23rd position, just behind Australia. We are second in the Commonwealth behind Canada.

The chief co-ordinator gives a report on the exams and co-ordination. These days the IMO scripts are scanned and on permanent record, so if evidence of irregularities is found in the future, it will be possible to revisit and re-examine past scripts.

The IMO Advisory Board secretary John Webb announces the lists of names of people who have been nominated for various IMOAB positions. The actual elections will be held next year. He also explains that negotiations are in train for future IMOs. The next few are already set: 2010 Kazakhstan, 2011 Netherlands and 2012 Argentina. I will suppress further details since the information is not yet official, but it seems that we have excellent candidates to host IMOs in 2013, 2014 and 2015.

Our German hosts have inserted an extra day in the programme to celebrate the 50 years of the IMO. We are treated to a series of short lectures by luminaries from IMOs past. The full list of speakers is Béla Bollobás, Tim Gowers (both based in the UK), László Lovász, Stanislav Smirnov, Terence Tao and Jean-Christophe Yoccoz. The UK team know the charming young man László Lovász Jr. through our joint winter camps with the Hungarians. Father and son both have IMO Gold Medals.

Between lectures there are breaks, and the stars (including three Fields Medallists) sit on stools and chat to the students, many of whom are determined to gather autographs. I was reminded of the febrile atmosphere in IMO 2001 in Washington when the students treated Andrew Wiles as if he were Jagger in his pomp. I try sitting on a stool and it works. A queue forms. Now who shall I pretend to be?

Former UK leader and 2002 Jury Chair Adam McBride made a very welcome short visit to the IMO in the context of the anniversary celebrations. There are many old IMO friends who have made short visits, and it is a delight to see them all.

July 20 Today is the outing. I have a long standing and well grounded aversion to IMO excursions, especially those which involve boat trips. Who can forget the *Hell on the Potomac* at IMO 2001, or the *Waverley Steamer Ordeal* of 2002? For some strange reason (stupidity?) I decide to risk the boat trip to Wangerooge, a Frisian Island. These islands are close to the shore, and run from the Netherlands through Germany to Denmark. We have an early morning start, so I get some sleep on the bus. As we arrive at the coast, we see extraordinary numbers of wind turbines. The journey out into the Wadden Sea is punctuated by an announcement that a child is missing. My heart sinks but soon the news comes through that she is safe. There is a significant quantity of rain.

As we land, the weather improves a little. Lunch is being served in a multi-purpose hall from giant saucepans. Enough said. I make my way into town and sit next to some statues of seals. I then adjourn to a bar and drink a glass or three. The team are having officially sanctioned fun elsewhere, with the organizers laying on a beach Sudoku treasure hunt. I sit for a while staring at the sea to acquire the Wangerooge sunburn effect. This is not associated with dangerous exposure to UV-radiation, but rather depends on sand-blasting, as the grains of silica are blown against your tender skin by robust winds.

July 21 One feature of this IMO is that events keep being held in different places. The closing ceremony includes some excellent Beethoven, and the usual medal ceremony.

The compere has an extraordinary talent for saying not quite the same thing over and over, congratulating people for existing and so on. He really does it very well, but there is a difficult moment when he mentions 'The United Kingdom of England', an object rather akin to 'The United States of California' or the 'Federal Republic of Bremen'. Now, to an Englishman, this remark is of little consequence, but I know that Adam McBride, the Scottish national treasure, is in the hall. If he had any hair, it would be standing on end. I worry that we are about to witness a brutal scene from *Braveheart*.

It was sad that some competitors felt it appropriate to boo other students. Until now, the IMO has been free of negative political gestures, and I hope that this situation can be restored.

We returned to the Jacobs University Campus for a party in the evening. I am feeling rather exhausted, but stay around because of accurate rumours that I have won the *Microphone d'Or* again. This is the award for the most garrulous juror.

July 22 The journey home was straightforward for the UK team (although this seemed not to have been the case for the Irish team).

There are hundreds of UKMT volunteers whose work, directly and indirectly, supports the UK effort at the IMO. There is also the contribution of the administrators in our Leeds HQ, and our sponsors. We are assisted by various academic institutions, including Trinity College Cambridge, The University of Bath and Oundle School. We must also tip our hat to the Bolyai Society in Hungary and the Australian Mathematics Trust, sister organizations with which we run mathematics camps. Thanks to all concerned.

UKMT Mentoring Schemes (Administered by BMOS)

The UKMT Mentoring Schemes are now used in well over 300 schools as well as by a significant number of people who have enrolled individually. The aim is to provide stimulating and challenging questions for pupils to work on in addition to their normal school syllabus work. The schemes cater for pupils from Years 7 to 13 and we very much hope that they will give a glimpse of different areas of Mathematics and encourage youngsters to delve into the subject and see its rich diversity.

Each person is linked up with a mentor who can offer help, guidance and encouragement and they read and give feedback on the solutions offered by their mentees. At the Junior and Intermediate levels, we encourage teachers to mentor their own pupils because regular contact is important at this stage. At the Senior and Advanced levels, mentees tend to be mentored by undergraduates, postgraduates and teachers who are more familiar with problem-solving techniques, though of course any teacher who is willing to act as a mentor to their own pupils is warmly encouraged to do so. Anyone who is interested in either being a mentee, a mentor or using the sheets with their classes is welcome to register with Janet Clark who administers the schemes from the UKMT Leeds office. The e-mail address is mentoring@ukmt.org.uk .

There are four schemes, which run from October through to May. In each scheme a sheet of about eight graded problems is issued at the beginning of each month and just before the end of the month mentees submit to their mentor the solutions or partial solutions they have managed to achieve. These are then read and returned with helpful feedback and comments.

Junior Scheme

This has been brilliantly run for the sixth year by John Slater, who comes up with an abundance of new ideas and interesting problems. It caters for those of roughly Years 7 - 9 who have perhaps done well in the Junior Maths Challenge and are looking at Junior Olympiad papers. A few hints are given with the questions which aim to introduce pupils to problem-solving at an accessible level, though the later questions will usually be quite challenging. All pupils are currently mentored by their teachers and teachers are welcome to enrol in order to use the problem sheets with their classes. This is often a good way to stimulate the interest of a whole class, rather than just one or two individuals, though it is likely that only one or two will rise to producing good solutions to the later questions. Thanks are due to all teachers and others who have acted as mentors this year.

Intermediate Scheme

The questions are currently set by Richard Atkins, and Alan Slomson produces the solutions. The scheme is aimed at those approximately in Years 9 - 11, who have done well in the Intermediate Maths Challenge and are preparing for Intermediate Olympiad papers or who have attended one of the UKMT National Mathematics Summer Schools. There is quite a gradient in these problems, from some which can be approached without knowledge of any special techniques to others which require modular arithmetic, some knowledge of number theory and geometrical theorems etc. The aim is gradually to introduce these techniques through the year. Hopefully as mentees come across these they will ask questions or look at the internet to find out about these methods. Most pupils are mentored by their teachers, but some external mentors are available where necessary. An innovation this year has been the introduction of a Hints and Comments for Mentors sheet, which is designed to help busy mentors and those less familiar with the material. The point being that polished solutions are not necessarily the most helpful thing for giving hints; what is wanted is some idea of the possible ways of tackling the problem and the motivation behind the steps involved. We hope that this has been a helpful initiative. Thanks are due to all teachers who have acted as mentors, and to the external mentors: Anne Andrews, Mary Teresa Fyfe, Yi Feng, Vesna Kadelburg, Vcky Neale, Ian Slater, and Mark Taylor.

Senior Scheme

The questions were set again this year by André Rzym and the solutions produced by James Cranch. Both André and James have put a huge amount of time and energy into this scheme for several years which is much appreciated. This scheme is aimed approximately at those in Years 11 - 13 and the questions are set at quite a challenging level, aimed at those who are tackling BMO papers or who have outgrown the Intermediate scheme. Typically just two or three people at any school might enrol with this scheme and most of the mentors are undergraduates or postgraduates, though it is good to see that several teachers are keen to act as mentors at this level. Doing the questions is a stimulating experience for any teacher and in my view one of the best ways to add freshness and innovation to one's regular teaching. An important role of mentors at this level is to encourage their mentees because the questions are generally more taxing than anything they confront at A-level, and each problem solved is a distinct achievement which should give huge satisfaction. Thanks are due to all teachers involved and the external mentors: Anne Andrews, Brian Brooks, Chris Bryant, Miguel Carrion, Cong Chen, Tom Close, Owen Cotton-Barratt, James Cranch, Janet

Dangerfield, Julia Erhard, Ben Fairbairn, David Foster, Mary-Teresa Fyfe, James Gazet, Jeffrey Giansiracusa, Julian Gilbey, Saul Glasman, Victoria Gregson, Michael Griffiths, Ina Hughes, Michael Illing, Vinay Kathotia, André Kueh, Kate Land, James Lawrence, Jonathan Lee, Kelvin Lee, Charles Leedham-Green, Sam Maltby, Freddie Manners, Lilian Matthiesen, Oliver McFarlane, Tristan Melen, Gerry Netto, Peter Neumann, Jerome Ripp, Hannah Roberts, Julia Robson, AndréRzym, Imdad Sardharwalla, Peter Scott, Alexander Shannon, Jack Shotton, Paul Smith, Balazs Szendroi, Oliver Thomas, Madoc Troup, Damjan Vukcevic, James elham, Dominic Yeo and Alison Zhu.

Advanced Scheme

This scheme is aimed at UK IMO squad members and those who have outgrown the Senior scheme, the questions being very hard and mainly of interest to those who are aiming to at selection for the UK team in the annual International Mathematics Olympiad. This comprised 20 people this year and huge thanks are due to the select band of mentors who are able to cope with questions at this level: Robin Bhattacharyya, Paul Jefferys, Toby Kenney, Henry Liu, Tom Lovering, Joseph Myers and Martin Orr.

We are grateful for the support of Trinity College, Cambridge in allowing us to hold the Mentoring Conference in October and to our patrons Professors Imre Leader and Tim Gowers particularly for their lectures at the Mentoring Conference; to Janet Clark for the huge amount of work she has done in administering the schemes this year and helping them run smoothly and to all mentors and setters for their time and effort. We are grateful for several letters of appreciation which show how widely the problem sheets are used in schools and how much they are valued. It is always lovely to receive such letters – many thanks to those who were kind enough to write. For the first time, the annual Mentoring Conference is going to be held in Oxford this year on Saturday 24th October 2009 and we hope to see as many mentors as possible on that occasion.

Richard Atkins, Director of Mentoring

UKMT Team Maths Challenge 2009

Overview

The Team Maths Challenge (TMC) is a national maths competition which gives pupils the opportunity to participate in a wide range of maths activities and compete against other pupils from schools in their region. The TMC promotes team working, and unlike the Junior, Intermediate and Senior Challenges, students work in groups and are given practical tasks as well as theoretical problems to add another dimension to mathematics.

The TMC is designed for teams of four pupils in:

- Y8 & Y9 (England and Wales)
- S1 & S2 (Scotland)
- Y9 & Y10 (Northern Ireland)

with no more than two pupils from the older year group.

Sample TMC material is available to download from the UKMT website (www.ukmt.org.uk) for use in school and to help teachers to select a team to represent their school at the Regional Finals.

Report on the 2009 TMC

The seventh year of the TMC saw the competition continue to grow, with the number of Regional Finals increasing from 56 to 60 and a total of 1500 teams registering to take part (compared to 1429 last year) from which 1395 turned up to participate.

The CD-ROM of materials from the 2008 TMC was sent in September to all schools that participated in that year's competition and was also included in the general mailing of 2009 competition details and entry forms to schools in early October. As usual, full details of the competition, including Regional Final dates and venues (kept up-to-date to show availability of places) were also made available on the UKMT website, along with additional past materials for the use of schools in selecting and preparing their team of four. Participants from the 2008 TMC also received a copy of the winning poster from the 2008 National Final, originally created by St Thomas More RC High School and professionally reproduced by Andrew Jobbings.

Each team signed up to participate in one of 60 Regional Finals, held between late February and the middle of May at a widely-spread set of venues. Each Regional Final comprised four rounds which encouraged the teams to think mathematically in a variety of ways. The Group Round is the only round in which the whole team work together and they are faced with a set of ten challenging questions. In the Crossnumber the team splits into two pairs; one pair get the across clues and the other pair get the down clues. The two pairs then work independently to complete the Crossnumber using logic and deduction. For the Head-to-Head, a new activity called the Mini Relay (which had been piloted at previous National Finals) was rolled-out to the Regional Finals in 2009. In this new round, teams are paired up and compete against their opponents to be the first to correctly answer a series of questions, with each pair working on different questions and the solution of each question dependent on the previous answer. The final round of the day, the Relay, is a fast and furious race involving much movement to answer a series of questions in pairs. Each Regional Final was run by a regional lead coordinator with support from an assistant coordinator and, at some venues, other local helpers. The teachers who accompanied the teams were fully occupied too – they were involved in the delivery and marking of all the rounds.

TMC National Final

Winners from the 60 Regional Finals (including one tie for first place) plus 9 runners-up were invited to the National Final on 22nd June 2009, which was once again held at the Camden Centre in London. As in the Regional Finals there were 4 main rounds, but as usual the Group Round was replaced by the Group Circus (a similar round but with the addition of some practical materials for use in solving the questions) and the day began with the additional Poster Competition, which was judged and scored separately from the main event and for which the theme for 2009 was 'Tiling'.

The following schools participated at the National Final (a good mix between the state and independent sectors):

Altrincham Girls' Grammar School	Altrincham, Cheshire
Amery Hill School	Alton, Hampshire
Ashcroft Technology Academy	London
Bancrofts School	Woodford Green, Essex
Bedford School	Bedfordshire
Bishop's Stortford High School	Hertfordshire
Bournemouth School	Bournemouth
Bristol Grammar School	Clifton, Bristol
Caistor Grammar School	Lincolnshire

Caroline Chisholm School	Wootton, Northants
Cheadle Hulme School	Cheshire
City of London School (for Boys)	London
Colyton Grammar School	Colyford, Devon
Comberton Village College	Cambridge
Commonweal School	Swindon
Crypt School	Gloucester
Denny High School	Falkirk
Dr Challoner's Grammar School	Amersham, Buckinghamshire
Dragon School	Oxford
Durrington High School	Worthing, West Sussex
Emmanuel College	Gateshead, Tyne & Wear
Grange School	Hartford, Cheshire
Harrogate Grammar School	North Yorkshire
Heathfield Community College	Old Heathfield, East Sussex
Heckmondwike Grammar School	West Yorkshire
Highgate School	London
Ian Ramsey CE School	Stockton-on-Tees
Ivanhoe College	Ashby de la Zouch, Leicestershire
Judd School	Tonbridge, Kent
Kenilworth School	Warwickshire
King Edward VI Camp Hill Boys' School	Kings Heath, Birmingham
King Edward VI High School for Girls	Birmingham
King Edward's School	Birmingham
King's School	Peterborough
Lancaster Royal Grammar School	Lancaster
Lancing College	West Sussex
Linton Village College	Cambridge
Loughborough Grammar School	Leicestershire
Lumen Christi College	Derry, N Ireland
Manchester Grammar School	Manchester
Merchant Taylors' Girls' School	Crosby, Liverpool
Millfield School	Street, Somerset
Northgate High School	Ipswich, Suffolk
Norwich School	Norfolk
Nottingham High School	Nottingham

Penair School	Truro, Cornwall
Plymouth High School for Girls	Devon
Queen Elizabeth Grammar School	Penrith, Cumbria
Queen Elizabeth High School	Gainsborough, Lincolnshire
Queen Elizabeth's School	Barnet, Hertfordshire
Reading School	Berkshire
Red House School	Norton, Stockton-on-Tees
Reigate Grammar School	Surrey
Richmond School	North Yorkshire
Robert Gordon's College	Aberdeen
Royal Belfast Academical Institution	Belfast
Sheldon School	Chippenham, Wiltshire
Sir Roger Manwood's School	Sandwich, Kent
Southend High School for Girls	Southend-on-Sea, Essex
St John's College	Old St Mellons, Cardiff
St Olave's Grammar School	Orpington, Kent
St Paul's School	Barnes, London
Stewart's Melville College	Edinburgh
Tadcaster Grammar School	Tadcaster, North Yorkshire
The King's School	Worcester
Tiffin School	Kingston-upon-Thames, Surrey
Victoria College	St Helier, Jersey
Windermere St Anne's School	Windermere
Wolverhampton Girls' High School	West Midlands
Ysgol Friars	Bangor, Gwynedd

The International School of Aberdeen also qualified for the event by winning their Regional Final, but sadly could not participate due to their early end of term.

We were delighted to have in attendance David Acheson, who presented the prizes at the end of the day (including signed copies of his book '1089 and All That'), as well as Steve Loveday and Emma Watkins, representing our joint TMC sponsors Helix and Winton Capital Management respectively. We are also grateful to Arbelos for their sponsorship in providing additional prizes for the event and to UKMT volunteer Andrew Bell for capturing the day's excitement in his additional role as official photographer. Finally, as we are moving to a new, bigger venue for next year's National Final to accommodate the continued growth of the competition, we would like to thank the staff at the Camden Centre for their fantastic support and efficiency over the past few years.

We would like to congratulate the winning school, St Paul's School (London), who retain the title they shared as joint winners last year, and the winners of the Poster Competition, The King's School (Worcester).

As usual, thanks are due to a great number of people for ensuring another successful year of the TMC: the team of volunteers who generously give up their time to write, check and refine materials, run Regional Finals and readily carry out countless other jobs behind the scenes; the staff in the Maths Challenges office in Leeds for the way in which the competition is administered (particularly Nicky Bray who has responsibility for the central coordination of the competition, newly assisted by Jo Williams who joined the Leeds office in September 2008) and the team of packers for their efficient and precise preparation and packing of materials; the teachers who continue to support the competition and take part so willingly, some of whom also organise and host a Regional Final at their own school and, of course, the pupils who participate so enthusiastically in the competition at all levels.

For 2008-2009 the volunteers were as follows (members of the TMC Subtrust shown by *):

Anne Andrews, Ann Ault, Anne Baker, Martin Bailey, Bridget Ballantyne, Andrew Bell, Kerry Burnham, Keith Cadman, Alex Crews, Graeme de Sainte Croix, Geoffrey Dolamore, Sally-Jane Fell, Sheldon Fernandes, Jackie Fox, Roy Fraser, Mary Teresa Fyfe, Miyoba Habanyana, Peter Hall, Mark Harwood, Karl Hayward-Bradley, Terry Heard, Rita Holland, Sue Hughes, Sally Anne Huk, Claire Hunt, Pam Hunt*, Andrina Inglis, Andrew Jobbings, Nathan Keeling, Andy Kemp, Jacqui Lewis*, Simon Lewis, Tricia Lunel, Pat Lyden, Holly McLean, Hilary Monaghan, Mike Moon, Steve Mulligan*, Helen Mumby, Paul Murray, Peter Neumann*, Pauline Noble, Andy Parkinson, Martin Perkins*, Dennis Pinshon, Vivian Pinto, Stephen Power*, Jenny Ramsden, Mary Read, Nikki Shepherd, Alan Slomson, Anne Strong, Penny Thompson, Alex Voice, James Welham*, Helen Wigglesworth, Rosie Wiltshire.

Our thanks also go to additional contacts at schools and other host venues responsible for organising and helping with Regional Finals:

Graeme Addison, Morag Anderson, Martin Armstrong, Catherine Beater, Irene Bell, Helena Benzinski, Anna Bigland, Caroline Bowker, David

Bowyer, Nigel Brookes, Jane Chadwick, Amanda Clayton, Denise Cook, Andy Crabtree, Matt Curran, Alan Darlington, Colin Dixon, Elin Dupasquier, Patricia Eaton, Nadia El-Taha, Michael Evans, Christine Godfrey, Val Heward, Gary Higham, Lizzy Howes, Linsey Kemp, Eddie Latch, Sean Lawrence, Helen Martin, Rebecca Martin, Joanne McCloskey, Marijike Molenaar, Julie Mundy, Jayne Needham, Carolyn Osborne, Ally Ravenhill, Lois Rollings, Mick Rye, Gilbert Simmons, Judith Singleton, Hilary Sugden, Beth Sweet, Bryn Tailford, Anna Witcher, Mick Young.

The venues for the 2009 Regional Finals (some of which hosted two events) were:

Aberdeen	University of Aberdeen
Belfast	Stranmillis College
Berkshire	Furze Platt School, Maidenhead
Blackpool	Arnold School
Bradford	Bradford Grammar School
Bristol	Clifton College
Cambridge (2 events)	Centre for Mathematical Sciences, University of Cambridge
Cardiff	Howells School
Carlisle	The Richard Rose Morton Academy
Channel Islands	St Sampson's High School, Guernsey
Cheshire	The Grange School, Hartford
Cornwall	Penair School, Truro
Cumbria	Barrow in Furness Sixth Form College
Derbyshire	Swanwick Hall School
Derry	St Columb's College
Devon	Exmouth Community College
Doncaster	Danum School Technology College
Dorset	Corfe Hills School, Broadstone
Durham	College of St Hild & St Bede, Durham University
East Sussex	Robertsbridge Community School
Edinburgh	University of Edinburgh
Essex	Bancroft's School, Woodford Green
Glasgow	University of Strathclyde
Gloucester	Wycliffe College
Hampshire (2 events)	Lord Wandsworth College, Hook
Hertfordshire	Ashlyns School, Berkhamsted

Hertfordshire	Haberdashers' Aske's School for Girls, Elstree
Hull	Newland School for Girls
Kent	Hartsdown Technology College, Margate
Kent	Tonbridge Grammar School
Leeds	Lawnswood School
Leicestershire	Ratcliffe College
Liverpool	University of Liverpool
London, Central (2 events)	City of London School
London, North	Preston Manor High School, Wembley
London, Outer	St Olave's Grammar School, Orpington
London, South	Trinity School, Croydon
Manchester (2 events)	University of Manchester
Norfolk	Hamond High School, Swaffham
Northampton	Caroline Chisholm School
Northumberland	Knott Hall, Heddon-on-the-Wall
Oxford	University of Oxford
Peterborough	Oundle School
Plymouth	Plymouth Guildhall
Rugby	Rugby High School
Somerset	Ansford Community School, Castle Cary
Stockport	Poynton High School
Stockton-on-Tees	Yarm School
Suffolk	Framlingham College
Swindon	Wootton Bassett School
Warwick	Myton School
West Sussex	Great Walstead School, Lindfield
West Sussex	Lancing College
Wolverhampton (2 events)	Jennie Lee Centre
York	The Mount School

TMC Regional Finals Material

Each of the 60 Regional Finals held across the UK involved four rounds:

1. Group Round
2. Crossnumber
3. Head-to-Head
4. Relay Race

Group Round

Teams are given a set of 10 questions, which they should divide up among themselves so that they can answer, individually or in pairs, as many as possible in the allotted time (45 minutes).

Question 1

A tile is fixed to a wall and then painted with four different colours, one for each quarter. One way of doing this is

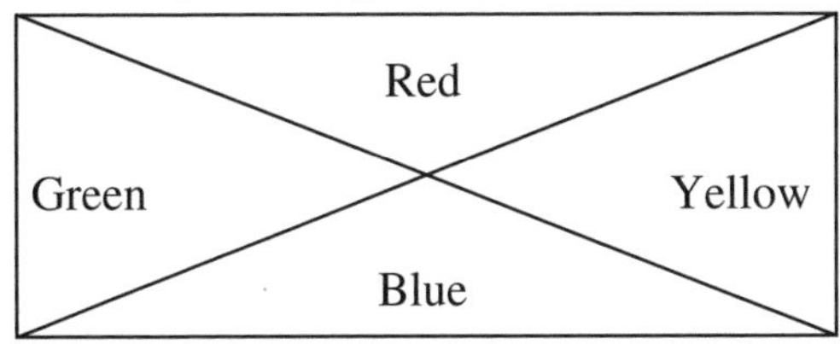

In how many **other** ways can the tile be painted?

Question 2

Sarah goes up a hill and then down again the same way. On the way up she averages 2 miles per hour. On the way down she averages 4 miles per hour. What is Sarah's average speed in miles per hour for the whole journey? Give an exact answer.

Question 3

The name Matilda is written repetitively like this:

MatildaMatildaMatildaMatilda……

What is the 1000th letter?

Question 4

The ten digits of a digital clock are shown below.

I have a 12 hour digital clock which shows the time, using four digits, on a piece of glass, so it can be seen from both sides. At what time between 3 o'clock and 10 o'clock does the time look the same from both sides?

Question 5

ABCD is a square; *BCGFE* is a regular pentagon, not overlapping the square. *AB* and *BE* are adjacent sides of a regular polygon. How many sides does this polygon have?

Question 6

Some students (fewer than 100) are having trouble lining up for a school production.

When they line up in 3s, two people are left over.

When they line up in 4s, three people are left over.

When they line up in 5s, four people are left over.

When they line up in 6s, five people are left over.

How many students are there in the group?

Question 7

The digits of Alberta's age are interchanged and 1 is added. The answer is half of Alberta's present age. How old is Alberta now?

Question 8

35 teenagers were asked what takeaways they liked to eat.

24 answered Chinese

16 answered Indian

10 answered pizza

None of the teenagers liked all three. All who liked pizza also liked Chinese and 9 of the Chinese fans didn't like either Indian or pizza.

If all the teenagers liked at least one, how many liked only Indian?

Question 9

12345 can be expressed as the sum of two primes in exactly one way. What is the larger of the two primes?

Question 10

Three squirrels, Steve, Keith and Benjamin, have spent all day collecting nuts. At the end of the day they are very tired and go to bed.

During the night, Steve wakes up and eats a nut. He then decides to take half of the remaining pile and hides it before going back to sleep.

Keith then wakes up. He too is hungry, so eats a nut. He also takes half of the remaining pile and hides it before going back to sleep.

Finally, Benjamin wakes up, eats a nut and hides half of the remaining pile.

In the morning, all of the squirrels share the remaining nuts equally between them and each goes off with four more nuts. Each squirrel then eats all the nuts he now has.

How many nuts has Steve eaten in total?

Crossnumber

Teams are divided into pairs, with one pair given the across clues and one pair given the down clues. Each pair answer as many questions as possible on the grid, showing their answers to the supervising teacher who either confirms or corrects them. The correct version is then shown to both pairs. Pairs only communicate through the supervisor, but they may make a request for particular clues to be solved. This round lasts up to 45 minutes.

1	■	2		3		■	4	■
5			■		■	6		7
	■	8	9	■	10		■	
11	12	■	13		■	14	15	
■		■		■	16	■		■
17		18	■	19		■	20	21
	■	22		■	23	24	■	
25	26		■	27	■	28		
■		■	29				■	

Across:

2. A power of two (4)
5. A prime factor of 12345 (3)
6. Six more than a multiple of 13 Across (3)
8. A cube number (2)
10. The product of the digits of 25 Across and also less than half of 23 Across (2)
11. The mean of 4 Down, 8 Across, 10 Across, 13 Across and 20 Across, and more than 3 Down (2)
13. A Fibonacci number (2)
14. A multiple of seven (3)
17. Eight less than a square number (3)
19. Seven less than 26 Down (2)
20. A number that is greater than 3 Down and less than 27 Down (2)
22. An even number which is the sum of a square and a triangle number in two different ways (2)
23. A prime number whose digits add up to five (2)
25. A square number and a multiple of five (3)
28. A multiple of 14 which includes a two and an eight amongst its digits (3)
29. Nine more than a power of 20 Across (4)

Down:

1. One hundred and ninety-five less than a square number (4)
2. One less than a Fibonacci number (3)
3. Highest common factor of 9 Down and 15 Down (2)
4. The sum of two powers of two (2)
6. (25 Across) percent of 24 Down (3)
7. The shortest side of a right-angled triangle whose longer sides are 24 Down and 25 Across (3)
9. The square of a triangle number and one less than a multiple of five (3)
12. A factor of 732, each of whose digits are powers of two (3)
15. Five multiplied by 3 Down (3)
16. An even square number and multiple of 8 Across (3)
17. A multiple of 17, the product of whose digits is a square number multiplied by seven (3)
18. A multiple of nine (3)

21. A power of 21 (4)
24. A factor of 360 (3)
26. Seven more than 19 Across (2)
27. A cube number (2)

Head-to-Head

Teams are divided into pairs, with one pair given Questions 1 and 3 (along with the record sheet on which to record their answers) and the other pair given Questions 2 and 4. The first pair work on Question 1 and then pass their answer to the other pair who use it to help them answer Question 2, for which they can first carry out some preparatory work. This continues with the second pair passing the answer to Question 2 back to the first pair and so on until a full set of answers is presented for marking.

Each team is paired up with another team for this activity and bonus points are awarded to the first team in each pair to present a correct set of answers before their opponents. Six of these mini relays are attempted in the time given.

A1 Write down the value of

$$(4^2 + 5^2) \times 7^2$$

A2 *T is the number that you will receive.*

At which number will the minute hand of a clock be pointing $T + 1$ minutes after midnight?

A3 *T is the number that you will receive.*

John has three sticks that he has formed into a triangle. The length of each stick is a whole number of centimetres.

One of the sticks is $(T + 1)$ cm long and another is $(T - 1)$ cm long.

How many different lengths could John's third stick be?

A4 *T is the number that you will receive.*

A polygon-based pyramid has T faces. How many edges does the pyramid have?

B1 Write down the value of

$$\frac{2^6 + 3^5 - 4^4 + 5^3 - 6^2}{7^1 \times 8^0}$$

B2 *T is the number that you will receive.*

Write down the answer to the following:

$$\left(\frac{5}{2} \times \frac{13}{5} \times \frac{T}{3} \times \frac{1}{5} \times \frac{7}{2} \times \frac{5}{14}\right) - \left(\frac{6}{5} \times \frac{15}{8} \times \frac{T}{3} \times \frac{5}{6} \times \frac{1}{3} \times \frac{1}{5}\right)$$

B3 *T is the number that you will receive.*

Mark can run at 12 km/h. Holly can run $20T$ metres in 45 seconds.

In a 3200m race what is the difference, in minutes, in their finishing times?

B4 *T is the number that you will receive.*

Five numbers have the following properties:

The median of the numbers is T;
The mode of the numbers is 2;
The mean of the numbers is 5;
The range of the numbers is $2T$.

Write down the product of the five numbers.

C1 Write down the value of

$$\frac{1 + 2 - (-3) - (4 - 5) - (6 - 7 - 8)}{16 - 15 - 14 + 13 + 12 - 11 + 10 - 9}$$

C2 *T is the number that you will receive.*

A red die and a blue die numbered from 1 to 6 are both rolled and the scores added together.
Find the number of ways of scoring more than T.

C3 *T is the number that you will receive.*

A cylinder with base radius T cm and height 12 cm is full of paint. The paint is poured into some smaller cylinders of base radius 6 cm and height T cm.

How many of these smaller cylinders can be **completely** filled with the paint?

C4 *T is the number that you will receive.*

Write down the lowest common multiple of $12(T - 1)$ and $9(T + 1)$.

D1 Write down the value of

$$\frac{(8^2 - 6^2)(4^2 - 2^2)}{(4^2 - 3^2)(2^2 - 1^2)}$$

D2 *T is the number that you will receive.*

The value of T is a square number less than 50. Write down the number of factors of T.

D3 *T is the number that you will receive.*

We define the factorial of the number n to be

$$n! = n \times (n - 1) \times (n - 2) \times \ldots \times 3 \times 2 \times 1.$$

Write down the value of $\dfrac{(T + 1)!}{20}$.

D4 *T is the number that you will receive.*

John drives at T metres per second around a circular track. Kevin drives at $(2T - 30)$ metres per second around the same track. They start together.

When John finishes his 15th lap, on which lap is Kevin?

E1 Calculate the number of sides of a polygon with internal angles summing to 2880°.

E2 *T is the number that you will receive.*

The diagram shows three isosceles triangles (the unequal sides form a straight line which is the base of the diagram). All angles are measured in degrees.

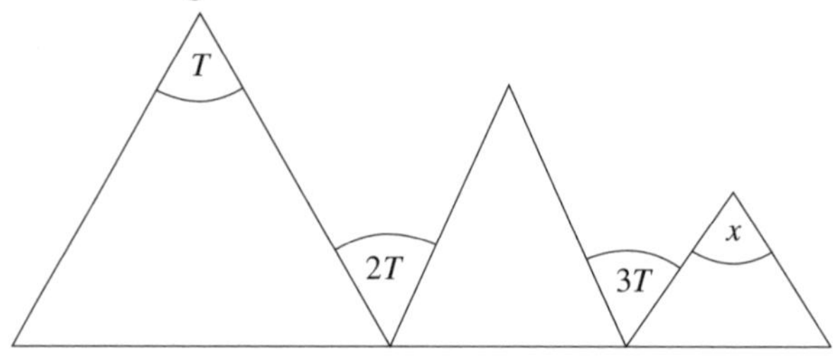

Find the value of x.

E3 *T is the number that you will receive.*

Each term in a sequence of numbers differs from the previous one by the same number. The first term is T and the 10th term is $2T$.

Write down the 12th term.

E4 *T is the number that you will receive.*

A cuboid with volume T cm^3 has sides with lengths x cm, $(x + 1)$ cm and $(x + 2)$ cm, where x is an integer.

Find the total length, in cm, of all the edges.

F1 The digits from 1 to 9 can be placed once each into the boxes to make the four equations (three horizontal and one vertical) all true. One digit has been filled in to help you. What digit must be placed in the middle box?

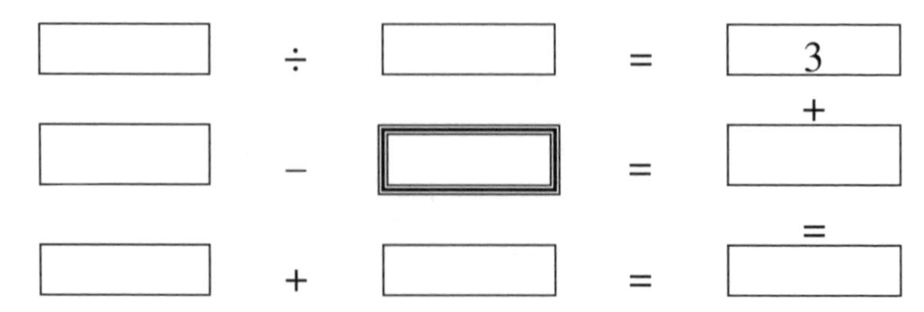

F2 *T is the number that you will receive.*

Write down the value of

$$5\left(\frac{T}{2} + \frac{T}{3} - \frac{T}{4} - \frac{T}{5} + \frac{T}{6}\right)$$

F3 *T is the number that you will receive.*

Write down the value of x in this pair of simultaneous equations:

$$x + y = T$$

$$5x - 3y = 7$$

F4 *T is the number that you will receive.*

Calculate the difference between the sum of the first T square numbers and the sum of the first T triangular numbers.

Relay Race

The aim here is to have a speed competition with teams working in pairs to answer alternate questions. Each team is divided into two pairs, with each pair seated at a different desk away from the other pair and their supervising teacher. This round lasts up to 45 minutes.

One member of Pair A from a team collects question A1 from the supervising teacher and returns to his/her partner to answer the question together. When the pair are certain that they have answered the question, the runner returns to the front and submits their answer. If it is correct, the runner is given question B1 to give to the other pair (Pair B) from their team. If it is incorrect, Pair A then have another go at answering the question, then the runner returns to the front to receive question B1 to deliver to pair B. (Pair A can only have one extra attempt.) The runner then returns, empty handed, to his/her partner. Pair B answer question B1 and a runner from this pair brings the answer to the front, as above, then takes question A2 to Pair A. Pair A answer question A2, return it to the front, collect question B2 for the other pair and so on until all questions are answered or time runs out. Thus the A pairs answer only A questions and the B pairs answer only B questions. Only one pair from a team should be working on a question at any time and each pair must work independently of the other.

A1 Calculate $\frac{6}{49} - \frac{5}{41}$.

A2 The speed of light is 3×10^8 metres per second. The sun is 150 million kilometres away from the earth.

How many seconds does it take light to reach the earth from the sun?

A3 There are 24 students in my form, 13 girls (one called Josie) and 11 boys (one called James). I choose *at random* one boy and one girl. What is the probability that James and Josie are chosen?

A4 On a recent school trip I had to pay for the train tickets. Our first group consisted of 3 adults and 12 children and cost £75. The second group consisted of 2 adults and 9 children and cost £54. There were no special offers or group rates. How much would a group of 1 adult and 5 children cost?

A5 With my cold tap on full I can fill my bath in 4 minutes, with my hot tap on full I can fill my bath in 6 minutes. If I pull the plug out of a full bath then it empties in 3 minutes. If I have both taps on full and the plug out how long will it take to fill the bath?

A6 What is the area of the shape shown below? Give your answer in terms of π.

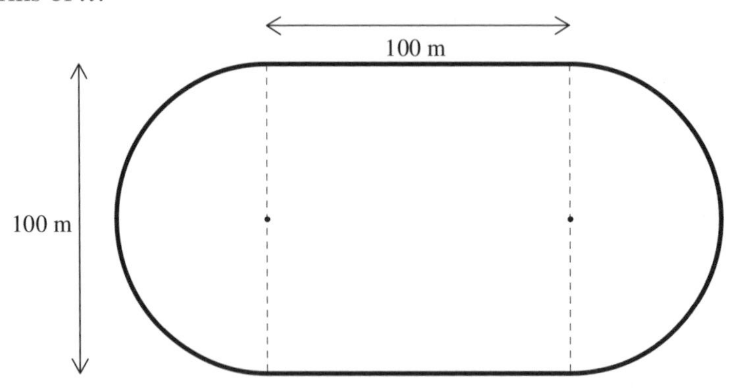

A7 What is the total of the numbers between 20 and 30 which are neither prime numbers nor multiples of 3 or 4?

A8 The first four numbers in a constantly increasing sequence are 7, 12, 17 and 22. What is the 20th number in the sequence?

A9 An arrow is drawn on a set of axes with the point at (3,1) and the other end at (2,4).
After a rotation of 90° clockwise the point is at (4,2) and the other end is at (7,3). What are the coordinates of the centre of rotation?

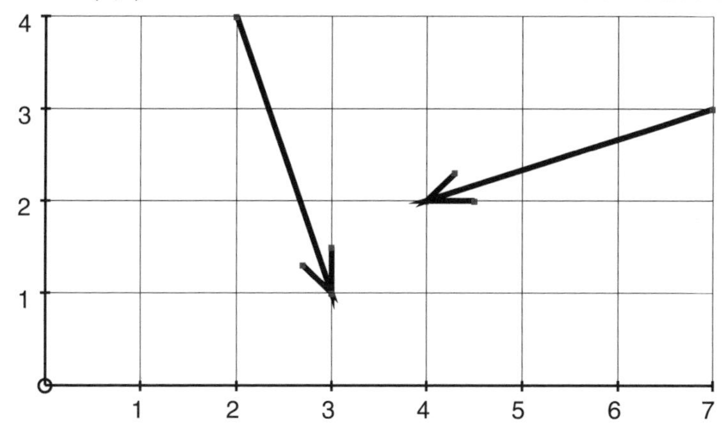

A10 What is the size of the smallest angle in this triangle?

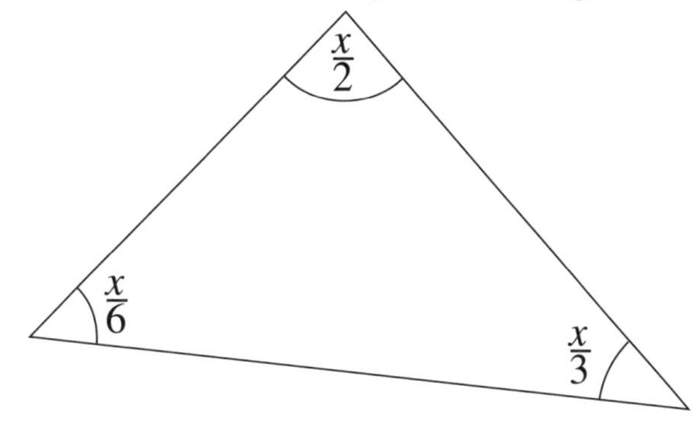

A11 What is the length of the diagonal of a rectangular field measuring 500m by 1200m?

A12 What is the median of the odd integers from 1 to 99 (inclusive)?

A13 Kepler was a mathematician and astronomer who lived around 400 years ago. His third law says that the square of the orbital period of a planet is equal to the cube of the distance from the sun, if the distance is measured in 'astronomical units' (AU) and the time in years. Jupiter is 5AU from the sun. What is the orbital period of Jupiter (to the nearest year)?

A14 I have an unfair die that has probability $\frac{1}{2}$ of landing on a six, with all the other numbers equally likely. If the die is thrown twice then what is the probability of obtaining a total score of 10?

A15 Some computers measure time by keeping count of the number of seconds that have passed since the beginning of 1970. At midnight at the start of the 1st of February 2009 this number was 1233446400.
Calculate what this number was on the 13th of February at 23:31 and 30 seconds.

B1 Calculate the total of 20% of 75 and $\frac{7}{8}$ of 128.

B2 To the nearest foot, what is the longest direct shot that can be played on a snooker table 12 feet long and 6 feet wide?

B3 A set of five cards has the numbers 1, 2, 3, 4 and 5 written on them, one number on each card. Two cards are chosen, without replacing the first, and their numbers are totalled. How many different totals are there?

B4 What is the mean of the whole numbers from 2001 to 2020?

B5 On a good day I can run to school at 15 km/h and it takes me 15 minutes. On a bad day it takes me 25 minutes. How fast do I run on a bad day?

B6 Bob thinks of two numbers. Twice the smaller added to four times the larger is 44. The sum of the numbers is 14. What is the smaller of the two numbers?

B7 What is the size of the largest angle in this quadrilateral?

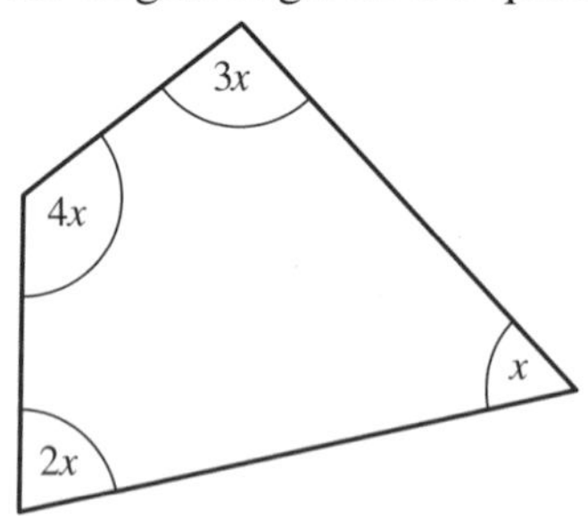

B8 A slug in my garden travels 18 m from the lettuce plants to the spinach plants in 4 hours. What is its average speed in cm/s?

B9 Our school swimming pool needs a complete change of water. It measures 8 m by 20 m and is, on average, 1.5 m deep. Our pump can remove water at the rate of 50 litres per second. How many **minutes** will it take to empty the pool? [1 m^3 = 1000 litres]

B10 The first four numbers in a constantly increasing sequence are 103, 117, 131, 145.

What is the total of the first seven numbers in the sequence?

B11 The number of pets owned by a group of pupils is shown in the table.

Number of pets	1	2	3	4
Frequency	10	8	7	x

If the median number of pets is 2, what is the largest possible value of x?

B12 What is the volume of a cylindrical tin of soup? It is 11 cm tall and has a base radius of 7cm. Give your answer in terms of π.

B13 What is the total of the whole numbers from 1 to 30 which are *neither* multiples of 2 *nor* square numbers?

B14 A bag contains five green counters, two yellow counters and three purple counters. Five more counters are added, and the probability of a counter taken out at random being yellow becomes $\frac{1}{3}$. How many of the extra counters were yellow?

B15 What is the chance of throwing HHT (in that order) when I throw one fair coin three times?

At the National Final, the Group Round was replaced by the Group Circus and the Head-to-Head featured four mini relays as opposed to six at the Regional Finals.

Group Circus

Teams move around a number of stations (ten at the 2009 National Final) to tackle a variety of activities, some of which involve practical materials.

Station 1

Harry, Christine and Betty are packing 36 boxes of chocolates. It would take Harry and Christine 2 hours to pack the boxes; Harry and Betty would take 3 hours; Christine and Betty would take 4 hours.
How many boxes does Christine pack in one hour?

Station 2

The boxes show the product of the circles at either end of the line. Given that a, b and c are positive, find c.

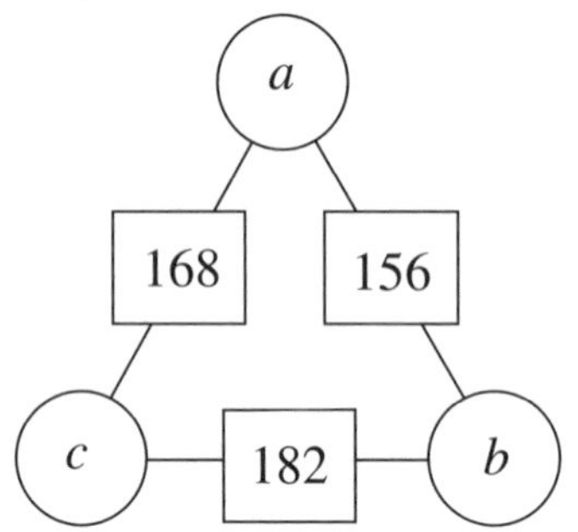

Station 3

Here is a **sheet** of a newspaper.
Each sheet has four pages.
How many sheets are there altogether?

Station 4

The diagram shows three touching circles each of radius 5 cm and a line which touches two of them.

Find the total length of the perimeter of the two shaded shapes.

Leave π in your answer.

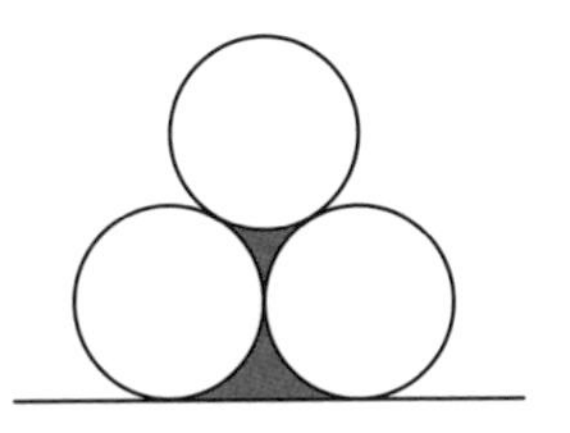

Station 5

Using each of the number cards 1 to 9 once and once only, find two whole numbers one of which is double the other.

Station 6

A pair of dice is thrown and the score is obtained by finding the product of the two numbers on top of the dice when they land.

In five throws of both dice: the second score is 5 more than the first; the third score is 6 less than the second; the fourth score is 11 more than the third; the fifth score is 8 less than the fourth.

What was the score for each of these five throws?

Station 7

Each different letter in the multiplication below stands for a different digit. Identical letters stand for the same digit. Work out the value which each letter represents.

$$\begin{array}{r} E\ G\ G \\ E\ \times \\ \hline J\ A\ M \end{array}$$

Station 8

When you add the square of Thomas's age to Lauren's age the total is 62.
When you add the square of Lauren's age to Thomas's age the total is 176.
How old are Thomas and Lauren?

Station 9

Find the number:

it's less than 100;
it's one more than a multiple of 3;
exactly one of its digits is prime;
if you reverse its digits, you get a prime;
it has exactly four factors;
the sum of its digits is prime;
if you multiply it by 5, the answer is greater than 100.

Station 10

Put the nine number cards

$$\left(1,\ 2,\ 3,\ 6,\ \tfrac{1}{6},\ \tfrac{1}{3},\ \tfrac{1}{2},\ \tfrac{2}{3},\ \tfrac{3}{2}\right)$$

onto a square 3 by 3 grid so that each card occupies one square and the product of every row, column and diagonal is equal to 1.

Crossnumber

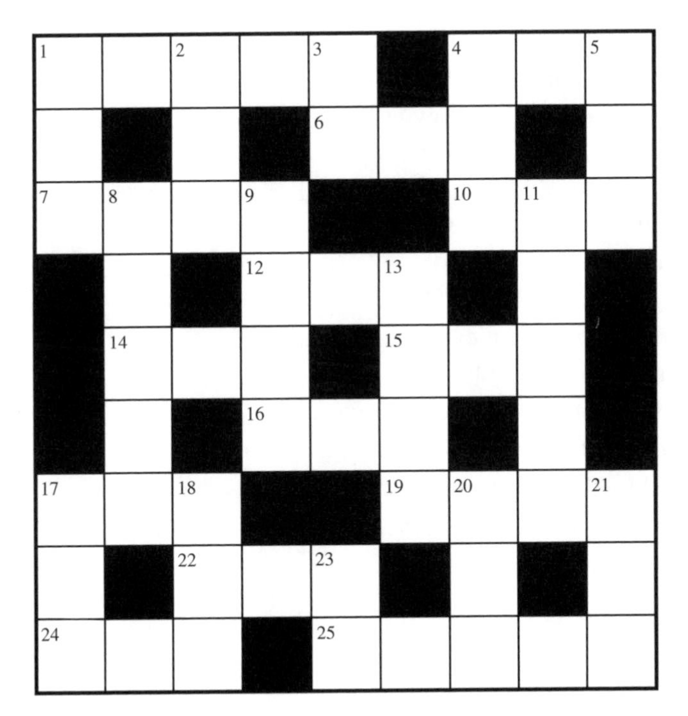

Across:

1. A square number cubed (5)
4. Eight less than 5 Down (3)
6. One less than a multiple of seven (3)
7. A prime factor of 20902 (4)
10. A number whose digits successively decrease by one (3)
12. Sixty percent of 20 Down (3)
14. A multiple of seven (3)
15. A multiple of three whose digits have an even sum (3)
16. A square number squared (3)
17. A prime number which is one less than a multiple of six (3)
19. Eleven more than a cube number (4)
22. A number all of whose digits are the same (3)
24. A number which leaves a remainder of eleven when divided by thirteen (3)
25. The square of a prime number. The sum of the digits of this square is ten (5)

Down:

1. A number with an odd number of factors (3)
2. Four less than a triangle number (3)
3. The square root of 9 Down (2)
4. A factor of 12 Across (3)
5. The longest side of a right-angled triangle whose shorter sides are 3 Down and 4 Across (3)
8. A Fibonacci number (5)
9. The square of 3 Down (4)
11. Three more than an even cube number (5)
13. A prime factor of 34567 (4)
17. The mean of 10 Across, 16 Across, 18 Down, 20 Down and 21 Down (3)
18. A power of eighteen (3)
20. Two less than 22 Across (3)
21. The digits of 12 Across reversed (3)
23. A multiple of twenty-three (2)

Head-to-Head

A1 A grandfather clock strikes once at 1 o'clock, twice at 2 o'clock etc.

Calculate one-thirteenth of the total number of strikes per day.

A2 *T is the number that you will receive.*

Ten identical tiles, each measuring (T − 7) cm by 3 cm, are arranged in the pattern shown.

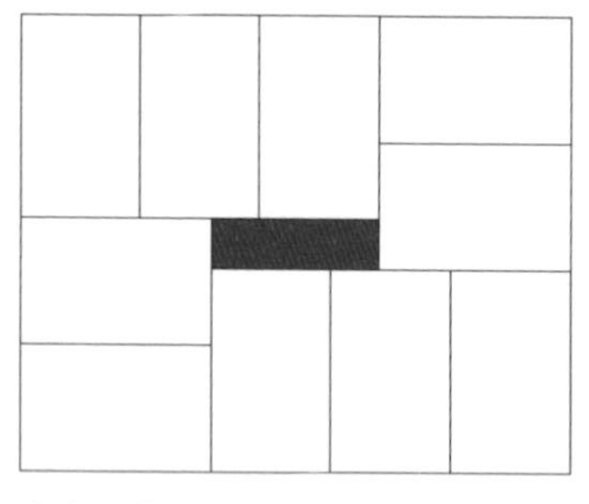

Calculate the area of the shaded section, giving your answer in cm^2.

A3 *T is the number that you will receive.*

Points D, E and F on the sides of the triangle ABC form an equilateral triangle.

Given that $\angle BED = 81°$, $\angle BAC = (9T + 40)°$ and $\angle CDF = 80°$, calculate $\angle DCF$.

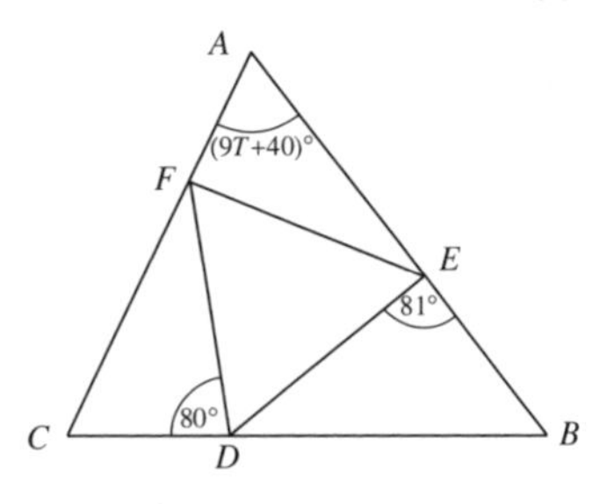

A4 *T is the number that you will receive.*

Calculate the value of

$$2\left(\frac{T}{5} + \frac{T}{9} \times \frac{2T}{3}\right) \div \frac{T}{15}$$

B1 The nth term of the sequence below is $pn^2 + qn$, where p and q are integers.

$$2,\ 6,\ 12,\ 20,\ 30,\ \ldots$$

Calculate the value of:

$$\frac{15^{\text{th}}\text{ term}}{(10^{\text{th}}\text{ term}) + 10}$$

B2 *T is the number that you will receive.*

The diagram shows three concentric circles. The radii of the circles are T units, $2T$ units and $4T$ units.

The value of the **unshaded** area can be written in the form $a\pi$ units^2, where a is an integer.

Work out the value of a.

B3 *T is the number that you will receive.*

The prime factorisation of 1500 can be written in the form

$$2^{\left(2a - \frac{T}{13}\right)} \times b \times c^{\left(8d - \frac{T}{4}\right)}.$$

Work out the value of $\dfrac{ad}{b}$.

B4 *T is the number that you will receive.*

A plot of land with its associated measurements (in metres) is shown.
The length of the perimeter of the plot is 148 metres.
Calculate the value of x.

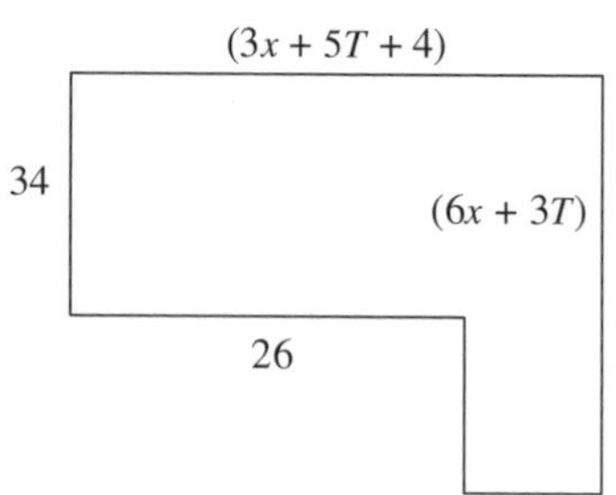

C1 Eight standard cubical dice (numbered 1 to 6, with spots totalling 7 on opposite faces) are stacked in a $2 \times 2 \times 2$ formation on a table.
What is the largest number of spots that could possibly be seen from a single viewpoint?

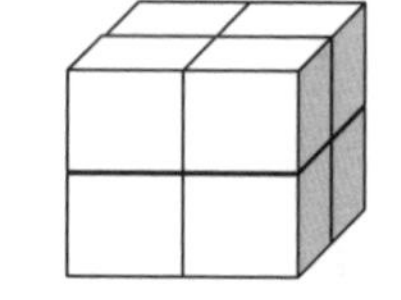

C2 *T is the number that you will receive.*

A bag contains $T - 3$ wooden blocks, painted one of three colours.

If I pick out one block at random, the probability of picking a red block is twice that of picking a green block, and the probability of picking a green block is twice that of picking a blue block.

How many blue blocks are there?

C3 *T is the number that you will receive.*

Slugs have a head but no legs.

Ravens have 2 legs and a head.

Spiders have 8 legs and a head.

Colin's creepy collection contains only these types of creatures and has 8 heads and $4T$ legs.

How many slugs does he have?

C4 *T is the number that you will receive.*

Gertie the Gorilla has 100 bananas numbered from 1 to 100.

For her starter, she eats all bananas that have a multiple of 9 on them.

For her main course, she eats all bananas with a multiple of $3T$ on them.

How many bananas are left?

D1 A rectangle sits inside a regular pentagon, sharing one edge, as shown in the diagram.

How many degrees is angle x?

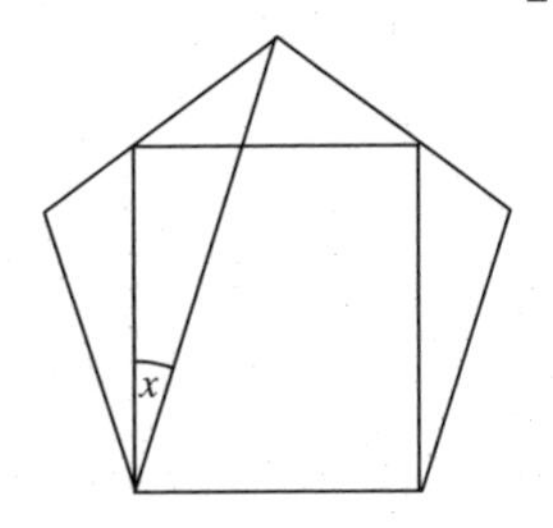

D2 *T is the number that you will receive.*

Anthony and Bertrand have 12 marbles between them.

Bertrand and Charlie have T marbles between them.

Charlie and Anthony have $3T - 40$ marbles between them.

How many marbles does Charlie have?

D3 *T is the number that you will receive.*

Gabby and her sister Harriet go from home to the shop and back.

Gabby runs to the shop at 3 m/s, spends 100 seconds there, and runs back at 5 m/s.

Harriet cycles to the shop at T m/s, spends 3 minutes there, and cycles back at 6 m/s.

They leave and arrive at the same time.

How many metres away is the shop?

D4 *T is the number that you will receive.*

Rip Van Winkle's younger brother falls asleep on the first of January 2008, a leap year. He wakes up T days later.

On which date does he wake up?

Give your answer in the form dd/mm/yy.

Relay Race

A1 I think of a number. When I divide 24 by one more than my number I get the same answer as when I divide 12 by one less than my number.

What is my number?

A2 A circle has the same area as this trapezium. What is the radius of the circle, to the nearest cm?

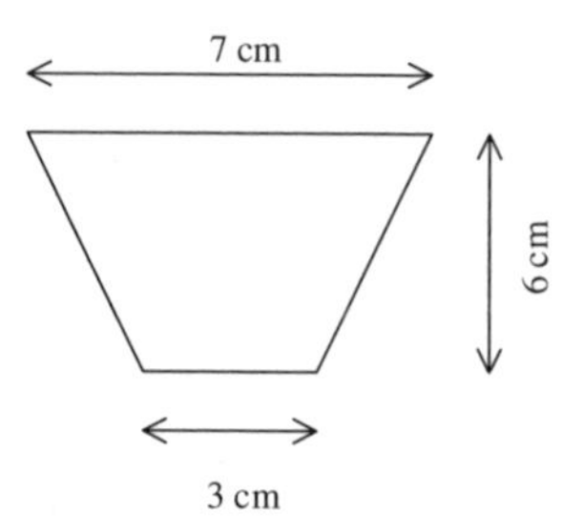

A3 Two of the angles of an isosceles triangle are $x°$ and $(x + 15)°$. What is the difference between the two possible values of x?

A4 Place cubes A, B and C in increasing order of size.

Cube A has volume 130 cm^3.

Cube B has volume 27 cubic inches.

Cube C has surface area 147 cm^2.

A5 A metal sphere with radius 6 cm has a spherical space, radius 3 cm, hollowed out inside it. Giving your answer as a multiple of π, what is the volume of metal?

Note: the volume of a sphere with radius r is given by $\frac{4}{3}\pi r^3$.

A6 This frequency table showing the number of pets of each child is not complete, the frequency for 5 pets has not yet been given.
The mean number of pets is 3.
How many children have 5 pets?

Number of pets	0	1	2	3	4	5
Frequency	6	7	4	9	10	

A7 Find the length h marked in the diagram.

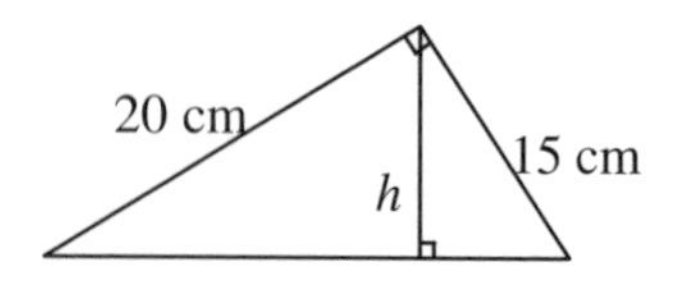

A8 A patriotic Italian baker is making muffins, each of which must use all three of the colours in the Italian flag. He has red, white and green paper cases, red and white icing, and red and green sweets to go on top.
How many different-looking muffins can he make?

A9 Calculate the value of $5x^2 + 2x + 0.4$ when $x = 1.2$.

A10 The Highway Code gives the stopping distance of a car driving at V mph as V feet for the driver to think and then $\frac{V^2}{20}$ feet to brake.

What is the stopping distance for a car being driven at 35 mph?

A11 The n th term of a sequence is equal to $(n + a)^2 + 2a$, where a is a positive whole number. The 5th term is 89.
Calculate the 3rd term.

A12 I think of a number. When I add five to my number and square the result I get twenty more than when I subtract five from my number and square the result. What was my number?

A13 Find the area of the trapezium.

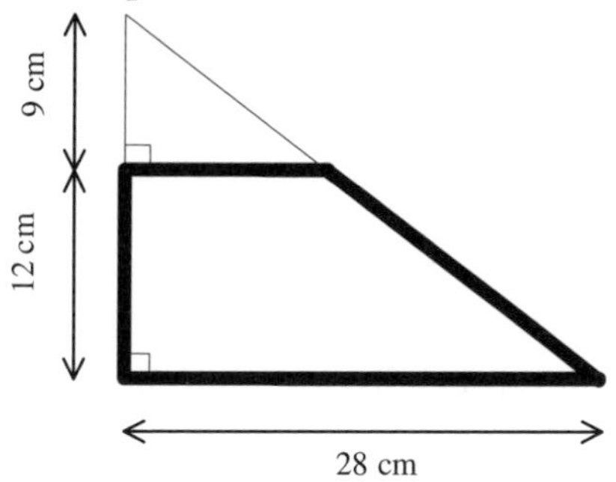

A14 Calculate 35% of 45% of £5500.

A15 Sir Arthur Conan Doyle was born 150 years ago. In *Silver Blaze*, Sherlock Holmes calculates a train's speed from how many telegraph posts they pass in one minute. The posts are 55 yards apart and they go from post 1 to post 33 in one minute. How fast are they going in miles per hour?

[1 mile = 1760 yards]

B1 Two of the angles of an isosceles triangle are $x°$ and $(x + 18)°$. What is the difference between the two possible values of x?

B2 Calculate 4% of 40% of 400 kg.

B3 Place cubes A, B and C in increasing order of size.

Cube A has surface area 147 cm^2.

Cube B has volume 216 cubic inches.

Cube C has volume 130 cm^3.

B4 A semicircle has the same area as this trapezium. What is the radius of the semicircle, to the nearest cm?

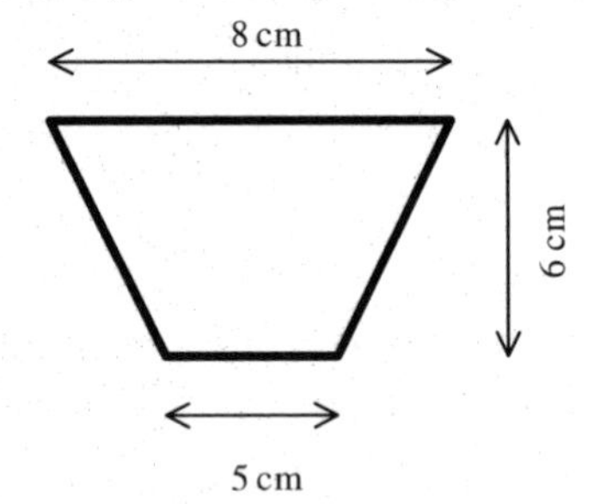

B5 I think of a number. When I divide 72 by one more than my number I get the same answer as when I divide 54 by one less than my number.
What is my number?

B6 Four cards have the numbers 1, 2, 4 and 5 written on them.
The cards are shuffled and two cards are selected at random.
What is the probability that the total of the cards chosen is 6?

[*Give your answer as a fraction in its lowest terms.*]

B7 The nth term of a sequence is equal to $(n + a)^2 + 3a$, where a is a positive whole number. The 3rd term is 145.
Find the value of the 2nd term.

B8 A metal sphere with radius 9 cm has a spherical space, radius 6 cm, hollowed out inside it. Giving your answer as a multiple of π, what is the volume of metal?

Note: the volume of a sphere with radius r is given by $\frac{4}{3}\pi r^3$.

B9 Calculate the value of $3x^2 + 5x + 1.87$ when $x = 1.1$.

B10 The cuboid and right-angled triangular prism shown below have the same volume. Find the height of the prism.

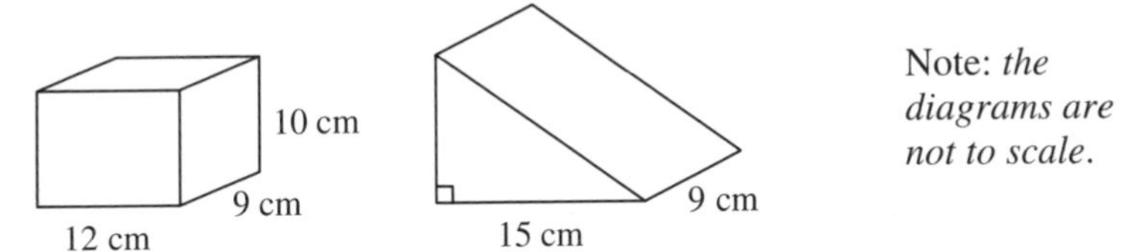

B11 Find the length h marked in the diagram.

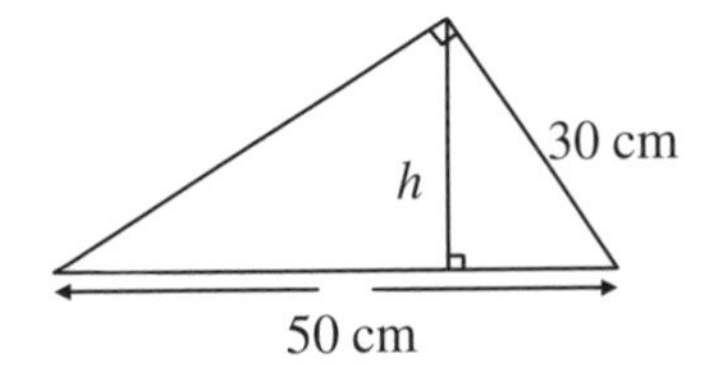

B12 A mathematical granny is knitting hats for her grandchildren from leftover wool. She has shiny wool in red, blue, yellow and green, fluffy wool in green, blue and red, and bobbly wool in yellow and blue. How many different hats can she make using three different colours and all three wool types in each hat?

B13 Sir Arthur Conan Doyle was born 150 years ago. In *Silver Blaze*, Sherlock Holmes calculates a train's speed from how many telegraph posts they pass in one minute. When going at 72 miles per hour they go from post 1 to post 34 in one minute. How many yards apart are the posts?
[1 mile = 1760 yards]

B14 Find the length of the perimeter of the smaller triangle.

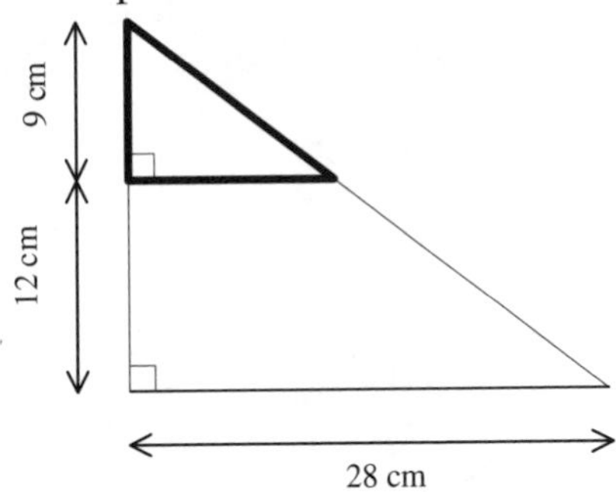

B15 The Highway Code gives the stopping distance of a car driving at V mph as V feet for the driver to think and then $\dfrac{V^2}{20}$ feet to brake.

If the stopping distance is 240 feet what is the speed of the car?

Solutions from the Regional Finals

Group Round

	Solution
1	Number of other ways a tile can be painted is 23
2	Average speed $2\frac{2}{3}$ (or $\frac{8}{3}$) miles per hour
3	1000th letter is d
4	Time 0 5 2 0
5	Number of sides is 20
6	Number of students is 59
7	Alberta's age is 52
8	Number of teenagers is 11
9	Larger of two primes whose sum is 12345 is 12343
10	Number of nuts is 56

Crossnumber

<table>
<tr><td>(1) 9</td><td>■</td><td>(2) 2</td><td>0</td><td>(3) 4</td><td>8</td><td>■</td><td>(4) 6</td><td>■</td></tr>
<tr><td>(5) 8</td><td>2</td><td>3</td><td>■</td><td>9</td><td>■</td><td>(6) 4</td><td>5</td><td>(7) 1</td></tr>
<tr><td>0</td><td>■</td><td>(8) 2</td><td>(9) 7</td><td>■</td><td>(10) 2</td><td>0</td><td>■</td><td>3</td></tr>
<tr><td>(11) 5</td><td>(12) 2</td><td>■</td><td>(13) 8</td><td>9</td><td>■</td><td>(14) 5</td><td>(15) 2</td><td>5</td></tr>
<tr><td>■</td><td>4</td><td>■</td><td>4</td><td>■</td><td>(16) 3</td><td>■</td><td>4</td><td>■</td></tr>
<tr><td>(17) 2</td><td>4</td><td>(18) 8</td><td>■</td><td>(19) 2</td><td>2</td><td>■</td><td>(20) 5</td><td>(21) 9</td></tr>
<tr><td>7</td><td>■</td><td>(22) 5</td><td>2</td><td>■</td><td>(23) 4</td><td>(24) 1</td><td>■</td><td>2</td></tr>
<tr><td>(25) 2</td><td>(26) 2</td><td>5</td><td>■</td><td>(27) 6</td><td>■</td><td>(28) 8</td><td>2</td><td>6</td></tr>
<tr><td>■</td><td>9</td><td>■</td><td>(29) 3</td><td>4</td><td>9</td><td>0</td><td>■</td><td>1</td></tr>
</table>

Head-to-Head

A1	**2009**
A2	**6**
A3	**9**
A4	**16**

B1	**20**
B2	**10**
B3	**4**
B4	**1120**

C1	**8**
C2	**10**
C3	**3**
C4	**72**

D1	**16**
D2	**5**
D3	**36**
D4	**18**

E1	**18**
E2	**54**
E3	**120**
E4	**60**

F1	**4**
F2	**11**
F3	**5**
F4	**20**

Relay Race

A1 $\frac{1}{2009}$
A2 500 seconds
A3 $\frac{1}{143}$
A4 £29
A5 12 minutes
A6 $10000 + 2500\pi$ m^2
A7 73
A8 102
A9 (4, 1)
A10 30°
A11 1300 m
A12 50
A13 11 years
A14 $\frac{11}{100}$ or 0.11
A15 1234567890

B1 127
B2 13 feet
B3 7
B4 2010.5
B5 9 km/h
B6 6
B7 144°
B8 0.125 or $\frac{1}{8}$ cm/s
B9 80 minutes
B10 1015
B11 10
B12 539π cm^2
B13 190
B14 3
B15 $\frac{1}{8}$

Solutions from the National Final

Group Circus

1 $7\frac{1}{2}$

2 $c = 14$

3 17 sheets

4 $10 + 10\pi$

5 (*any one of*):
(6729, 13458), (6792, 13584), (6927, 13854), (7269, 14538),
(7293, 14586), (7329, 14658), (7692, 15384), (7923, 15846),
(7932, 15864), (9267, 18534), (9273, 18546), (9327, 18654)

6 (*in this order*): 10, 15, 9, 20, 12

7 E = 2, G = 8, J = 5, A = 7, M = 6

8 Thomas: 7; Lauren: 13

9 34

10 One answer is:
(seven others are possible
by rotation & reflection)

2	$\frac{1}{6}$	3
$\frac{3}{2}$	1	$\frac{2}{3}$
$\frac{1}{3}$	6	$\frac{1}{2}$

Crossnumber

[1] 1	5	[2] 6	2	[3] 5	■	[4] 1	9	[5] 2
2	■	9	■	[6] 6	4	3	■	0
[7] 1	[8] 4	9	[9] 3	■	■	[10] 2	[11] 1	0
■	6	■	[12] 1	3	[13] 2	■	3	■
■	[14] 3	4	3	■	[15] 6	4	8	■
■	6	■	[16] 6	2	5	■	2	■
[17] 3	8	[18] 3	■	■	[19] 9	[20] 2	7	[21] 2
2	■	[22] 2	2	[23] 2	■	2	■	3
[24] 2	8	4	■	[25] 3	2	0	4	1

Head-to-Head

A1	**12**
A2	**4**
A3	**45**
A4	**106**

C1	**66**
C2	**9**
C3	**2**
C4	**78**

B1	**2**
B2	**52**
B3	**2**
B4	**6**

D1	**18**
D2	**10**
D3	**300**
D4	**27/10/08**

Relay Race

A1 3

A2 3 (cm)

A3 5

A4 C A B

A5 252π (cm^3)

A6 13

A7 12 (cm)

A8 3

A9 10

A10 96.25 (ft)

A11 57

A12 1

A13 240 (cm^2)

A14 £866.25

A15 60 (mph)

B1 6

B2 6.4 (kg)

B3 A C B

B4 5 (cm)

B5 7

B6 $\frac{1}{3}$

B7 124

B8 684π (cm^3)

B9 11

B10 16 (cm)

B11 24 (cm)

B12 10

B13 64 (yards)

B14 36 (cm)

B15 60 (mph)

UKMT and Further Maths Network Senior Team Maths Challenge 2009

Following the highly successful pilot Senior Team Maths Challenge of 2007-08, a fully-fledged competition took place in 2008-09 with 51 Regional Finals held across the United Kingdom (and one in the Channel Islands). The competition was run in collaboration with the Further Mathematics Network and their time and effort contributed greatly to its smooth running and success. In all, almost 900 teams of four competed, the students being chosen in the main from Years 11, 12 and 13 with at most two from Year 13. The culmination of the competition was the National Final in London with the title of National Champions going to Westminster School.

The 2008-09 Senior Team Challenge followed a similar pattern to the pilot competition with three Rounds: the Group Round consisting of ten questions to be answered by the team in 40 minutes; the Crossnumber where one pair has the Across clues and the other pair has the Down clues; the Mini-Relay which has sets of four linked questions that, in a change for this year, were answered by pairs of students rather than individuals. This change to the rules was made to emphasize the fact that this is a team competition and that co-operation and team-work are essential for success.

Exactly the same structure was used for the National Final in February except that in addition a Poster Competition was completed as the first event. Teams had to answer questions inspired by two sets of interlinking ring patterns spotted by Dr Peter Neumann in a church in Paris. This round did not count for the overall competition, but the work of the top three teams has been turned into a professionally produced poster that will be sent to all the schools that took part in the competition.

Unfortunately the National Final was due to be held in the middle of the national transport paralysis caused by snow in February and had to be postponed at very short notice. Luckily the Camden Centre was able to offer us the same day the following week and the UKMT Office in Leeds moved mountains to ensure that a smooth transition was brought about. In the end only two of the sixty invited teams were unable to make the rearranged National Final. The event was wonderful to watch, with 232 competitors working with enthusiasm and energy throughout the day. Westminster School, the eventual winners, were presented with their prize by writer and broadcaster Simon Singh.

As with any UKMT competition, thanks must be given to all the volunteers who wrote questions, acted as checkers for the materials produced, ran Regional Finals alongside FMNetwork Managers and who helped on the day at the National Final.

The writers: Kerry Burnham, Tony Cheslett, David Crawford, Alex Crews, Sheldon Fernandes, Karen Fogden, Mark Harwood, Sally Anne Huk, Richard Lissaman, Becky Lovelock, Holly McLean, Dennis Pinshon, Penny Thompson and James Welham.

The checkers: Martin Perkins, Jenny Ramsden and John Silvester.

The UKMT representatives who ran Regional Finals or who helped at the National Final: Ann Ault, Martin Bailey, Anne Baker, Kerry Burnham, Keith Cadman, Mary Teresa Fyfe, Peter Hall, Paul Harper, Terry Heard, Rita Holland, Sally Anne Huk, Pam Hunt, Nathan Keeling, Andy Kemp, Jacqui Lewis, Simon Lewis, Pat Lyden, Helen Mumby, Peter Neumann, Martin Perkins, Dennis Pinshon, Jenny Ramsden, John Slater, Alan Slomson, Penny Thompson, James Welham and Rosie Wiltshire.

The Senior Team Maths Challenge can now claim to be a major national mathematical competition with a prestigious title at stake. I do hope that more and more schools and colleges will compete in and enjoy this event in the coming years.

Stephen Power, Lead Volunteer Senior Team Maths Challenge

The following pages contain much of the material which was used in both the Regional Rounds and the National Final.

Regional Group Round

1 When $10^{30} - 90$ is written in full, what is the sum of the digits?

2 In the diagram $ABDE$ is a parallelogram, ABC is a straight line, $AB = x$ cm and $BC = y$ cm. If the area of triangle BCD is Q cm^2, what is the area of the parallelogram?

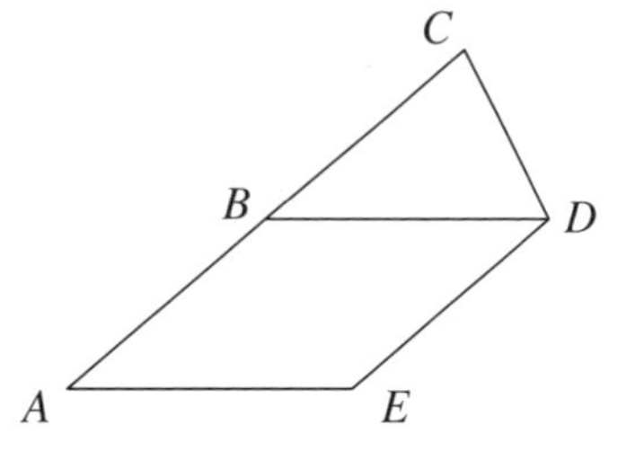

3 How many positive whole numbers less than 100 have exactly 4 positive factors?

4 Factorise $120x^2 + 97x - 84$.

5 A researcher is sent to a certain address where he knows the house-owner has three daughters. Part of the conversation was:

Researcher: "How old are your daughters"

House-owner (and amateur Mathematician): "The product of their ages is 36 and the sum of their ages equals this house number."

The house-owner pointed to the number on the front door.

Researcher: "You haven't given me enough information."

House-owner: "My oldest daughter is a lot older than her sisters."

The researcher is then able to work out the ages of the daughters.

What are the ages of the daughters?

6 Solve $2^{8 + 6x + x^2} = \dfrac{2008}{2^8 - 5}$.

7 $PQRS$ is a rectangle in which $PQ = 2QR$.

Point E is such that PQE is an equilateral triangle which overlaps rectangle $PQRS$.

M is the mid-point of EQ.

Find the size of angle QMR.

8 Three touching circles have centres P, Q and R as shown. Find the diameters of these three circles if $PQ = 9$, $PR = 7$ and $QR = 5$.

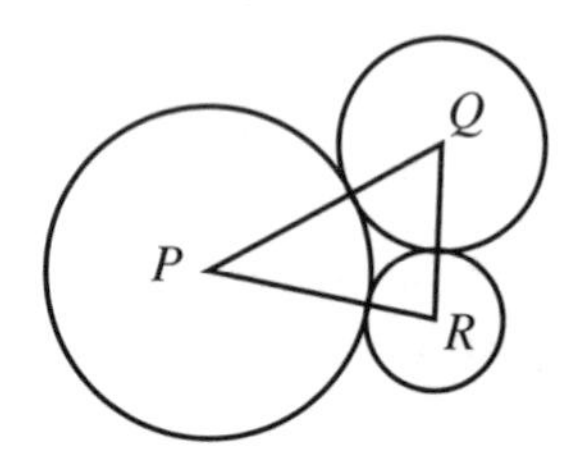

(diagram not to scale)

9 The centres of the faces of a cube of side $2a$ are joined to create a regular octahedron. What fraction of the volume of the cube does the octahedron occupy?

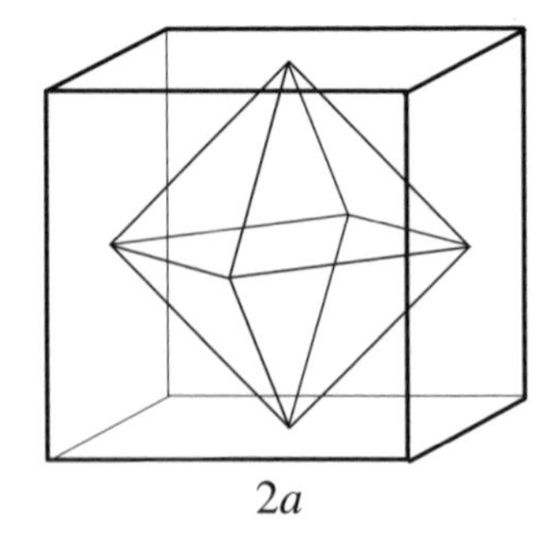

10 The sum of 101 consecutive positive integers is p^3 where p is a prime number.

What is the smallest of the 101 integers?

Regional Final Crossnumber Round

Across

1 $p^3 - p^2 - 3$ where p is a prime number
3 Half the product of the distinct prime factors of 12 Across
4 x where $x^2 - 40x + 144 = 0$
6 Mean of 1 Across, 8 Across and 9 Across
8 Sum of the prime factors of 15 Down
9 A triangle number squared
12 7 Down times 2 Down minus twice 1 Down
14 Multiple of both the square root of 4 Across and 7 Down
16 Twice a Fibonacci number
18 8 Across plus a multiple of 10 Down but not divisible by four
20 27 Across minus 7 Down
22 To the nearest whole number, the result of twice 11 Down divided by 1 Down
23 The difference between 25 Across and 23 Across is 2 Down
25 see 23 Across
26 20 Across plus the smallest difference between 27 Across and a Fibonacci number
27 A cube

Down

1 $p^2 + 2(p - 7)$ where p is a prime number
2 Exterior angle in degrees of a regular polygon
3 Multiple of 1 Down
5 One more than a multiple of four and one less than a multiple of three
7 Four more than a triangle number, two less than a square number
10 Twice a Fibonacci number
11 One more than the difference between 5 Down and 15 Down
12 Half the lowest common multiple of 6 Across and 8 Across
13 Number where consecutive digits differ by two
15 Product of two consecutive primes, its digit product being less than its digit sum
17 $x^2 + 2x + 2$ where x is an integer
19 Eight more than a multiple of eleven
20 Product of one sixth of 24 Down and one more than one sixth of 24 Down
21 Multiple of 7 Down
22 Number whose digit sum is equal to the highest common factor of 4 Across and 8 Across
24 Two thirds of a square number 24

Regional Mini-relay

A1 Solve the simultaneous equations:

$$2x + 5y - 2z = 4$$
$$7x - y + 2z = 13$$
$$9x - 4y = 1$$

Write down the value of $\dfrac{z^2 - yx}{2}$.

A2 T is the number that you will receive
The expression $\dfrac{T - 4}{x + 1} + \dfrac{Tx}{2x^2 + 7x + 5}$ can be written in the form $\dfrac{px + q}{2x^2 + 7x + 5}$.
Write down the value of p.

A3 T is the number that you will receive

The ratio of the volumes of these two similar cuboids, shown similarly situated, is 64:1.

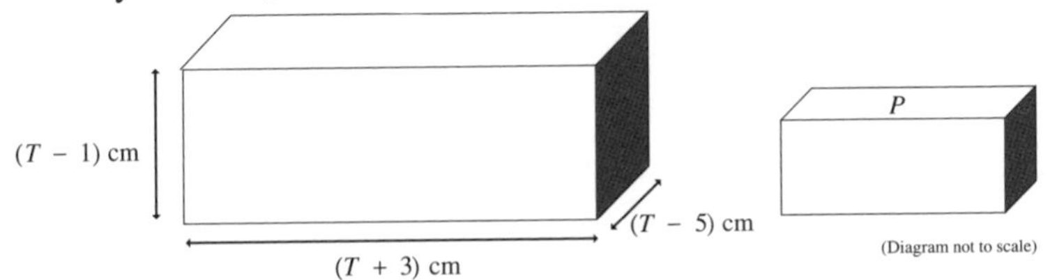

Calculate the perimeter of face P.

A4 T is the number that you will receive

A solid is formed by joining a right circular cone with base of radius 3 cm, to a hemisphere of radius 3 cm, as shown. The cone has a slant height of $(T - 7)$ cm. Calculate the volume of the solid in terms of π.

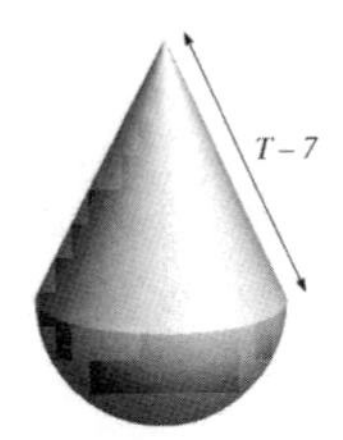

B1 Given that

$$125 = 5^{4x+1}$$

calculate the value of x.

B2 T is the number that you will receive

The equation $(2^{2x}) - 5(2^x) + 4 = 0$ has two solutions, a and b. Using the substitution $y = 2^x$, or otherwise, calculate $T(a + b)$.

B3 T is the number that you will receive

Let $x = \dfrac{2\sqrt{3} + T}{T} \div \dfrac{T}{2\sqrt{3} - T}$.

Calculate the value of x.

B4 T is the number that you will receive

Let $A = \sqrt{11T} + \sqrt{75} - T\sqrt{12}$.

A can be written in the form $a + b\sqrt{c}$, where a, b and c are integers.

Write A in the form $a + b\sqrt{c}$.

C1 $2y + x + 4 = 0$ is the equation of the line L_1

$y + 5x = 2$ is the equation of the line L_2

$y = ax + b$ is the equation of the line L_3

The line L_3 passes through the y-intercept of L_1 and the x-intercept of L_2.

Calculate ab.

C2 T is the number that you will receive

The coordinates $\left(T, \frac{T}{2}\right)$, $\left(0, \frac{T}{10}\right)$, $\left(0, \frac{-T}{10}\right)$ and $(T, 0)$ give the vertices of a quadrilateral.

Calculate the area of this quadrilateral.

C3 T is the number that you will receive

The graphs with equations $y = 2x^2 + x + T$ and $y = 6x + 33$ intersect at two points, (x_1, x_2) and (x_2, y_2).

Calculate the difference between x_1 and x_2.

C4 T is the number that you will receive

The circle $x^2 + y^2 + 8Tx - 6Ty - 8 = 0$ intersects the line $y = 2x$ at points (x_1, y_1) and (x_2, y_2).

Calculate $x_1 + x_2$.

D1 The digits of 2008 can be arranged in different orders, for example 0208.

In how many different orders can these digits be arranged?

D2 T is the number that you will receive

A combination lock has $(T \div 3)$ digits, where each digit is one of 0-9. Burglar Bill attempts every possible combination in sequence.

It takes him 2 seconds to try each combination.

Calculate, to the nearest hour, the longest time it could take him to open the safe.

D3 T is the number that you will receive

Worthington-upon-Mud has a tug-of-war squad of 10 men. A team of $(T + 2)$ men is needed for their next event.

How many different teams could be selected?

D4 T is the number that you will receive

$(T \div 5)$ people are in a room.

Everyone shakes everyone else's hand once.

Calculate the total number of handshakes.

E1 Triangle ABC has a right-angle at A. Semicircles are drawn with BA, AC and BC as diameters as shown. Given that $AC = 8$ and $BC = 10$, write down the value of one third of the total shaded area.

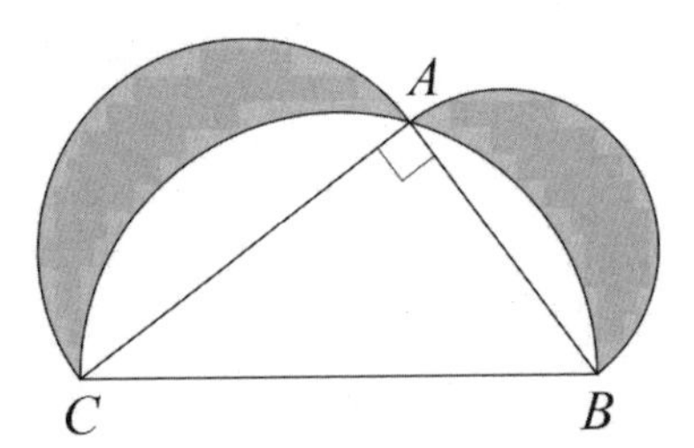

E2 T is the number that you will receive

The value of $\dfrac{T}{3 - \sqrt{5}}$ can be expressed in the form $a + b\sqrt{5}$, where a and b are integers.

Write down the value of $8(a - b)$.

E3 T is the number that you will receive

A parallelogram $ABCD$ is such that

$\angle DAB = (2w - 70)^\circ$, $\angle BCD = (w + 30)^\circ$ and

$\angle ABC = \angle CDA = (x + T)^\circ$.

Write down the value of $x + 6$.

E4 T is the number that you will receive

The angles of a certain hexagon form an arithmetic sequence with common difference $\frac{1}{2}T$.

Write down the size, in degrees, of the smallest angle of the hexagon.

F1 Write down the value of

$$\frac{48}{\sqrt{16^{\frac{3}{2}}}} - 3^{\frac{1}{2}}\left(\sqrt{\frac{4 + \sqrt{4}}{2}}\right).$$

F2 T is the number that you will receive

A cylinder of radius 4 cm and height $(T + 6)$ cm has the same volume as a different cylinder of radius $(4 + y)$ cm and height $(T - 2)$ cm.

Calculate the value of y.

F3 T is the number that you will receive

Given that

$$(T + 16)c + 7d = 4$$
$$d + e = 20$$
$$e + f = 36$$
$$f + 5c = 15$$

find the value of c.

F4 T is the number that you will receive

In the diagram, all angles are measured in degrees. Write down the value of x.

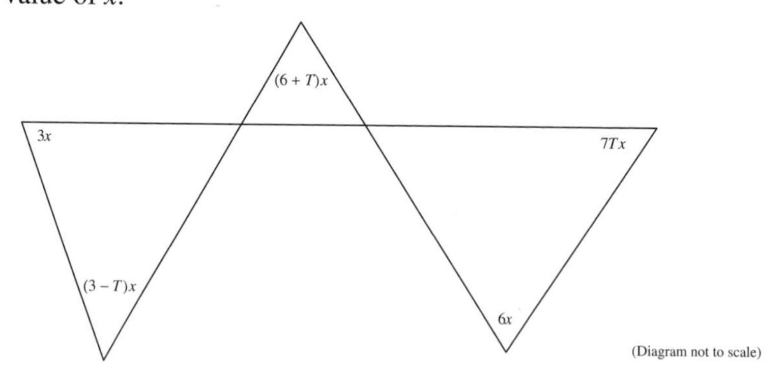

(Diagram not to scale)

Regional Final Answers

Group round answers

1. Sum of digits	253
2. Area of parallelogram	$\frac{2Qx}{y}$ cm^2
3. Number of numbers	32
4. Factorised quadratic	$(3x + 4)(40x - 21)$
5. Ages of daughters (in any order):	2, 2, 9
6. Values of x:	$-1, -5$
7. Angle QMR	75°
8. Diameters of the circles (in any order):	3, 7, 11
9. Fraction of the volume of the cube	$\frac{1}{6}$
10. Smallest of the 101 integers	10151

Crossnumber: Completed grid

[1] 2	9	[2] 1	■	[3] 2	7	3	■	[4] 3	[5] 6
1	■	[6] 2	5	4	■	■	[7] 1	■	4
■	[8] 3	0	■	3	■	■	[9] 4	[10] 4	1
[11] 4	■	■	[12] 1	6	3	[13] 8		6	
2	■	■	9	■	■	[14] 6	7	6	[15] 2
[16] 1	[17] 2	2	0	■	■	4	■	■	2
■	9	■	[18] 5	6	[19] 2	2	■	■	1
[20] 2	0	[21] 2	■	■	2	■	[22] 4	0	■
7	■	8	■	■	[23] 1	4	0	■	[24] 9
[25] 2	0	■	[26] 2	1	9	■	[27] 2	1	6

Mini-relay answers

	A	B	C	D	E	F
1	7	$\frac{1}{2}$	−10	12	8	3
2	13	1	35	6	32	8
3	12	11	1.5	45	45	−1
4	30π	$11 - 47\sqrt{3}$	1.2 or $\frac{6}{5}$	36	36	12

National Final Group Round

1 What is the ratio of the area of a square inscribed in a semicircle to the area of a square inscribed in the whole circle?

2 $N = 10 \times 9 \times 8 \times 7 \times 6 \times 5 \times 4 \times 3 \times 2 \times 1$

How many positive factors does N have?

3 A 3 by 4 rectangle is folded along one of its diagonals to form the pentagon $ABCDE$, as shown. Calculate the perimeter of this pentagon.

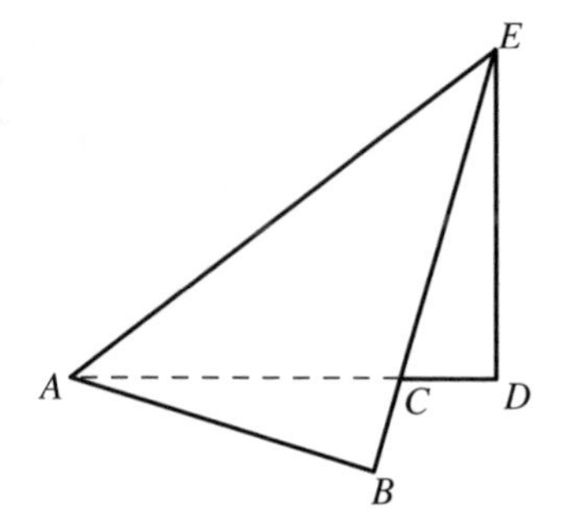

4 Six dots are arranged on the page so that they form the vertices of two adjacent squares. Three of these dots are chosen at random and joined with straight lines. What is the probability that a right-angled triangle will be formed?

5 The number

$$(10^2 - 8^2)(9^2 - 7^2)(8^2 - 6^2)(7^2 - 5^2)(6^2 - 4^2)(5^2 - 3^2)(4^2 - 2^2)(3^2 - 1^2)$$

can be written in the form $k \times 2^n$, where k and n are positive integers. What are the values of k and n?

6 Put a single digit in each of the six squares shown, with no repetitions, so that the two columns, reading downwards, each contain a three-digit perfect square, and the middle two rows, reading across, each contain a two-digit perfect square. What is the sum of the six digits used?

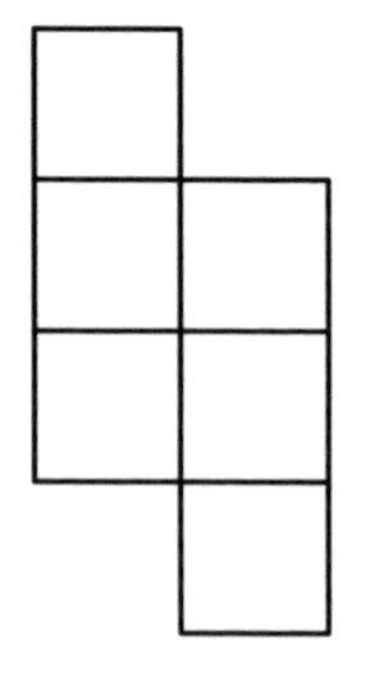

7 M is the smallest positive integer which has the property that, for $n = 2, 3, 4, 5, 6, 7, 8, 9$ and 10, the remainder when M is divided by n is $n - 1$.

What is the value of M ?

8 A club with x members is organized into four committees in accordance with the following rules:

1) Each member belongs to two and only two committees.
2) Each pair of committees has one and only one member in common.

What is the value of x?

9 Three students (Tony, Becky and Jenny) are doing some surveying work on a piece of level ground and are currently standing at points T, B and J respectively.

Jenny says to Becky, "I've noticed that the mean of our distances from Tony is the same as the distance between us."

Becky replied, "Yes, and the cosine of the angle BJT is equal to $\frac{TB}{TJ}$."

At that point, Tony said, "Ah, now I can work out the numerical value of cos BJT."

What is it?

10 In southern Iraq, during an excavation of the ancient city of Ur, a set of dice was found. Each of these dice was the shape of a regular tetrahedron with one of the vertices marked with a dot. If three of these dice are thrown the score is the number of marked vertices that appear at the top. What is the probability that the total score on two consecutive throws of the three dice is 2?

National Final Crossnumber Round

	1	2		3		4			
5				6					7
		8				9	10		
11	12				13				
			14	15			16	17	
18		19		20					
							21		22
23			24		25				
			26						
	27				28				

Across

1 p^{p-3} where p is prime

4 16 Across + 14 Across – 27 Across + half the difference of 13 Down and 15 Down

6 Product of two consecutive integers

8 Odd multiple of eight, the highest common factor of 8 Across and 18 Across is two

9 The sum of 3 Down, 4 Across and twice 1 Across

11 Palindrome, the square of whose digit sum is equal to four times its digit product

14 27 Across minus a multiple of thirteen

16 x^4 where x is an integer

18 Multiple of three

20 Half the product of two consecutive Fibonacci numbers

21 Divisible by three but not nine

23 Two more than 28 Across minus 7 Down

25 21 Across plus 4 Down

26 Multiple of thirteen

27 16 Across + 11 Across

28 One more than the cube of a prime number

Down

2 One third the product of two consecutive Fibonacci numbers
3 Triangle number
4 Square
5 One more than a square and three less than a cube
7 Two more than 28 Across minus 23 Across
10 Five less than a triangle number
12 Multiple of 3 Down, not divisible by five or nine
13 Twice the digit product plus half the digit sum of 15 Down
15 Product of two consecutive primes
17 2^{n+1} where n is an even integer
18 $[1 \times 2 \times 3 \times \ldots \times n] - [1 \times 2 \times 3 \times \ldots \times (n - 1)]$ where n is an integer
19 Prime three less than a multiple of eleven
21 The mean of 17 Down, 19 Down and 21 Down is one more than 1 Across
22 Palindrome which is twice a number one less than a multiple of twelve
24 Digit sum of 24 Down is a multiple of six
25 Multiple of half 10 Down

National Final Mini-relay

A1 Five perfect squares have a mean of 59, a median of 4 and a mode of 1. The second largest of the five numbers is a two digit number 'ab'. What is the value of $a - b$?

A2 T is the number that you will receive.
Calculate the maximum possible volume of the cuboid shown, as x varies.

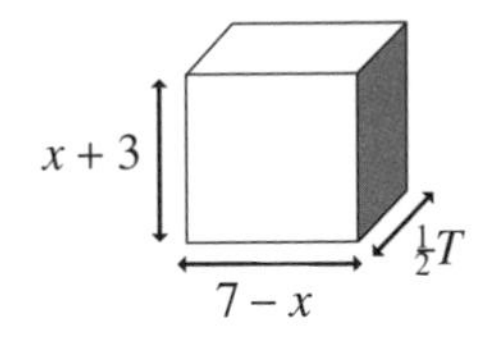

A3 T is the number that you will receive.
Prism A has a cross-sectional area of T cm^2.
Cuboid B has the same volume as prism A.
Cuboid B has a square base and a height of 3 cm.
Calculate the surface area of the cuboid.

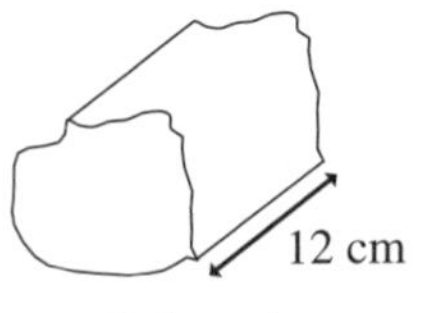

Prism A

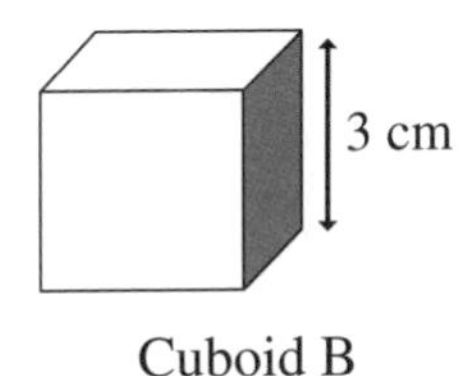

Cuboid B

A4 T is the number that you will receive

$T = 32d$ where d is the diameter of the circle shown.

The rectangle has a height equal to twice its width.

Calculate the shaded area, giving your answer in terms of π.

B1 The function $f(y)$ is defined for values of y, ($y \neq 0$ or 1), by

$$f(y) = \frac{1 + \frac{1}{y}}{1 - \frac{1}{y}}$$

Calculate $f(f(f(6)))$ and write your answer in the form $\frac{a}{b}$, where a and b are positive integers with no common factors except 1, and then find the value of $a + b$.

B2 T is the number that you will receive.

Find the value of x.

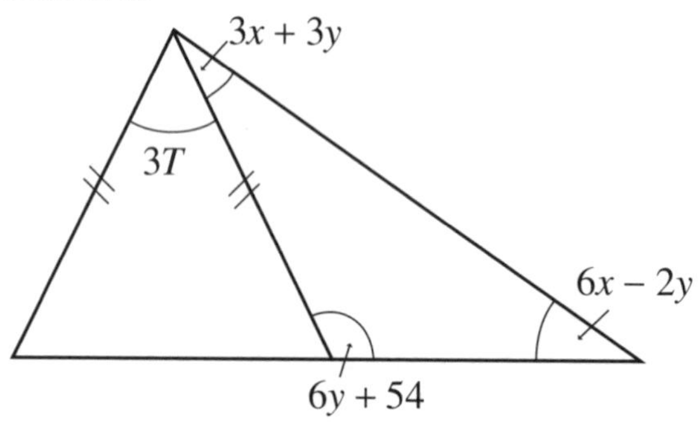

B3 T is the number that you will receive

Find the smallest positive multiple of T which leaves a remainder of 1 upon division by each of the numbers 2, 3, 4, 5 or 6.

B4 T is the number that you will receive.

For any positive integer y, we define

$y! = 1 \times 2 \times 3 \times 4 \times 5 \times \ \ldots \ \times y$.

Write down the number of zeros at the end of 10!

C1 A quadrilateral has angles such that, when put in order of increasing size, they form a sequence where each term is twice the previous term. Find the size of the second smallest angle.

C2 T is the number that you will receive

If $\left(\frac{T}{6}\right)^{3y+1} = 16^{y+1}$, find the value of $\frac{1}{y}$.

C3 T is the number that you will receive

The points with co-ordinates $(0, 0)$, $(T, 1)$ and $(1, T)$ are the vertices of a triangle.

Find the area of the triangle.

C4 T is the number that you will receive.

Lance cycles up a hill at an average speed of 4 m/s and then back via the same route at an average speed of T m/s. Find his average speed for the whole journey.

D1 The diagram shows three semicircles, and $AB = BC = CD$.

What fraction of the largest semicircle is shaded?

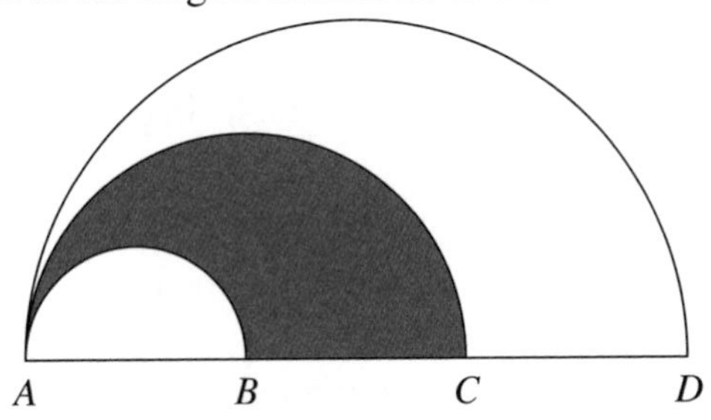

D2 T is the number that you will receive.

The value of the expression below can be written as a fraction in the form $\frac{a}{b}$, where a and b are positive integers with no common factors except 1.

$$1 + \frac{T}{1 + \frac{T+1}{1 + \frac{1}{1+1}}}$$

Calculate the value of $a - b$.

D3 T is the number that you will receive.

The area of the circle alongside is $(T + 13)$ cm^2. If the area of the square is written in the form $\frac{m}{\pi}$, what is the value of m?

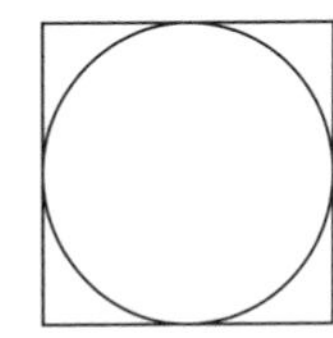

D4 T is the number that you will receive.
Suppose x and y are positive real numbers where

$$x(x + y) = T - 60$$

and

$$y(x + y) = T - 55$$

Calculate the value of $x + y$, giving your answer as a surd.

E1 If $x = \sqrt{5}$ and $y = \dfrac{x - \frac{1}{x}}{x + \frac{1}{x}}$, find the value of $\dfrac{\frac{1}{y} - y}{\frac{1}{y} + y}$ and express your answer as a fraction in the form $\dfrac{a}{b}$, where a and b are positive integers with no common factors except 1.
Calculate the value of $b - a$.

E2 T is the number that you will receive.
By rationalising the denominator, express the fraction $\dfrac{T\sqrt{2}}{\sqrt{8} - \sqrt{7}}$ in the form $a + b\sqrt{c}$, for suitable integers a, b and . What is the value of $\dfrac{a + b}{c + 6}$?

E3 T is the number that you will receive.
When the expression $(T - \sqrt{2})^3 + (T + \sqrt{2})^2 + (T - \sqrt{2})$ is simplified, it can be expressed in the form $a - b\sqrt{c}$. What is the value of $a - bc$?

E4 T is the number that you will receive.
Define the operation Δ by $a \, \Delta \, b = ab - 2a - 2b + 6$.
What is the value of $(a \, \Delta \, b) \, \Delta \, c - a \, \Delta \, (b \, \Delta \, c) + 2T$?

F1 For any triangle, the incircle of a triangle is the largest circle contained inside the triangle; it touches (is tangent to) the three sides.
Find the radius of the incircle for a triangle with sides of length 8 units, 15 units and 17 units.

F2 T is the number that you will receive.
A train leaves London for Edinburgh every hour on the hour. A train leaves Edinburgh for London every hour on the half hour. Each train takes $T + 2$ hours to reach its destination. If you travel on the London to Edinburgh train, how many trains from Edinburgh to London would the driver see on your journey?

F3 T is the number that you will receive.
The system of equations

$$x + y = 1$$
$$kx + y = T - 8$$
$$x + ky = T - 7$$

has a unique solution. Find the value of $\frac{1}{2}k$.

F4 T is the number that you will receive.
For the circle centre C, find the value of y.

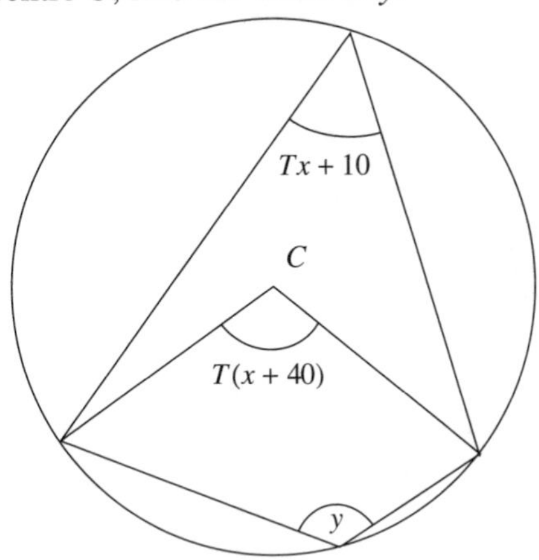

National Final Answers

Group Round answers

1. Ratio	2 : 5
2. Number of positive factors	270
3. Perimeter of pentagon	$12\frac{3}{4}$ or $\frac{51}{4}$
4. Probability of a right-angled triangle	$\frac{7}{10}$
5. k and n	$k = 2835$; $n = 23$
6. Sum of the digits	35
7. M	2519
8. x	6
9. Numerical value of cos BJT	$\frac{5}{7}$
10. Probability of total score 2	$\frac{1215}{4096}$

Crossnumber: Completed grid

■	[1] 2	[2] 4	0	[3] 1	■	[4] 2	3	6	■
[5] 1	■	2	■	[6] 3	4	2	■	■	[7] 4
2	■	[8] 7	7	6	■	[9] 5	[10] 1	7	4
[11] 2	[12] 4	2	■	■	[13] 1	■	6	■	2
■	0	■	[14] 3	[15] 4	7	■	[16] 6	[17] 2	5
[18] 4	8	[19] 6	■	[20] 3	5	7	■	5	■
3	■	1	■	7	■	■	[21] 6	7	[22] 8
[23] 2	4	3	[24] 7	■	[25] 9	0	3	■	3
0	■	■	[26] 4	2	9	■	3	■	8
■	[27] 8	6	7	■	[28] 6	8	6	0	■

Mini-relay answers

	A	B	C	D	E	F
1	2	12	48	$\frac{1}{3}$	8	3
2	25	7	5	3	2	10
3	320	301	12	64	6	2
4	$25\pi - 40$	7	6	$\sqrt{13}$	12	110

Other aspects of the UKMT and other similar bodies overseas

As well as the Maths Challenges, the UKMT is involved in other events and activities.

Enriching Mathematical Thinking
UKMT Teacher Meetings 2009

In 2009 we held seven meetings. The venues were Belfast (W5 @ Odyssey), Cambridge (University of Cambridge), Cardiff (University of Cardiff), Glasgow (University of Strathclyde), London (University of Greenwich), Manchester (University of Manchester), and Leeds (University of Leeds).

In total over 550 teachers attended the one-day meetings. Each meeting featured three plenary sessions with lunch and refreshment breaks, and delegates received a resource pack to take back to the classroom.

Nrich (www.nrich.maths.org.uk) gave sessions at all seven meetings and we are grateful to Charlie Gilderdale, Alison Kiddle, Jenny Piggott and Liz Woodham for the quality of these sessions and the accompanying resources.

UKMT spokespeople gave an insight into using challenge material in the classroom at each event. Material from the Junior, Intermediate, Senior, Team and Senior Team Challenges was used. The speakers were Ceri Fiddes, Jacqui Lewis, Alan Slomson, James Welham, and Mary Wimbury.

Liz Meenan gave an interactive, practical and fun session of measuring, calculating and folding with Fibonacci numbers and the golden ratio at Belfast, Glasgow and Manchester. Colin Wright talked about marine mathematics at Cardiff and Cambridge. Rob Eastaway illustrated extracts from his book How many socks make a pair in Leeds and Simon Singh gave an insight into the making of the Fermat's Last Theorem documentary in Greenwich.

This year we also finished with an optional session on the UKMT's Olympiad papers. These were given by Mary Teresa Fyfe, Vinay Kathotia, Alan Slomson, Andrew Jobbings, Howard Groves, Dean Bunnell and Peter Neumann.

The delegate fee was £40, which included refreshments, lunch and resource pack. Feedback from those attending was, once again, extremely positive.

Website – www.ukmt.org.uk

Visit the UKMT's website for information about all the UKMT's activities, including the Maths Challenges, latest UKMT news, contact details, the national team competition and how to buy past papers. There's an online quiz featuring past questions from the Challenges, and links to sponsors, supporters and other mathematical organisations providing resources for young mathematicians.

Overseas bodies

The UKMT has links of varying degrees of formality with several similar organisations in other countries. It is also a member of the World Federation of National Mathematics Competitions (WFNMC). What follows is a brief description of some of these other organisations. Some of the information is taken from the organisations' web sites but a UK slant has been applied.

"Kangourou des Mathématiques"

The European Kangaroo Competition

http://www.math-ksf.org/

The obvious question is: why Kangaroo? The name was given in tribute to the pioneering efforts of the Australian Mathematics Trust. The Kangaroo contest is run by local organisers in each country under the auspices of the 'Association Kangourou sans Frontières', which was founded by a small group of countries in 1991. There are now 41 countries involved and more than five million participants throughout Europe and beyond, from the UK to Kazakhstan and from Norway to Cyprus.

In the UK in 2009, around 7000 children in the years equivalent to English Years 9, 10 and 11 took part in the 'Cadet' and 'Junior' levels of the Kangaroo competition, as a follow-up to the Intermediate Maths Challenge. Four representatives of the UK Mathematics Trust, Andrew Jobbings, Paul Murray, Mary Read and Alex Voice, attended the meeting in Berlin, at which the 2009 Kangaroo papers were constructed.

The main objective of the Kangaroo, like all the competitions described in this section, is to stimulate and motivate large numbers of pupils, as well as to contribute to the development of a mathematical culture which will be accessible to, and enjoyed by, many children and young people. The Association also encourages cross-cultural activities; in some countries, for example, prize-winners are invited to attend a mathematics 'camp' with similar participants from other nations.

The Australian Mathematics Trust

www.amt.canberra.edu.au

For over twenty-five years, the Australian Mathematics Competition has been one of the major events on the Australian Education Calendar, with about one in three Australian secondary students entering each year to test their skills. That's over half a million participants a year.

The Competition commenced in 1978 under the leadership of the late Professor Peter O'Halloran, of the University of Canberra, after a successful pilot scheme had run in Canberra for two years.

The questions are multiple-choice and students have 75 minutes in which to answer 30 questions. There are follow-up rounds for high scorers.

In common with the other organisations described here, the AMC also extends its mathematical enrichment activities by publishing high quality material which can be used in the classroom.

Whilst the AMC provides students all over Australia with an opportunity to solve the same problems on the same day, it is also an international event, with most of the countries of the Pacific and South-East Asia participating, as well as a few schools from further afield. New Zealand and Singapore each enter a further 30,000 students to help give the Competition an international flavour.

World Federation of National Mathematics Competitions – WFNMC

www.amt.canberra.edu.au/wfnmc.html

The Federation was created in 1984 during the Fifth International Congress for Mathematical Education.

The Federation aims to provide a focal point for those interested in, and concerned with, conducting national mathematics competitions for the purpose of stimulating the learning of mathematics. Its objectives include:

- Serving as a resource for the exchange of information and ideas on mathematics competitions through publications and conferences.

- Assisting with the development and improvement of mathematics competitions.
- Increasing public awareness of the role of mathematics competitions in the education of all students and ensuring that the importance of that role is properly recognised in academic circles.
- Creating and enhancing professional links between mathematicians involved in competitions around the world.

The World Federation of National Mathematics Competitions is an organisation of national mathematics competitions affiliated as a Special Interest Group of the International Commission for Mathematical Instruction (ICMI).

It administers a number of activities, including

- The Journal *Mathematics Competitions*
- An international conference every four years. Previous conferences were held in Waterloo, Canada (1990), Pravets, Bulgaria (1994), Zhong Shan, China (1998). In 2002, the WFNMC met in Melbourne, Australia. In 2006, the conference was in the UK.
- David Hilbert and Paul Erdős Awards for mathematicians prominent on an international or national scale in mathematical enrichment activities.

The UKMT sent two delegates, Tony Gardiner and Bill Richardson, to the WFNMC conference in Zhong Shan in 1998 and provided support for several delegates who attended ICME 9 in Tokyo in August 2000, at which the WFNMC provided a strand.

In August 2002, the WFNMC held another conference, similar to the one in 1998. The venue for this was Melbourne, Victoria. On this occasion, the UKMT provided support for two delegates: Howard Groves and Bill Richardson.

In July 2006, WFNMC 5 was held in the UK at Robinson College, Cambridge. This event was a tremendous success with around 100 delegates from many parts of the world.

In July 2007, WFNMC had a strand at ICME 11 in Mexico. UKMT was represented by Bill Richardson.

Lists of volunteers involved in the UKMT's activities

UKMT officer bearers

Chair: Professor Bernard Silverman

Secretary: Dr Alan Slomson *Treasurer*: Prof. Adam McBride

The Council

Professor Bernard Silverman (Chair)
Mr Richard Atkins
Professor John Brindley (from April 2009)
Mr Dean Bunnell (to April 2009)
Dr Colin Campbell
Dr Katie Chicot (from April 2009)
Dr Ceri Fiddes
Dr Tony Gardiner (to October 2008)
Dr Sara Santos (from October 2008)
Professor Tom Korner
Professor Adam McBride
Mr Tony Mann
Mr Steve Mulligan (Vice-Chair)
Miss Jenny Ramsden
Mr Bill Richardson (Vice-Chair)
Dr John Silvester
Dr Geoff Smith
Mr Alex Voice
Mr James Welham

Members of the Trust who are not on the Council or members of a Subtrust

The Mathematical Association
The Royal Institution
Mr Dennis Archer
Dr Roger Bray
Sir Alan Budd
Mrs Mary Teresa Fyfe
Mr Howard Groves
Mr Terry Heard
Dr Andrew Jobbings
Dr Frances Kirwan
Mrs Margaret Jackson
Miss Susie Jameson
Professor Imre Leader
Dr Gerry Leversha
Mr Nick Lord
Mr Dennis Orton
Dr Peter Neumann
Mr Peter Ransom
Dr Adrian Sanders
Mr Robert Smart
Dr Brian Stewart
Mr Peter Thomas.

The Subtrusts

British Mathematical Olympiad Subtrust

Dr Geoff Smith (Chair)
Dr Don Collins (Treasurer)
Mr Richard Atkins
Dr James Cranch
Dr Ceri Fiddes
Dr Vesna Kadelberg (Secretary)
Professor Imre Leader

Team Maths Challenge Subtrust

Mr Steve Mulligan (Chair)
Miss Pam Hunt (Secretary)
Ms Jacqui Lewis
Mr Martin Perkins (Treasurer)
Mr Stephen Power
Dr Peter Neumann
Mr James Welham

Challenges Subtrust

Mr Bill Richardson (Chair)
Professor John Brindley
Mr Colin Dixon
Mr Howard Groves
Professor Adam McBride
Mr Stephen Power
Professor Chris Robson
Dr Alan Slomson
Ms Anne Baker
Mr David Crawford
Mrs Karen Fogden
Dr Calum Kilgour
Mr Paul Murray
Miss Jenny Ramsden (Secretary)
Mrs Mary Read
Mr Alex Voice (Treasurer)

Other Committees

Finance and General Purposes Committee

Mr Richard Atkins
Mr Stephen Mulligan
Professor Bernard Silverman
Ms Mary Wimbury (UKMT Director)
Professor Adam McBride
Mr Bill Richardson
Dr Alan Slomson

Nominations Committee

Mr Tony Mann (Chair)
Mr Bill Richardson
Professor Adam McBride
Mr James Welham

Outreach Committee

Mr Tony Mann (Chair)
Mrs Mary Teresa Fyfe
Dr Vinay Kathotia
Miss Jenny Ramsden
Ms Mary Wimbury
Professor John Brindley (Chair)
Miss Pam Hunt
Mr Nick Lord
Mr James Welham

Publications Committee

Dr Gerry Leversha (Chair)
Mr Nick Lord
Dr Christopher Bradley

Members of the BMOS Extended Committee

Philip Coggins (Bedford School)
Ben Green (Trinity College, Cambridge)
Gerry Leversha (St Paul's School)
David Monk (ex Edinburgh University)
Alan Pears (ex King's College, London)
Bernard Silverman (St. Peter's, Oxford)
Alan West (ex Leeds University)
Tim Cross (KES, Birmingham)
Patricia King (ex Benenden School, Kent)
Adam McBride (Uni. of Strathclyde)
Peter Neumann (Queen's Coll., Oxford)
Adrian Sanders (ex Trinity College, Camb.)
Zhivko Stoyanov (University of Bath)
Brian Wilson (Royal Holloway, London)

BMOS Markers

Richard Atkins (Oundle School)
Robin Bhattacharrya (Derby)
Brian Brooks (Millfield School)
Philip Coggins (ex Bedford School)
James Cranch (Uni. of Sheffield)
Paul Fannon (Sevenoaks School)
Ceri Fiddes (Millfield School)
David Forster (Oratory School)
Jenny Gardner (Bank of England)
James Gazet (Eton College)
John Haslegrave (Trinity College)
Ina Hughes (University of Leeds)
Ian Jackson (Tonbridge School)
Paul Jeffreys (ex Trinity College)
Andrew Jobbings (Shipley)
Vesna Kadelburg (MPW, Cambridge)
Nathan Kettle (Trinity College)
Jeremy King (Tonbridge School)
Gerry Leversha (St Paul's School)
Tom Lovering (Trinity College)
Joseph Myers (Codesourcery Inc.)
Vicky Neale (Trinity College)
Martin Orr (Trinity College)
Hannah Roberts (Trinity College)
Paul Russell (Churchill College)
Geoff Smith (University of Bath)
Jerome Watson (Bedford School)
Dominic Yeo (Trinity College)
Alison Zhu (Trinity College)

Markers for IMOK and JMO

Anne Andrews	(Buckingham)	IMOK
Anne Ault	(Hampshire)	IMOK
Dean Bunnell	(Queen Elizabeth GS, Wakefield)	JMO
Philip Coggins	(Bedford School)	IMOK
David Crawford	(Leicester Grammar School)	IMOK / JMO
Mary Teresa Fyfe	(Hutchesons' Grammar School, Glasgow)	IMOK / JMO
James Gazet	(Eton College)	IMOK
Gwyn Gardiner	(KES, Birmingham)	JMO
Tony Gardiner	(University of Birmingham)	JMO
Valeriu Gutu	(Romania)	JMO
Mark Harwood	(St Bede's Grammar School, Bradford)	IMOK
Rita Holland	(ex Wisbech Grammar School)	IMOK
Ina Hughes	(University of Leeds)	IMOK
Carl James	(Leicester Grammar School)	IMOK / JMO
Andrew Jobbings	(Shipley)	IMOK / JMO
Calum Kilgour	(St Aloysius College, Glasgow)	IMOK
Gerry Leversha	(St Paul's School)	IMOK
Nick Lord	(Tonbridge School)	IMOK
Holly McLean	(Bingley Grammar School)	IMOK
Sam Maltby	(Touch Vision)	IMOK
Linda Moon	(Glasgow Academy)	IMOK
Philip Moon	(The High School of Glasgow)	IMOK

Peter Neumann	(The Queen's College, Oxford)	IMOK / JMO
Sylvia Neumann	(Oxford)	IMOK / JMO
Stephen Power	(St Swithuns School, Winchester)	IMOK / JMO
Jenny Ramsden	(High Wycombe)	IMOK / JMO
Bill Richardson	(Elgin)	JMO
Mary Read	(Haberdashers' Aske's Hatcham College)	IMOK
Chris Robson	(Harrogate)	IMOK
Paul Russell	(Churchill College, Cambridge)	IMOK / JMO
John Slater	(Market Rasen)	IMOK / JMO
Alan Slomson	(University of Leeds)	JMO
Jon Stone	(St Paul's School, London)	IMOK
Alex Voice	(Westminster Choir School, London)	IMOK / JMO
Christopher Walker	(Summer Fields School, Oxford)	IMOK
Jerome Watson	(Bedford School)	IMOK
James Welham	(Wycliffe College)	IMOK
Brian Wilson	(Royal Holloway, London)	IMOK

Problems Groups

There are currently five groups. The first being the BMO Setting Committee.

The BMO Setting Committee

Gerry Leversha	(Chair)
Tim Cross	(KES, Birmingham)
David Forster	(Abingdon School)
Jenny Gardner	(ex Trinity College, Cambridge)
Paul Jefferys	(ex Trinity College, Cambridge)
Jeremy King	(Tonbridge School)
Jack Shotton	(Trinity College, Cambridge)
Geoff Smith	(University of Bath)

The other four groups have overlapping membership. There is one group for each of the Senior Mathematical Challenge (S), the Junior and Intermediate Mathematical Challenges (I&J), the Junior Mathematical Olympiad (JMO) and the IMOK olympiad papers. These first two were chaired by Howard Groves and the others by Alex Voice and Andrew Jobbings respectively. Those involved are listed below.

Steve Barge	(Sacred Heart Catholic College)	S
Dean Bunnell	(Queen Elizabeth GS, Wakefield)	S / IMOK / JMO
Kerry Burnham	(Torquay Boys' Grammar School)	I&J
James Cranch	(University of Sheffield)	IMOK
Colin Dixon	(Newcastle)	S
Karen Fogden	(Henry Box School, Witney)	I&J / JMO

Mary Teresa Fyfe	(Hutchesons' GS, Glasgow)	S / IMOK / JMO
Carol Gainlall	(Park House School, Newbury)	I&J
Tony Gardiner	(University of Birmingham)	I&J / IMOK / JMO
Howard Groves	(RGSAO, Worcester)	S / I&J / IMOK / JMO
Andrew Jobbings	(Shipley)	S / I&J / IMOK / JMO
Gerry Leversha	(St Paul's School)	IMOK
Toby Lockyer	(Lord Williams School, Thame)	I&J
Paul Murray	(Lord Williams School, Thame)	I&J / JMO
Andy Parkinson	(Beckfoot School, Bingley)	IMOK
Stephen Power	(St. Swithun's Schol, Winchester)	I&J
Mary Read	(Haberdashers' Aske's Hatcham C.)	IMOK
Alan Slomson	(University of Leeds)	S / I&J
Alex Voice	(St Christopher's School, Hove)	I&J / JMO

It is appropriate at this stage to acknowledge and thank those who helped at various stages with the moderation and checking of these papers: Adam McBride, Peter Neumann, Chris Robson and Stephen Power.

TMC coordinators and regional helpers

Anne Andrews	Ann Ault	Anne Baker
Martin Bailey	Bridget Ballantyne	Andrew Bell
Kerry Burnham	Keith Cadman	Alex Crews
Graeme de Sainte Croix	Geoffrey Dolamore	Sally-Jane Fell
Sheldon Fernandes	Roy Fraser	Jackie Fox
Mary Teresa Fyfe	Miyoba Habanyana	Peter Hall
Mark Harwood	Karl Hayward-Bradley	Terry Heard
Rita Holland	Sue Hughes	Sally Anne Huk
Claire Hunt	Pam Hunt	Andrina Inglis
Andrew Jobbings	Nathan Keeling	Andy Kemp
Jacqui Lewis	Simon Lewis	Tricia Lunel
Pat Lyden	Holly Mclean	Hilary Monaghan
Mike Moon	Steve Mulligan	Helen Mumby
Paul Murray	Peter Neumann	Pauline Noble
Andy Parkinson	Martin Perkins	Dennis Pinshon
Vivan Pinto	Stephen Power	Jenny Ramsden
Mary Read	Nikki Shepherd	Alan Slomson
Anne Strong	Penny Thompson	Alex Voice
James Welham	Helen Wigglesworth	Rosie Wiltshire

BMOS Mentoring Schemes
Richard Atkins (Director)

Junior Scheme Coordinator: John Slater

Intermediate Scheme Coordinators: Richard Atkins, Alan Slomson

Senior Scheme Coordinators: Andre Rzym; James Cranch

Other mentors were:

Anne Andrews
Brian Brooks
Chris Bryant
Miguel Carrion
Cong Chen
Tom Close
Owen Cotton-Barratt
Janet Dangerfield
Julia Erhard
Ben Fairbairn
Yi Feng
MT Fyfe
James Gazet
Jeffrey Giansiracusa
Julian Gilbey
Saul Glasman
Victoria Gregson
Michael Griffiths
Ina Hughes
Vesna Kadelburg
Vinay Kathotia
Andre Kueh
Kate Land
James Lawrence
Jonathan Lee
Kelvin Lee
Charles Leedham-Greem
Lilian Matthiesen
Sam Maltby
Freddie Manners
Oliver McFarlane
Tristan Melen
Vicky Neale
Gerry Netto
Peter Neumann
Jerome Ripp
Hannah Roberts
Julia Robson
Indad Sardharwalla
Peter Scott
Alexander Shannon
Jack Shotton
Ian Slater
Paul Smith
Balazs Szendroi
Mark Taylor
Oliver Thomas
Madoc Troup
Damjan Vukcevic
James Welham
Dominic Yeo
Alison Zhu

Advanced Scheme Coordinators: Paul Jefferys; Jenny Gardner

Other mentors were:

Robin Bhattacharyya
Toby Kenney
Henry Liu
Tom Lovering
Joseph Myers
Martin Or

UKMT Maths Challenges 2009–10

We hope you have enjoyed the 2008–09 Yearbook.

The dates for the 2009–10 Maths Challenges are:

Senior Maths Challenge	Thursday 5 November 2009
Intermediate Maths Challenge	Thursday 4 February 2010
Junior Maths Challenge	Thursday 29 April 2010

Follow-on Rounds

British Mathematical Olympiad Round 1	Thursday 3 December 2009
British Mathematical Olympiad Round 2	Thursday 28 January 2010
Intermediate Mathematical Olympiad and Kangaroo	Thursday 18 March 2010
Junior Mathematical Olympiad	Tuesday 15 June 2010

Please contact the Maths Challenges Office for entry details.

Our contact details are:

UKMT Maths Challenges Office,
School of Mathematics,
University of Leeds,
Leeds LS2 9JT

Tel: 0113 343 2339; Fax: 0113 343 5500
Email: enquiry@ukmt.org.uk

Or visit our website at
www.ukmt.org.uk

UKMT Publications

UKMT Yearbook

The 2008-2009 Yearbook is our eleventh Yearbook, having published one a year since 1998-1999. Edited by Bill Richardson, the Yearbook documents all the UKMT activities from that particular year. They include all the challenge papers and solutions at every level; lists of high scorers; tales from the IMO and Olympiad training camps; details of the UKMT's other activities; and a round-up of global maths associations.

Past Paper Booklets – Junior, Intermediate and Senior Challenges.

If you would like further copies of our Challenge past papers, we also sell booklets containing the Mathematics Challenge question papers, solutions, and a summary chart of all the answers.
The Junior and Intermediate booklets contain material for five years, and the Senior Challenge booklet for four years.

Past Paper Booklets – Follow-on Rounds

The JMO booklet contains four years' papers and solutions for the Junior Mathematical Olympiad, the follow up to the JMC.
The 2009 IMOK booklet contains the papers and solutions for the suite of Intermediate follow-on rounds – the Kangaroo Grey, the Kangaroo Pink, Cayley, Hamilton and Maclaurin. We also have IMOK booklets currently available from 2008, 2007 and 2006.
The two BMO booklets contain material for the British Mathematical Olympiad Round 1. One contains papers and solutions for 2001-2004, and the other for 1997-2000.

Ten Years of Mathematical Challenges 1997 to 2006

Edited by Bill Richardson, this book was published to celebrate the tenth anniversary of the founding of UKMT. This 188-page book contains question papers and solutions for nine Senior Challenges, ten Intermediate Challenges, and ten Junior Challenges.

A Mathematical Olympiad Primer by GC Smith

This UKMT publication, provides an excellent guide for young mathematicians preparing for competitions such as the British Mathematical Olympiad. The book contains theory including algebra, combinatorics and geometry, and BMO1 problems and solutions from 1996 onwards.

The Backbone of Pascal's Triangle by Martin Griffiths

Everything covered in this book is connected to the sequence of numbers: 2, 6, 20, 70, 252, 924, 3432,... Some readers might recognize this list straight away, while others will not have seen it before. Either way, students and teachers alike may well be astounded at both the variety and the depth of mathematical ideas that it can lead to.

Plane Euclidean Geometry: Theory and Problems
by CJ Bradley and AD Gardiner

An excellent book for students aged 15-18 and teachers who want to learn how to solve problems in elementary Euclidean geometry. The book follows the development of Euclid; contents include Pythagoras, trigonometry, circle theorems, and Ceva and Menelaus. Along with much explanatory material, the book contains hundreds of problems, many with hints and solutions.

Introductions to Number Theory and Inequalities by CJ Bradley

This publication is currently out of print but a revised, updated edition should be available in early 2010.

Crossing the Bridge by Gerry Leversha

This book provides a course on geometry for use in the classroom, re-emphasising some traditional features of geometrical education. The bulk of the text is devoted to carefully constructed exercises for classroom discussion or individual study. It is suitable for students aged 13 and upwards.

New Problems in Euclidean Geometry by David Monk

This recently published book should appeal to anyone 16+ who enjoys solving the kind of challenging and attractive geometry problems that have virtually vanished from the school curriculum, but which still play a central role in national and international mathematics competitions. It is a treasure trove of wonderful geometrical problems, with hints for their solution.

To order any UKMT publications, please complete the form on the next page or see our website at www.ukmt.org.uk

In addition to the books above, UKMT continues to publish:

Newsletter
The UKMT's newsletter, "Maths Challenges News", is sent out once a term, giving the latest news from the Trust, mathematical articles, examples from Challenge papers and occasional posters for the classroom wall! Free to all schools participating in the Maths Challenges.

Order Form for UKMT Publications

Please photocopy this form and send a cheque payable to 'UKMT(Leeds)' to:

UKMT (Publications), Maths Challenges Office,
School of Mathematics, University of Leeds, Leeds LS2 9JT

		Quantity	Price	Subtotal
Yearbooks	2008-2009		£8	
	2007-2008		£8	
	2006-2007		£8	
Past Paper Booklets	Junior Challenge		£2.50	
	Intermediate Challenge		£2.50	
	Senior Challenge		£2.50	
	Set of all three		£6	
Follow-on Rounds	JMO		£2.50	
	IMOK 2009		£2.50	
	BMO1 (2001-2004)		£2.50	
	BMO1 (1997-2000)		£2.50	

We have limited stock of Yearbooks from before 2006. Please contact the Maths Challenges Office for availability and prices.

	Quantity	*Price*	*Subtotal*
Ten Years of Mathematical Challenges		£10 + p&p*	
A Mathematical Olympiad Primer		£10 + p&p*	
The Backbone of Pascal's Triangle		£12 + p&p*	
Plane Euclidean Geometry: Theory and Problems		£10 + p&p*	
Crossing the Bridge		£10 + p&p*	
New Problems in Euclidean Geometry		£10 + p&p*	

*p&p: £1 on all UK orders less than 5 copies; £5 per book on all overseas orders; p&p is free on all UK orders of 5 copies or more.

Total: I enclose a cheque for £ payable to 'UKMT(Leeds)'.

Your details:

Name . . . .

Address . . . .

. . . .

Postcode . . . .

Telephone . . . . Email . . . .